TOPICS
IN MATHEMATICS

FOR
ELEMENTARY
SCHOOL
TEACHERS

TWENTY-NINTH
YEARBOOK

NATIONAL COUNCIL OF TEACHERS OF MATHEMATICS
Washington, D.C., 1964

PREFACE

The past decade has been described as a period of revolution in school mathematics. The curriculum changes brought about by this revolution were evident first at the secondary level, but are now apparent from the kindergarten through the high school. At the elementary level, the changes have been of two kinds: new topics have been introduced, frequently from geometry and from elementary number theory; and familiar topics—the whole numbers, fractional numbers, problem solving—have been treated in greater depth than was formerly the case.

It is with problems created by the changes in treatment of familiar topics that this, the Twenty-Ninth Yearbook, is primarily concerned. Many teachers have found that their professional education did not give them sufficient understanding of mathematical concepts to teach in depth the topics traditionally included in the arithmetic curriculum which is now considered important. This yearbook is offered in the hope that it may be of service to these teachers.

The eight topics presented in this yearbook were first published in August 1964 as eight separate booklets. The booklets, now combined under one cover, give an introduction to the topics considered, not an exhaustive treatment; the interested reader may study each subject in greater depth in other publications.

The eight booklets were written in the summer of 1963 by a writing group which was organized and sponsored by the 1962-63 NCTM Supplementary Publications Committee and financed by the NCTM. The committee consisted of Kenneth B. Henderson (chairman), Marguerite Brydegaard, M. Albert Linton, Henrietta Mazen, Eugene D. Nichols, Helen A. Schneider, and Daniel W. Snader. The manuscripts completed in the summer of 1963 were read critically by the members of the

1963-64 NCTM Supplementary Publications Committee: Kenneth B. Henderson (chairman), Don E. Edmondson, M. Albert Linton, Henrietta Mazen, Marian A. Moore, Daniel W. Snader, and William Wooton.

The Twenty-Ninth Yearbook Editorial Committee (composed of the members of the original writing group) is grateful for the warm support given this project by Frank B. Allen, NCTM President, 1962-64, and Bruce E. Meserve, NCTM President, 1964-66. The Editorial Committee is also grateful for the many valuable suggestions made by members of the two NCTM Supplementary Publications Committees and for the assistance of James D. Gates, NCTM Executive Secretary; Doris D. Wigglesworth, NCTM Editorial Associate; and other staff members at the Washington office. The painstaking care of the printing craftsmen at the Port City Press and the artists at the Waverly Press is also much appreciated.

The Editorial Committee

Edwin F. Beckenbach
Helen Curran
Walter Fleming
Geraldine Green

Lola May
Marlene Schroeder
Margaret F. Willerding
William Wooton

Lenore John, *Chairman*

CONTENTS

vi

BOOKLET NO. 5: *NUMBERS AND THEIR FACTORS*

BOOKLET NO. 6: *THE RATIONAL NUMBERS*

BOOKLET NO. 7: *NUMERATION SYSTEMS FOR RATIONAL NUMBERS*

BOOKLET NO. 8: *NUMBER SENTENCES*

●●●

BOOKLET NUMBER ONE:

SETS

BASIC CONCEPTS OF SETS

Importance of Set Concepts in Elementary School Mathematics

There are many answers to the often-raised question: "Why are sets important in mathematics?" The response one receives to this question depends to some degree on the person who is asked. In this booklet, we shall narrow the question and ask: "Why are sets important in elementary school mathematics?," since we are primarily concerned with the importance of set concepts as they bear upon the initial experiences that boys and girls have with mathematics and upon the effective use to which teachers at the elementary level can put these concepts in their classroom activities.

In some ways, the introduction of sets to elementary school children does not constitute a new or novel development in mathematics education. Sets have been used for many years in teaching boys and girls to count and to answer questions involving the notion of "how many". For instance, it is quite common to use a collection of blocks, a row of chairs, a set of dishes, and so on, to provide concrete representations for number ideas. There is little question that the use of sets of concrete items is of value in the development of an understanding of number. In this sense, sets have always been of importance in elementary school teaching.

There are good reasons to expect the teaching of set concepts and terminology to very young children to produce a marked improvement in the understanding of the number concepts children are (and have always been) expected to acquire as a part of their general education. Let us examine a few of these reasons:

1. Many people now believe that the concept of a whole number may be approached more meaningfully through set concepts. Sets have always played a role in developing children's notions of the nature of a number. In many cases, however, the connection between the

sets being used and the word "number" has not been explicitly made. Quite often, the sets and their members have been simply visual or tactile experiences poorly related to the essentially abstract concept of number.

2. Because geometric as well as arithmetic ideas can be very clearly and concisely formulated in terms of sets, the children, at an early age, should come to realize that it is possible to use sets of one kind (say, points) to talk about sets of another kind (say, numbers). Thus, the set concepts and terminology learned in connection with an introduction to numbers can be applied directly to first experiences with point sets, and can serve as a strong bridge between number ideas and geometric ideas.

3. Set concepts, if acquired in the early grades, constitute a solid foundation upon which to base the more advanced mathematical concepts the children will encounter in their later school years.

The set notions needed by children in the early years are few and simple. Moreover, the symbolism and terminology necessary to discuss them have been shown to be readily accessible to boys and girls. Let us examine some of these ideas, and the terms and symbols used in talking about them.

Sets

What is a set? Instead of trying to define this fundamental notion, let us arrive at an agreement about what a set is by citing a number of examples:

1. A herd of cattle is a set (of cattle).
2. A pride of lions is a set (of lions).
3. A covey of quail is a set (of quail).
4. An army is a set (of soldiers).
5. A lawn is a set (of blades of grass).
6. A set of dishes is a set (of dishes).

In short, a set is simply a collection of a particular kind. The things (whatever they may be) that constitute a given set are called *members* or *elements* of the set. For example, the members of a given covey of quail are the individual quail in that covey; the members of a given herd of buffalo are the individual buffalo in that herd; and the members of a given set of dishes are the individual cups, saucers, plates, and the like in that set.

A mathematical set is a *well-defined collection*. By this it is not meant that the word "set" is being defined, but that a specific collection is being described so clearly that its membership is unambiguous to all concerned. Some examples of well-defined collections are the following:

1. The set whose members are the letters in the alphabet,
2. The set whose members are the months of the calendar year,
3. The set whose members are all the commercial television channels in New York City.

In each of these sets no questions arise as to whether or not a member belongs to a particular set.

Consider, for example, a class of second graders in Room 5 at Winslow School. Does the statement, "The class of second grade children in Room 5 at Winslow School is a set," clearly define the collection which constitutes the set? The only way to answer this question completely is to see whether or not the description is clear-cut enough so that any given thing can be identified as being a member or not a member of the collection. Is the teacher in the set? The fact that the statement specifies "second grade children" assures us that the teacher is not a member of the set. Is John Jones, who is at home sick in bed but who will be in Room 5 at Winslow School as a second grade pupil tomorrow, a member of this set? At this point, the description as worded proves inadequate to permit us to render a clear yes or no answer. He may be thought of as a member, if "class" is taken to mean "those enrolled in the class," but, on the other hand, the intent might be "those who are in the class at this moment." In this latter case, might we want to include in the set Mary Smith, a second grade pupil who has dropped in to deliver a note to the teacher in Room 5 but who is really a pupil of Mrs. Adams, the teacher in Room 7 at Winslow School? This should suffice to illustrate that the collection under consideration is not clearly described, and cannot be classified as being well defined. Teachers can profitably use descriptions of this kind to impress upon the children the need for care in specifying the collection which makes up the set.

Most of the collections used in the early grades are well defined. Specific collections of blocks, for example, or specific collections of symbols on flannel boards, chalk-boards, or paper leave little room for doubt about what these collections do or do not contain.

Symbolism

Here is an example of one method by which sets are named:

$$A = \{\text{Mary, Jane, Betty}\}.$$

This is read, "The set whose members are Mary, Jane, and Betty." Capital letters are generally used to denote sets. Braces,* { }, (sometimes called

---

* This symbol and all the symbols used in this booklet are listed on pp. 41-42. Refer to the list whenever you are in doubt about how to read a symbol.

curly brackets) are also used in discussing sets; and symbols or names enclosed in braces are understood to refer to members of sets. Commas separate the symbols which represent the members of a set when the members are listed between braces.

Instead of listing all the members of a set, we could designate it equally well by describing its members. If we wanted to consider the teachers on the faculty of Winslow School as the members of a set, we could use W to denote the set, and thus avoid having to respecify the members each time we refer to this set. Thus, the set we named W, above, might be represented by

$$W = \{\text{teachers on the faculty of Winslow School}\},$$

which is read: "The set whose members are (all) the teachers on the faculty of Winslow School." If we wished to list the members of this set, we might write

$$W = \{\text{Mr. Smith, Mrs. Jones, Miss Adams}, \ldots, \text{Mrs. Brown}\},$$

which is read: "The set whose members are Mr. Smith, Mrs. Jones, Miss Adams, . . . , Mrs. Brown." (Here the three dots, . . . , mean there are other persons in the set of teachers; but since the list is long, we took this simple means of making the meaning clear, rather than naming every teacher. It is understood from the three dots that the name of every teacher is to be included.

Some sets have no members. The set that contains no members is called the *empty set* or *null set*, and is sometimes denoted by the letter $\emptyset$ from the Scandinavian alphabet; $\emptyset$ is then read, "the empty set," or "the null set." Alternatively, we may simply write $\{\ \}$ to denote the empty set. The set whose members are one-thousand-year-old women living today is an example of the empty or null set. If we used T to denote this set, we would write

$$T = \emptyset \qquad \text{or} \qquad T = \{\ \}.$$

The Greek letter epsilon, ϵ, is used to abbreviate "is a member of," or "is an element of." If E denotes the set of even numbers, the expression "$2 \epsilon E$" means "2 is a member of E." Symbols to denote individual members of sets are usually taken from the lower-case letters of the alphabet: a, b, c, x, y, z, for example. The expression

$$a \epsilon A$$

is therefore read, "a is a member, or element, of the set A," or simply "a is a member of A."

The slant bar, $/$, is frequently used as a *negation symbol* in mathematics. The symbol $\notin$ is read "is not a member (element) of." For example, if Mrs. Peterson does not teach at Winslow School, and if W denotes the set of teachers on the faculty of Winslow School, then we would write

Mrs. Peterson $\notin W$,

which is read: "Mrs. Peterson is not a member (element) of the set W."

Exercise Set 1

1. Specify the members of each of the following sets.

    (a) The set of states bordering the Pacific Ocean
    (b) The set of the first six months of the year
    (c) The set of the living Ex-Presidents of the United States of America in 1962
    (d) The set of Supreme Court Justices who are women
    (e) The set of the Great Lakes
    (f) The set of the first five letters of the English alphabet

2. Select the best description for each set in the following list.

    (a) $J = \{\text{June, July}\}$
        (1) The set of two warm months
        (2) The set of two consecutive months
        (3) The set of two consecutive months with names beginning with the letter J.

    (b) $L = \{x, y, z\}$
        (1) The set of the last three letters of the alphabet
        (2) The set of three consonants in the alphabet
        (3) The set of three letters in the alphabet

    (c) $P = \{\text{Washington, Adams, Jefferson, Madison, Monroe}\}$
        (1) The set of five early Presidents of the United States of America
        (2) The set of the first five Presidents of the United States of America
        (3) The set of five Presidents of the United States of America.

3. Let $A = \{a, b, c, d\}$,
        $B = \{e, f, g, h\}$,
        $C = \{a, e, i, o, u\}$.

Insert the correct symbol, ϵ or $\notin$, in the following blanks.

(a) a ____ A	(d) b ____ A	(g) f ____ A
(b) a ____ B	(e) b ____ B	(h) f ____ B
(c) a ____ C	(f) b ____ C	(i) f ____ C

Set Equality

Let $A = \{a, b, c, d\}$,

and $B = \{c, d, a, b\}$.

We notice that each set contains precisely the same members although they are not listed in the same order. This sameness can be indicated by the *equality symbol*, $=$, (read, "equals" or "is equal to"). Thus, we can say

$$A = B$$

because set A and set B contain precisely the same members.

It is important to note that the order in which the members of each set are listed is immaterial. Thus,

$$\{a, b, c, d\} = \{c, d, a, b\} = \{a, c, b, d\}.$$

In short, to say that two sets are equal is to say that you do not really have two sets, but only one. More formally, we can make the definition:

> *If A denotes a set, and B denotes a set, then for sets A and B, the statement*
>
> $$A = B$$
>
> *means that A and B denote the same set.*

When reading statements involving sets and the equality symbol, it is helpful consciously to interpret the equality symbol in terms of *sameness*. Thus, the symbolic statement

$$W = \{\text{teachers on the faculty of Winslow School}\}$$

should be interpreted as an assertion that we are agreeing to use two different symbols (or a symbol and a group of symbols) to represent the same set of people.

Subsets

Any part of a set can, itself, be viewed as a set. For example, the members of the set of children in a specific classroom at a specific time can be used to form two other sets, the set of boys in the classroom and the set of girls in the classroom. These latter two sets are called subsets of the set of children in the classroom. This subset relation can be indicated by the set-inclusion symbol, $\subseteq$, (read "is a subset of"). Thus the statement

$$\{\text{Gerry, Helen}\} \subseteq \{\text{Gerry, Helen, Marlene}\}$$

is read: "The set whose members are Gerry and Helen is a subset of the set whose members are Gerry, Helen, and Marlene." More formally, we have the following definition:

For sets A and B, the statement

$$A \subseteq B$$

means that all the members of A are members of B.

As another example, consider

$$\{John\} \subseteq \{John, Joe, Tom\}$$

(read: "The set whose only member is John is a subset of the set whose members are John, Joe, and Tom."). This asserts that we are considering a subset of {John, Joe, Tom} whose only member is John.

A given set may have many subsets. How many? Perhaps we can determine this by considering a few specific cases. Let us again consider the set

$$\{John\}.$$

At first glance, the only set A meeting the conditions laid down in our definition for

$$A \subseteq \{John\}$$

appears to be {John} itself. Certainly, by our definition, any set is a subset of itself, for it contains as members all of its own members. Let us, however, consider also the set containing no members, { }. Would such a set be a subset of {John}? According to our definition, the statement that

A is a subset of B

means that every member of A is a member of B. This implies that if A is not a subset of B, then it must contain at least one member that is not a member of B. But the null set contains no such member. Thus, the set {John}, which contains a single element, has two subsets, {John} and $\emptyset$.

Incidentally, we say *the* null set because, in accordance with the definition of equal sets, all null sets are equal.

Next consider the set

$$\{John, Joe\},$$

which contains two members. Its subsets are

$$\emptyset,$$
$$\{John\},$$
$$\{Joe\},$$
$$\{John, Joe\}.$$

Thus, a set containing two members has four subsets.

Similarly, the set {John, Joe, Tom} has eight subsets:

$\emptyset,$	{John, Joe},
{John},	{John, Tom},
{Joe},	{Joe, Tom},
{Tom},	{John, Joe, Tom}.

If you care to list them, you will find that the set {John, Joe, Tom, Bob} has sixteen subsets, and {John, Joe, Tom, Bob, Ralph} has thirty-two subsets. We have, then, a pattern (see Table I).

TABLE I *

Number of Members in Set	Number of Subsets
1	2, or 2^1
2	$4 = 2 \times 2$, or 2^2
3	$8 = 2 \times 2 \times 2$, or 2^3
4	$16 = 2 \times 2 \times 2 \times 2$, or 2^4
5	$32 = 2 \times 2 \times 2 \times 2 \times 2$, or 2^5

* The raised numerals in the table are called *exponents*. Using exponents is a convenient way to indicate how many times a number is used as a factor. Thus 2^1 indicates that 2 is used as a factor one time. Similarly, 2^2 indicates that 2 is used as a factor two times.

Though we shall not prove it here, these examples make it plausible that if a set has n members, then it has 2^n subsets; that is, as many subsets as the product of n factors, each of which is 2. Thus, a set containing ten members has precisely 2^{10}, or 1024, subsets; and a set containing twenty members has 2^{20}, or 1,048,576, subsets.

Proper Subsets

If A and B denote two sets such that A is a subset of B and B has at least one member that is not a member of A, then A is said to be a *proper subset* of (or to be properly included in) B; and symbolically we write

$$A \subset B.$$

The statement

{Gerry, Helen} $\subset$ {Gerry, Helen, Marlene}

asserts that the set {Gerry, Helen} is a subset of the set {Gerry, Helen, Marlene} and that the latter set has at least one member (in this case, Marlene) that is not a member of the first set.

Let us make this formal definition:

For sets A *and* B, *the statement*

A $\subset$ B

means that A $\subseteq$ B, *and that* B *has at least one member that is not a member of* A.

As we saw, {Gerry, Helen} ⊂ {Gerry, Helen, Marlene} is a statement that {Gerry, Helen} is a proper subset of {Gerry, Helen, Marlene}. It is still true that {Gerry, Helen} is a subset of {Gerry, Helen, Marlene} and that it is still acceptable to write

{Gerry, Helen} ⊆ {Gerry, Helen, Marlene}.

On the other hand, though we may write the true statement

{Gerry, Helen, Marlene} ⊆ {Gerry, Helen, Marlene},

it is *not* true that

{Gerry, Helen, Marlene} ⊂ {Gerry, Helen, Marlene},

since the set denoted by the right-hand member of this statement does not contain a member that is not in the set denoted by the left-hand member. The only difference between the notion of a subset and that of a proper subset is that a set is a subset of itself but not a proper subset of itself.

Exercise Set 2

1. List the subsets of the set {boat, car, airplane, train}.

2. If C = {Los Angeles, Seattle, Sacramento, Chicago, New York, Detroit, San Francisco, Philadelphia}, list the members of the following subsets of Set C:

   (a) Cities in California,
   (b) Cities east of the Mississippi River,
   (c) Cities that are state capitals.

3. Let G = {Jane, Mary, Sue, Ann, Carol},
   A = {Jane, Mary, Sue, Ann},
   B = {Jane, Mary, Ann, Sue},
   C = {Jane, Mary}.

   In which of the following can ⊂ be inserted to make a true statement? In which of the following can ⊆ be inserted to make a true statement?

   (a) A ____ G
   (b) A ____ B
   (c) C ____ B
   (d) C ____ G

Universal Sets

It is very helpful, when thinking and talking about sets, to have the members of a given set come from some specified "population." For example, if we wish to talk about sets of pupils, it is helpful if we have some general population of pupils whom we consider as possible and eligible members of our set. We might want to focus our attention on the

pupils in a single school, or we might want to consider all second grade
pupils in the school, or all the elementary school pupils in the United
States. If we specify a particular set of pupils to which we shall limit
ourselves in drawing members for other sets to be discussed, then this
specified set is called the *universal set,* or simply the *universe,* of our discussion. Thus, in any particular discussion involving sets, every set in the
discussion is a subset of the universal set. The universal set is generally
denoted by the capital letter U.

Venn Diagrams

There is a schematic means of depicting set concepts using what are
called *Venn* or *Euler diagrams.* Figure 1 is such a diagram. In general,
some closed geometric figure is used to represent the universal set, with

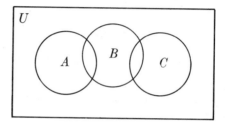

FIGURE 1

the understanding that the region interior to the boundary line represents
U, the universal set. Smaller closed geometric figures (we have used circles
in Figure 1) completely contained in U are then used to represent the sets
in a discussion (each being a subset of U), with the understanding that
the interior region of each of these smaller closed figures encompasses all
the members of the set being represented. The members of the set may
or may not be designated in the interior of the figure.

Figure 2 shows a Venn diagram in which letters of the alphabet are used

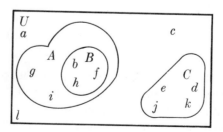

FIGURE 2

to denote individual members. This time we have used closed curves that are not circles to denote the sets under consideration. Thus, Figure 2 is a visual depiction of the following:

$$U = \{a, b, c, d, e, f, g, h, i, j, k, l\},$$
$$A = \{b, f, g, h, i\},$$
$$B = \{b, h, f\},$$
$$C = \{d, e, j, k\}.$$

We have

$$A \subset U, \quad B \subset U, \quad C \subset U, \quad \text{and} \quad B \subset A,$$

as you should verify from Figure 2 and also from the symbols within the braces.

COUNTING AND CARDINALITY

One-to-One Correspondence

The very important question of *how many* members belong to a set can be answered by appealing to a primitive notion, that of matching, or pairing, the elements of two sets. If the elements of two sets can be paired in some way so that each element of each set is associated with a single element of the other, then the elements in the sets are said to be in *one-to-one correspondence*.

Figure 3 shows two sets with a one-to-one correspondence exhibited between their members. Of course there are other ways of establishing a one-to-one correspondence here.

$$\{\text{Mary}, \quad \text{John}, \quad \text{Tom}\}$$
$$\uparrow \qquad \uparrow \qquad \uparrow$$
$$\downarrow \qquad \downarrow \qquad \downarrow$$
$$\{\text{Toby}, \quad \text{Rover}, \quad \text{Fido}\}$$

FIGURE 3

Figure 4 shows two additional possibilities, and there are others. It is important to note that regardless of how the correspondence is established, each member of each set is paired with one and only one member of the other. The existence of a one-to-one correspondence between sets has nothing to do with the way in which the correspondence is established.

$$\{\text{Mary}, \quad \text{John}, \quad \text{Tom}\} \qquad \{\text{Mary}, \quad \text{John}, \quad \text{Tom}\}$$
$$\uparrow \qquad \uparrow \qquad \uparrow \qquad\qquad \uparrow \qquad \uparrow \qquad \uparrow$$
$$\downarrow \qquad \downarrow \qquad \downarrow \qquad\qquad \downarrow \qquad \downarrow \qquad \downarrow$$
$$\{\text{Fido}, \quad \text{Toby}, \quad \text{Rover}\} \qquad \{\text{Rover}, \quad \text{Fido}, \quad \text{Toby}\}$$

FIGURE 4

One-to-one correspondences can be established by actually pairing the elements of the sets or by clearly specifying how such a pairing can be made in theory. We have already shown a specific pairing, but the sets in our example contain very few members and thus it was easy to show the correspondence by listing. If we were to have to show a one-to-one correspondence (assuming one existed) between the set of people in a football stadium and the set of seats in the stadium, we would have to specify precisely how such a correspondence could be established. One way might be to have each person take a seat, and then observe that each person was seated in a seat, and no seat was unoccupied.

Equivalent Sets

At this point in our discussion, we might profitably pause to inquire into just what kinds of ways we have thus far developed for comparing or relating one set with another. For example, we know that set-equality implies *sameness*. That is, if two sets are equal, they have the same members, and conversely. Also, we have compared sets by means of *subset* and *proper subset* considerations, where all of the elements of one set are elements of another, but where equality does not necessarily exist. In addition to the equality and subset relation, we can now define a new relation between sets based on the one-to-one correspondence concept.

> The statement that two sets are equivalent means that *the elements of the two sets can be placed in one-to-one correspondence.*

The equivalence relationship between sets is not the same as the equality relationship because equivalent sets need not be the same set; although equal sets are obviously equivalent since any set can be placed in one-to-one correspondence with itself.

The symbol $\sim$ (read, "is equivalent to") is used to denote equivalence. Thus if

$$A = \{a, b, c\}, \qquad B = \{l, m, n\},$$

and

$$C = \{x, y, z\},$$

we can indicate their equivalence by writing statements like $A \sim B$, $A \sim C$, and $B \sim C$. Again, do not think that for A to be equivalent to B it is necessary that a, b, and c denote the same kind of things that l, m, and n denote. Indeed, the very usefulness of the equivalence relation depends on the fact that it does not matter what kinds of elements the sets A and B contain. All that equivalence is concerned with is the fact that we can pair the elements in such a way that the sets are in one-to-one correspondence.

The notion of one-to-one correspondence was probably one of man's earliest mathematical ideas. The use of marks such as /////// on cave walls to match the members of the set of buffalo killed in a hunt, for example, is an application of this principle. Whether or not names existed for these sets of marks is questionable, but the marks themselves served very well to answer the question, "How many buffalo did you kill?" Moreover, such tallies could be compared with other similar sets of marks to determine who, among a group of hunters, had had the greatest success in the hunt. Questions involving more and fewer can be resolved by a one-to-one pairing of the elements of two sets and the observation of the existence of unpaired elements in one of the sets when the other is exhausted. For example, if we compare the sets A and B, where

$$A = \{a, \ b, \ c\}$$
$$\updownarrow \quad \updownarrow \quad \updownarrow$$
$$B = \{x, \ y, \ z, \ w\},$$

it is apparent that they are not equivalent; and we can describe this lack of equivalence in one of two ways: by saying that the set B contains more elements than A; or, alternatively, that A contains fewer elements than B.

Ordered Sets

The properties of sets in which we have thus far been interested have all centered around the notion of set membership. That is, we have been interested solely in talking about whether a given object is or is not in a given set, whether a given set does or does not share members with another, and whether or not there is equivalence between two given sets. In each of these considerations, we have observed that the order in which we considered the members of our sets was not of concern to us.

We wish now to consider some sets with the property that the *order* in which the elements are arranged is of importance. "What is order?" Answering this question, in a purely mathematical sense, is a matter of some difficulty if it is to be answered from abstract considerations only. There is, however, such a strong intuitive notion in most of us with regard to the concept of, say, *before*, that it is probably best to lean on this intuitive idea almost completely in discussing order. Essentially, to order things is to arrange them in some unambiguous fashion so that one can then say of each element which of the elements it precedes. This arrangement is made by comparing each pair of items in the list we are to arrange.

and deciding which of the two belongs before the other. The word "before" can be replaced with other words or phrases—for example, "earlier than," "less than," "preceding," "shorter than," "to the left of," or "below." Essentially, order in a set is a relationship among the elements in the set, which is specified clearly enough that one can determine whether each element does or does not have the specified relationship with any other element. When each item has been arranged so that it is in the proper relationship to all of the other items, then the items may be said to have been ordered.

Consider the set of letters from the alphabet:

$$A = \{\text{"}x\text{"}, \text{"}b\text{"}, \text{"}m\text{"}, \text{"}n\text{"}, \text{"}k\text{"}\}.$$

Here the quotation marks indicate that the members are the symbols themselves, and are not being used as names for other unspecified objects. There is an arbitrary order given to the letters in the alphabet, namely

$$\text{"}a\text{"}, \text{"}b\text{"}, \text{"}c\text{"}, \text{"}d\text{"}, \text{"}e\text{"}, \text{"}f\text{"}, \text{"}g\text{"}, \text{"}h\text{"}, \ldots, \text{"}x\text{"}, \text{"}y\text{"}, \text{"}z\text{"};$$

and "a" comes before (or earlier in the alphabet than) "b"; "b" is before "c"; and so on. If now we ask that the elements in the set A be ordered so that (reading from left-to-right in the braces) the symbols occur in their proper relationship to each other according to this criterion for order, we have

$$A_{\text{ordered}} = \{\text{"}b\text{"}, \text{"}k\text{"}, \text{"}m\text{"}, \text{"}n\text{"}, \text{"}x\text{"}\},$$

where A_{ordered} is used to denote the set whose elements are those of A, but considered in the specified order from left-to-right. A_{ordered} is an example of an *ordered set*.

Standard Sets and Cardinality

Now, let us establish some ordered sets of symbols beginning with the set $\{\text{"}1\text{"}\}$ (read, "the set whose element is the numeral 1") and continuing thus:

$$\{\text{"}1\text{"}, \text{"}2\text{"}\},$$
$$\{\text{"}1\text{"}, \text{"}2\text{"}, \text{"}3\text{"}\},$$
$$\{\text{"}1\text{"}, \text{"}2\text{"}, \text{"}3\text{"}, \text{"}4\text{"}\}.$$

If we continue this chain of sets to include symbols "5", "6", "7", "8", "9", and if we introduce the symbol "0" together with some agreements about how these symbols are to be combined in a systematic way to form new symbols, we can visualize an endless chain of sets as described. Moreover, it is observable that

$$\{\text{"}1\text{"}\} \subset \{\text{"}1\text{"}, \text{"}2\text{"}\} \subset \{\text{"}1\text{"}, \text{"}2\text{"}, \text{"}3\text{"}\} \subset \ldots$$

(the three dots indicate that the sequence extends indefinitely in the same pattern). By comparing any one of these sets with another, we can determine which belongs before which in this endless succession of proper subsets. These sets of symbols are called *standard sets;* and each member of any one of them is a *numeral.* In words, the numerals are read, "one," "two," "three," and so on.

We now have all of the concepts necessary to establish a clear way of answering the question: "How many members are in the set A?" Consider the sets $\{a\}$, $\{x\}$, $\{o\}$, and $\{Jack\}$. Each of these sets is equivalent to any other of them. That is, the elements of any two of the sets can be placed in one-to-one correspondence Now, consider all sets equivalent to any one of these, say, $\{a\}$. Among these sets is the standard set $\{"1"\}$. These sets all possess a property in common, namely, their equivalence to the standard set $\{"1"\}$; and this property is independent of the nature of the elements the sets contain. This common property we shall call the number one. Similarly, the property shared by all sets which are equivalent to the standard set $\{"1", "2"\}$ is called the number two.

The naming is accomplished by assigning to the number the last numeral occurring in the standard set for that number, and the set is said to contain that number of elements. Thus, the standard set for all sets equivalent to $A = \{a, b, c, d\}$ is $\{"1", "2", "3", "4"\}$; and since "4" is the last (right-hand) member of the standard set, A is said to have four members, and four is said to be the number of the set A.

If A is any set, the symbol

$$n(A)$$

(read, "the number of the set A") denotes the number of ("how many") elements in the set. For example, if

$$A = \{a, b, c\},$$

and

$$B = \{a, b, c, d, e, f\},$$

then

$$n(A) = 3 \text{ and } n(B) = 6.$$

The number of a set is sometimes called the *cardinality* of the set; and hence, for any set A, $n(A)$ is called a *cardinal number.* The empty set, $\emptyset$, is assigned the cardinality zero, and

$$n(\emptyset) = 0.$$

Numbers and Numerals

A number, as we have developed the concept here, is therefore an abstraction. Note that there is a distinction between a number and its name. Numerals, those elements in our standard sets, are *names for numbers*. It is as necessary upon occasion to distinguish between the number, 4, and the numeral, "4", as it is to distinguish between the boy, Jack, and his name, "Jack."

In the ordinary course of a discussion, there is usually little difficulty occasioned by the difference between an object and its name, the intent of a speaker or writer generally being quite evident from the context. In writing about matters where this distinction is not obvious as, for example, in writing a sentence such as "How many letters are there in 'the post office'?" in which words as such (in this case "the post office") are being discussed, it is customary to use single or double quotation marks to clarify the meaning. Thus, in our sample sentence, the intent is to ask for the number of letters from the alphabet in the words "the post office," rather than to talk about number of epistles in the post office. In mathematics, comparable situations are handled similarly, quotation marks generally being employed to indicate the fact that numerals are being discussed rather than the numbers they represent. This is not always done, however, when the intent is clear from context.

Cardinal Numbers and Order

Having developed what is meant by a cardinal number, we can now feel free to talk about sets whose elements are cardinal numbers. For example, we can write

$$A = \{1, \ 2, \ 3, \ 4\}$$

to denote the set whose elements are the cardinal numbers, (or simply numbers) 1, 2, 3, 4. Note that this set is not the same as the standard set

$$B = \{\text{"1"}, \ \text{"2"}, \ \text{"3"}, \ \text{"4"}\}$$

because in one case the elements of the set are numbers, and in the other numerals. They are, however, sets of the same cardinality, and we can write

$$n(A) = n(B),$$

meaning that "$n(A)$" and "$n(B)$" are different names for the same number—in this case, the number 4. The elements in $\{1, \ 2, \ 3, \ 4\}$ are shown in ordered sequence.

We can order cardinal numbers by means of standard sets. Let A and B be any two standard sets; then if $A \subset B$ but $B \not\subset A$, we define $n(A) < n(B)$. (Read: "The cardinal number for A is *less than* the cardinal number for B.") For example, consider the numbers 3 and 5. Since $\{\text{"1"}, \text{"2"}, \text{"3"}\} \subset \{\text{"1"}, \text{"2"}, \text{"3"}, \text{"4"}, \text{"5"}\}$, by our definition we have $3 < 5$. (Read: "Three is less than five.") When the elements of a set of cardinal numbers are arranged so that the standard set to which each corresponds contains as a proper subset the standard set of every cardinal number preceding it (and thus its standard set is a proper subset of the standard set of every cardinal number that succeeds it), then the set has been ordered. The elements of the set of cardinal numbers

$$\{7, 3, 6, 2\}$$

can be ordered $2 < 3 < 6 < 7$, by observing that

$$\{``1", ``2"\} \subset \{``1", ``2", ``3"\} \subset \{``1", ``2", ``3", ``4", ``5", ``6"\} \subset$$
$$\{``1", ``2", ``3", ``4", ``5", ``6", ``7"\}.$$

Since $\emptyset \subset A$ for every standard set A, $0 < n(A)$ for every nonempty set A. That is, 0 is the smallest cardinal number.

Cardinal Numbers and Counting

We have seen that cardinal numbers serve very well in some instances to tell us how many elements a set contains. Moreover, the cardinal numbers are ordered. Because of these two properties, they can be used to count items, and to order the elements in any other set in an arbitrary fashion.

Suppose we want to determine the number of marbles in a bag. We can do this by reaching into the bag and withdrawing one marble at a time and placing it in one-to-one correspondence with one of our standard sets in ordered sequence. Figure 5 shows a schematic depiction of this process. When the last marble has been associated with its standard set, we can examine the right-hand element of this set and determine the cardinal number of this standard set. This will be the number of marbles the bag contained.

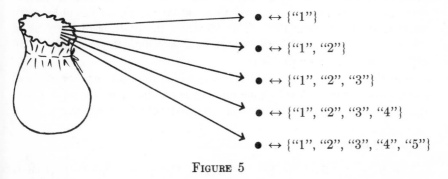

FIGURE 5

The process of associating objects sequentially with standard sets (and hence with cardinal numbers) is called *counting*. Notice that the counting of the marbles is independent of the particular marbles themselves. If they were all returned to the bag, and the process repeated, each marble need not be placed in correspondence with the same standard set to which it corresponded in the original matching. The order in which the marbles are withdrawn from the bag will have no effect on the count, and under any arrangement of the marbles the cardinality of the last standard set employed in the count will always be the same. If this were not the case we could not talk about *the* cardinal number of a set.

The counting process described here has another useful feature. If we wish, as soon as we have paired each marble with a standard set, we can note the cardinal number of the set and label the marble with the name of this number. We can then display the marbles as follows:

$$① \quad ② \quad ③ \quad ④ \quad ⑤ \quad ⑥ \quad . . . \, ,$$

and identify each of the particular marbles by the cardinal number with which it is associated.

When cardinal numbers are employed to designate individual elements in a set in some order, the elements or numbers are being used in what is called an *ordinal* sense. In fact, one frequently encounters the term *ordinal number* applied to numbers used in this way. This usage is confusing to the extent that it conveys to the reader the notion that there is a set of ordinal numbers that differs from the set of cardinal numbers in some way. The term "ordinal" refers to the usage and not to the essential nature of the numbers involved.

The ordinal usage of numbers can usually, but not always, be identified by the presence of the words "first," "second," "third," "twenty-second," and the like, as opposed to "one," "two," "three," and "twenty-two." Symbols for numbers being put to ordinal use frequently (but again, not always) appear in the form "7th," "32nd," or "51st." Perhaps the most common exceptions in this regard occur in dating, as, for example, when we talk about the year 1901. This identifies the position of the year in which we are interested with respect to a sequence of years, and is an ordinal use of the number 1901.

Sometimes numerals are used in a way which relates to neither cardinal nor ordinal number. A telephone number is one familiar illustration, and the number assigned to a member of a football squad is another.

Finite and Infinite Sets

The set of cardinal numbers is endless. Given any standard set, it is always possible to form another with greater cardinality by simply adding an additional numeral to the right of the last numeral in the given standard set.

Any nonempty set, A, whose elements can be placed in one-to-one correspondence with those of a standard set is said to be a *finite set*. This means that the elements in A can be counted according to the procedure developed in the preceding section, and that such a counting would terminate with a standard set. For example, the set of states in the United States of America in 1963 is a finite set, because the elements of this set can be counted, with the process ending when we come to the standard set whose cardinality is fifty. The empty set is also considered a finite set. All other sets are said to be *infinite sets*. The set of cardinal numbers, therefore, is an infinite set.

The properties of infinite sets cannot reasonably be expected to be discussed at the elementary school level. Presumably children can appreciate the intuitive notion that there is no greatest cardinal number, or that the elements of the set of cardinal numbers can be arranged in an endless sequence, but there seems little point in introducing the word "infinite" as such. Indeed, the use of the phrase "an infinite number of" can actually evoke in the children's minds the erroneous notion of some very large but quite specific number that is greater than any cardinal number. While it is true that a cardinality is assigned to the set of cardinal numbers in higher mathematics, this cardinality is not a number in the sense in which we have here discussed number.

Earlier, the point was made that if $A \subset B$, then it seems natural to expect that A has fewer members than B. Consider, however, the set of cardinal numbers,

$$C = \{0, 1, 2, 3, \ldots\},$$

in which the three dots indicate that these elements continue without end. Then consider the set of even cardinal numbers,

$$D = \{0, 2, 4, 6, \ldots\}.$$

By displaying these sets as follows,

$$C = \{0, 1, 2, 3, \ldots\}$$
$$\updownarrow \; \updownarrow \; \updownarrow \; \updownarrow$$
$$D = \{0, 2, 4, 6, \ldots\},$$

we see that their elements are in one-to-one correspondence. Indeed, we can specify a rule (pair the cardinal number n with the cardinal number $2n$) by which this correspondence can be made explicit. Therefore, by our definition of equivalence,

$$C \sim D.$$

But D is clearly a proper subset of C, because, for instance, it does not contain the cardinal number 1. Thus, it is possible for an infinite set to

be placed in a one-to-one correspondence with a proper subset of itself.
With finite sets this is impossible.

The Number Line

A useful model for visualizing the set of cardinal numbers is the number
line. Children generally have a very strong intuitive appreciation for
those properties of straight lines that we use in talking about numbers.
Among these intuitive notions are (a) that every point on a straight line
has a position, (b) that there is such a thing as a "distance" between every
two points on a straight line, and (c) that it is possible to compare the
"distance" between any two points with the "distance" between any other
two points.

To construct from a geometric straight line a model for the cardinal
numbers that will be meaningful to a student, we can begin by drawing a
representation of a part of a straight line on any flat surface. It is helpful
also if arrowheads are affixed to each end of the portion of a line

$$\longleftarrow\!\!\!\-----------------------\!\!\!\longrightarrow$$

to indicate that the picture is assumed to continue indefinitely in both
directions. Next, let us identify some specific points on the picture of a
line by marking any convenient point (call it P) and a second point
different from the first (call it Q). From these points mark off, by some
means, a series of points (of which P and Q are two consecutive points of
the series) equally spaced along the line. The method of doing this might
be to use the familiar pair of compasses, a pair of marks made on the edge
of a sheet of paper, or some other similar device (Fig. 6) for marking
equal spaces. Note that the location of the points P and Q is of no con-
sequence, and, once having chosen them, we can mark off the line in both
directions.

When the identification of points has been completed, we might find
something like Figure 7. At this point, we have a picture of a part of
what is conceived to be a line stretching off indefinitely in two directions;
and upon which, by means of repeatedly laying off a fixed distance, we
have identified some specific points. The picture we have is not a part of
the line itself, nor are the marks we have made to single out points the
points themselves. Points and lines in the sense we are thinking.of them
here are simply concepts or ideas, which we represent by means of paper
and pencil, or chalkboard and chalk. Our pictures have properties not
shared by the things they represent; for example, they can be seen. Moreover, in order to be seen, they have to have dimension, and the only
dimension we conceive our line as having is length, which is finite when
considered as a portion isolated between two points and infinite when

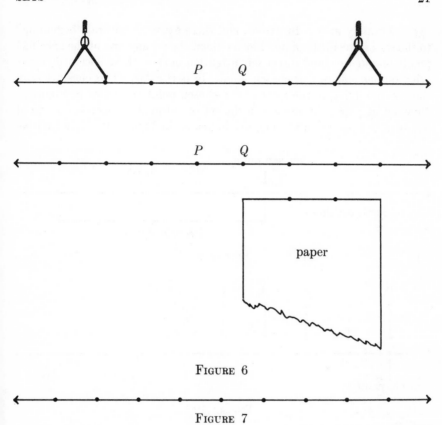

FIGURE 6

FIGURE 7

considered as extending endlessly in its entirety. Our points are conceived simply as dimensionless locations.

Our picture, however, is a vivid and useful one for the purposes to which we wish to put it. Next, let us visualize the set of whole numbers in its entirety and see how we can make a connection between this set of numbers and the set of points we have identified on the line. Figure 8 shows the two sets, one above the other. We know that there are infinitely many numbers in our set; and, conceptually, infinitely many *specified* points on our line. We propose to pair the elements of these sets. There is, however, the question of how to make this pairing. After all, while the set of whole numbers has a beginning (least member), our line is conceived as extend-

$$\{0, 1, 2, 3, 4, 5, \cdots\}$$

FIGURE 8

ing indefinitely in two directions, and there exists no natural "beginning" to the set of specified points. Let us, then, choose any one of the specified points on our line, and direct our attention only to those specified points lying on one side of this chosen point. In particular, let us consider only those points lying to the right of the chosen point, as shown in Figure 9. Now, let us pair each number in the set of cardinal numbers with one of our specified points, in the manner indicated in Figure 10. Note that we

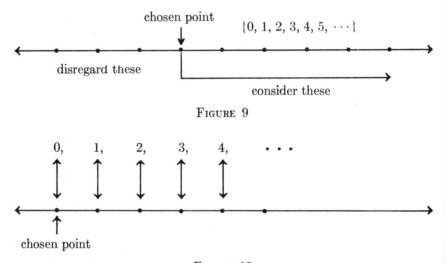

FIGURE 9

FIGURE 10

are making this pairing in a particular way. The number 0 is associated with the chosen (initial) point, and each successive cardinal number is assigned, in order, to a successive point. Figure 11 shows a picture of a

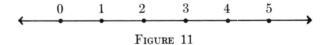

FIGURE 11

part of the finished product, with each specified point labeled with the numeral for the cardinal number with which it is paired. Conceptually, this labeling extends indefinitely far to the right, with each cardinal number matched, in order, with a specific point. The portion of the line to the left of the point corresponding to 0 (this point is called the *origin* of the number line) is of no interest or concern to us at this time. When the set of numbers is extended to include negative numbers, this part of the line can be used in a similar way to visualize these negative numbers.

If we wish to focus our attention on a picture of a set of cardinal numbers paired with points at some distance away from the origin, we need only sketch that part of the number line in which we have an interest. For example, if we wish to visualize that part of the number line associated with the set of cardinal numbers

$$\{265,\ 266,\ 267,\ 268,\ 269\},$$

our picture of the part of the number line might appear as shown in Figure 12, where it is understood that the origin is located 265 segments along the line to the left.

265   266   267   268   269

←——•————•————•————•————•——→

FIGURE 12

There are a number of valuable pedagogic purposes for which the number line can be used, although at this time we shall point out only one.* The number line gives a concrete means of visualizing order in the set of cardinal numbers. Of any two cardinal numbers, the point on the number line corresponding to the lesser of the two numbers will lie to the left of the point corresponding to the greater.

SET OPERATIONS

Union of Sets

Consider the set of second grade children present in Room 7 of Winslow School at some specific time. If we call this our universal set, U, then we can talk about a number of different subsets of U. For example, we can talk about the set of boys, the set of girls, the set of children seated in Row 1, Row 2, or some other row, or the set of children whose last names begin with the letter "W." There are many ways of specifying subsets of our universe. Using such subsets, we can illustrate how two (or more) sets can be employed to identify another subset of U.

Suppose we call U our universe as specified above, and let

$$A = \{\text{boys}\}, \qquad C = \{\text{children in Rows 1 and 2}\},$$
$$B = \{\text{girls}\}, \qquad D = \{\text{children in Rows 3 and 4}\},$$

where it is understood that $A \subseteq U$, $\quad B \subseteq U$, $\quad C \subseteq U$, $\quad$ and $\quad D \subseteq U$. (Read these symbols in words to make sure you know what they mean.) If we ask the members of set A to stand, all of the boys in the class should stand. Similarly, we can identify the members of each of the sets B, C, D

---

* Other booklets in this series will make heavy use of the number line concept.

by asking that their members stand. Of course, when those in sets C and D are asked to rise, we will possibly find both boys and girls on their feet. Now, suppose we ask those children who are members of either set A, or set C, or both, to stand. We should expect, this time, to find all of the boys on their feet as well as all girls in Rows 1 and 2. We have used A and C to form a new set, called the *union* of sets A and C. To formalize what we are talking about here, let us make the following definition.

> *If A and B are subsets of the universe, the union of A and B, denoted by the symbols $A \cup B$, is the set of all elements belonging to A or B or both.*

(Note that the symbol "$\cup$" differs from the letter U used to denote the universal set.)

The process of forming the union of two sets is called an *operation* on sets, and since it is defined so that it applies to just two sets at a time it is called a *binary operation*. Just as we can perform a binary operation on the numbers 2 and 3 to obtain another number (for example, $2+3=5$ or $2 \times 3 = 6$), we can perform a binary operation on two sets to obtain another set. (The prefix "bi" means two—compare its use in "bicycle," "biped," etc.) Moreover, since the union of any two subsets of a given universe is, itself, a subset of the same universe, the universe is said to be *closed* with respect to the formation of unions.

Let us give another example of the union of two sets, this time using sets whose members are simply identified by the names, a, b, c, d, e, f, g, and h. Let us agree that

$$U = \{a, b, c, d, e, f, g, h\},$$
$$A = \{a, b, c\},$$
$$B = \{b, c, d\},$$
$$C = \{d, e, f, g, h\},$$
$$D = \{h\}.$$

Now, verify that $A \cup B$ (read "the union of A and B" or, sometimes, "A union B") is $\{a, b, c, d\}$. Notice that $A \cup B$ is not written $\{a, b, c, b, c, d\}$ since there is no point in writing the name for a single member more than once. The set $A \cup B$ has four members, not six. Returning to the sets specified above, verify that

$$A \cup C = \{a, b, c, d, e, f, g, h\}.$$

Since this set contains all the members of U, we can write

$$A \cup C = U.$$

Also,

$$A \cup D = \{a, b, c, h\}$$

and

$$D \cup C = \{d, \ e, \ f, \ g, \ h\}.$$

This last set is the same as set C; thus,

$$D \cup C = C.$$

The Venn diagrams introduced in the preceding section offer a vivid means of visualizing unions of sets. Shading the regions being used to represent sets makes the union of two sets stand out quite clearly. Figures 13-16 depict the unions of the sets mentioned above.

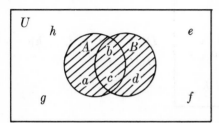
$$A \cup B = \{a, \ b, \ c, \ d\}$$

FIGURE 13

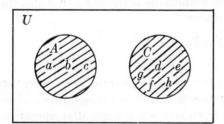
$$A \cup C = \{a, \ b, \ c, \ d, \ e, \ f, \ g, \ h\}$$

FIGURE 14

The last example (Fig. 16) illustrates another fact, namely, if a set is a subset of a second set then the union of the two sets is the second set. Symbolically, this is expressed as follows:

$$\text{If } A \subseteq B, \text{ then } A \cup B = B.$$

In particular then, the union of any set with the universal set will be the universal set, because every set is a subset of the universal set. In symbols, for every set

$$A \subseteq U, \ A \cup U = U.$$

Moreover, $\emptyset \cup A = A$ for every set A, since $\emptyset \subseteq A$. The definition of the union of two sets implies that the order in which the members of a set are

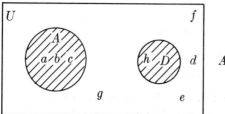

$$A \cup D = \{a,\ b,\ c,\ h\}$$

FIGURE 15

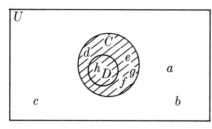

$$D \cup C = \{d,\ e,\ f,\ g,\ h\}$$
$$D \cup C = C$$

FIGURE 16

considered is immaterial in forming a union, as is the order in which the sets are considered. Thus, the statement

$$A \cup B = B \cup A$$

is true for any two sets A and B.

When the order in which we take two things in performing an operation has no effect on the result, the operation is said to be *commutative*. Thus, the process of forming the union of two sets is a commutative operation.

Let us make another definition here so that we can talk about the union of more than two sets. Thus, let us agree to the following: For any sets A, B, and C,

$$A \cup B \cup C \text{ denotes the set } (A \cup B) \cup C.$$

Translating this ·symbolism into words, we might put it this way: $A \cup B \cup C$ is the set formed by first forming the union of A and B (this is indicated by the parentheses) and then forming the union of this set with C. Similarly, by agreement we would work from the left in the repeated binary operation $A \cup B \cup C \cup D$. For an example, consider

$$U = \{2,\ 4,\ 6,\ 8,\ 10,\ 12\},$$
$$A = \{2,\ 4\},$$
$$B = \{4,\ 6,\ 8\},$$
$$C = \{4,\ 8,\ 12\}.$$

Forming $A \cup B$ first, we have

$$A \cup B = \{2,\ 4\} \cup \{4,\ 6,\ 8\},$$
$$= \{2,\ 4,\ 6,\ 8\}.$$

Then,

$$(A \cup B) \cup C = \{2,\ 4,\ 6,\ 8\} \cup \{4,\ 8,\ 12\},$$
$$= \{2,\ 4,\ 6,\ 8,\ 12\}.$$

This example can be used to point out another characteristic of the operation of forming the union of sets. Is $A \cup (B \cup C)$ the same set as $(A \cup B) C$? [In $A \cup (B \cup C)$, the parentheses indicate that the set $B \cup C$ is formed first, and then the union of this set with set A is formed.] If U, A, B, and C are specified as above, we have

$$B \cup C = \{4,\ 6,\ 8\} \cup \{4,\ 8,\ 12\},$$
$$= \{4,\ 6,\ 8,\ 12\}.$$

Now, if we form the union of this set with A, we find that

$$A \cup (B \cup C) = \{2,\ 4\} \cup \{4,\ 6,\ 8,\ 12\},$$
$$= \{2,\ 4,\ 6,\ 8,\ 12\},$$

which is precisely the same set as $(A \cup B) \cup C$. Of course, the fact that we obtained identical results in this particular case might be simply an accident. Can we expect that for every three sets A, B, and C,

$$(A \cup B) \cup C = A \cup (B \cup C)?$$

The answer is yes, and it can be illustrated by the Venn diagrams in Figures 17-20.

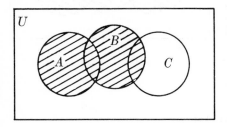

FIGURE 17   FIGURE 18

Figure 17 depicts three sets A, B, and C in a universe U, and the region corresponding to $A \cup B$ is shaded.

Figure 18 shows the same sets, but with the region corresponding to $(A \cup B) \cup C$ shaded.

Comparing Figures 18 and 20, we can see that

$$(A \cup B) \cup C = A \cup (B \cup C)$$

This property of the operation of forming union of sets is called the *associative property*. We also say that the operation is *associative*.

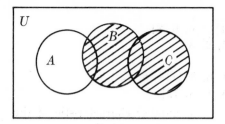

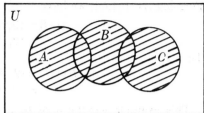

FIGURE 19

FIGURE 20

Figure 19 illustrates the same three sets, but with the region corresponding to $B \cup C$ shaded.

Figure 20 shows the same three sets with the region corresponding to $A \cup (B \cup C)$ shaded.

What this really means is that in $A \cup B \cup C$ it is immaterial which of the following sets is formed first: $A \cup B$ or $B \cup C$.

Figures 21 and 22 go one step further and illustrate that $(A \cup C) \cup B = (A \cup B) \cup C = A \cup (B \cup C)$. Comparing Figures 18, 20, and 22, you can see that $(A \cup B) \cup C = A \cup (B \cup C) = (A \cup C) \cup B$.

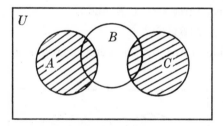

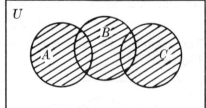

$A \cup C$

$(A \cup C) \cup B$

FIGURE 21

FIGURE 22

Exercise Set 3

1. Let $U = \{$The states of the U.S.A.$\}$,

$C = \{$Colorado, California, Connecticut$\}$,

$O = \{$Oregon, Oklahoma$\}$,

$P = \{$Alaska, California, Hawaii, Oregon, Washington$\}$.

List the members of each of the following.

(a) $C \cup O$

(b) $C \cup P$

(c) $O \cup P$

2. Let $U = \{$Children in Grade 5 at Winslow School$\}$,
$S = \{$Mary, Ellen, Anne, John, Bob$\}$,
$M = \{$John, Bob, Anne, Jimmy, Sue$\}$,
$C = \{$Don, Mary, Philip, Jimmy, Nora, Anne$\}$,
$W = \{$Mary, Anne, Joe, Nora$\}$.

List the members of each of the following.

(a) $S \cup M$
(b) $C \cup W$
(c) $(S \cup C) \cup W$
(d) $C \cup (W \cup M)$

3. Let $U = \{1, 2, 3, 4, 5, 6, 7, 8, 9, 10, 11, 12\}$,
$A = \{2, 4, 6, 8, 10, 12\}$,
$B = \{1, 3, 5, 7, 9, 11\}$,
$C = \{3, 6, 9, 12\}$,
$D = \{2, 3, 4, 5, 6, 7\}$.

List the members of each of the following.

(a) $A \cup B$
(b) $B \cup C$
(c) $C \cup D$
(d) $(A \cup C) \cup D$

Intersection of Sets

A second operation on sets is that of forming the *intersection* of two sets. Let us begin the discussion by using the same sets we used to illustrate the formation of the union of two sets. Thus,

$U = \{$second grade children present in Room 7 at Winslow School$\}$,

where it is understood that we are referring to some specific point in time when school is in session. Also, as before, we have

$$A = \{\text{boys}\},$$
$$B = \{\text{girls}\},$$
$$C = \{\text{children in Rows 1 and 2}\},$$
$$D = \{\text{children in Rows 3 and 4}\}.$$

A, B, C, and D are all subsets of U. If we ask the members who belong to both set A and set C to stand, we will have on their feet all the boys in Rows 1 and 2. Thus, we have used the two sets, A and C, to form a new set: this time, the set of those elements that are in *both* A and C. Consequently, we have performed a binary operation on sets A and C.

This is an example of what we mean by the intersection of two sets. In general, let us make the following definition.

> *If A and B are subsets of the universe, the intersection of*
> *A and B, denoted by $A \cap B$, is the set of all elements*
> *belonging to both A and B.*   °

The symbolism $A \cap B$ is read, "the intersection of A and B"; or sometimes read, "A intersection B." Since any members of both A and B must be members of U, the universe is closed with respect to the operation of forming intersections of sets. Also, since $A \cap B$ has exactly the same members as $B \cap A$, it is true that, for all sets A and B,

$$A \cap B = B \cap A,$$

and the operation of forming the intersection of two sets is commutative.

Let us also consider again the example

$$U = \{a, b, c, d, e, f, g, h\},$$
$$A = \{a, b, c\},$$
$$B = \{b, c, d\},$$
$$C = \{d, e, f, g, h\},$$
$$D = \{h\}.$$

You can verify that

$$A \cap B = \{a, b, c\} \cap \{b, c, d\},$$
$$= \{b, c\}.$$

(Are these symbols meaningful? What is in effect being said here is that the set of elements which are in both A and B is the set of elements in both $\{a, b, c\}$ and $\{b, c, d\}$. This is the set whose elements are b and c; that is, $\{b, c\}$.) Figure 23 is a Venn diagram illustrating this, where $A \cap B$ is depicted by shading.

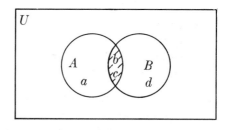

$$A \cap B = \{b, c\}$$

FIGURE 23

The sets A and C have no elements in common; hence the intersection of sets A and C has no elements and is, therefore, the empty set. This can be written

$$A \cap C = \emptyset,$$

which is read, "The intersection of A and C is the empty set." The Venn

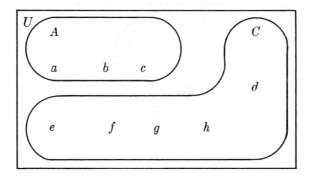

$$A \cap C = \emptyset$$

Figure 24

diagram in Figure 24 shows this situation. When two nonempty sets contain no members in common, they are called *disjoint* sets. More formally:

If A and B are nonempty sets, then A and B are disjoint if, and only if, $A \cap B = \emptyset$.

Now we are ready to consider a few more interesting intersections. A little thought should suffice to convince one that for any sets A and B, if $A \subseteq B$, then

$$A \cap B = A.$$

In words, if a first set is a subset of another set, then their intersection is the first set. Figure 25 is a Venn diagram depicting this situation.

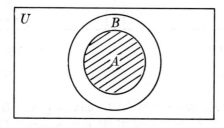

$$A \cap B = A$$

Figure 25

Since every set in a discussion is a subset of the universe, it follows that for every set A,

$$U \cap A = A.$$

This is shown by the Venn diagram in Figure 26.

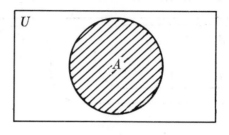

$$U \cap A = A$$

FIGURE 26

Although the process of forming the intersection of two sets, like that of forming their union, is a binary operation, we can extend it to more than two sets by means of the following definition:

For any sets A, B, *and* C, A∩B∩C *denotes the set* (A∩B)∩C.

The parentheses indicate that $A \cap B$ is formed first.

Now, consider Figures 27 and 28, which show first $A \cap B$, and then $(A \cap B) \cap C$.

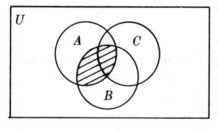

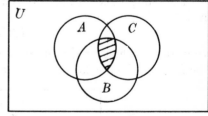

$A \cap B$ $(A \cap B) \cap C$

FIGURE 27   FIGURE 28

In Figures 29 and 30, we see first $B \cap C$, and then $A \cap (B \cap C)$.

When we compare Figures 28 and 30, it is apparent that, for any sets A, B, and C,

$$(A \cap B) \cap C = A \cap (B \cap C).$$

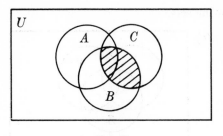

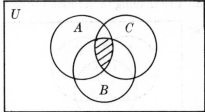

$B \cap C$

FIGURE 29

$A \cap (B \cap C)$

FIGURE 30

In other words, the operation of forming the intersection of sets is *associative*. This does not constitute a proof of associativity, but it does make it plausible.

Exercise Set 4

1. Let $U = \{$cities in Michigan$\}$,

   $B = \{$Detroit, Grand Rapids, Lansing, Saginaw, Flint$\}$,
   $C = \{$Lansing, Kalamazoo, Ann Arbor, Detroit$\}$,
   $D = \{$Grand Rapids, Detroit, Battle Creek$\}$,
   $E = \{$Ludington, Benton Harbor, Frankfort$\}$.

   List the members of each of the following.

   (a) $B \cap C$ (d) $(B \cap D) \cap C$
   (b) $C \cap D$ (e) $D \cap (C \cap B)$
   (c) $C \cap E$ (f) $(B \cap E) \cap C$

2. Let $U = \{1, 2, 3, 4, 5, \ldots, 15\}$,
   $A = \{2, 4, 6, 8, 10, 12, 14\}$,
   $B = \{1, 3, 5, 7, 9, 11, 13, 15\}$,
   $C = \{3, 6, 9, 12, 15\}$,
   $D = \{4, 8, 12\}$.

   List the members of each of the following.

   (a) $A \cap B$ (d) $(A \cap C) \cap D$
   (b) $B \cap C$ (e) $B \cap (C \cap D)$
   (c) $A \cap D$ (f) $(A \cap D) \cap C$

3. Use shading to indicate the following sets.

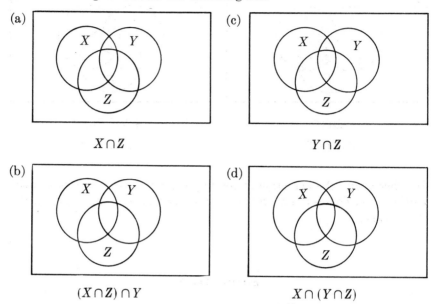

(a)

$X \cap Z$

(c)

$Y \cap Z$

(b)

$(X \cap Z) \cap Y$

(d)

$X \cap (Y \cap Z)$

Combining Set Operations

When the processes of forming unions and intersections of sets are combined, Venn diagrams become increasingly useful as an aid to visualizing the results. We shall consider only a few examples here; but, if you wish to do some experimenting on your own, you will find that combinations of these operations offer many possibilities for the formation of sets.

First, consider the statement

$$A \cap (B \cup C) = (A \cap B) \cup (A \cap C).$$

Is this a true assertion? In Figures 31-33 we have a sequence of Venn diagrams showing $A \cap (B \cap C)$: by first (Fig. 31) showing A, B, and C; second (Fig. 32), $B \cup C$; and third (Fig. 33), $A \cap (B \cup C)$.

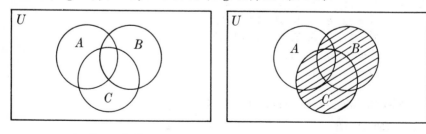

A, B, and C
FIGURE 31

$B \cup C$
FIGURE 32

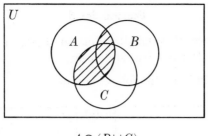

$$A \cap (B \cup C)$$

FIGURE 33

Now, compare this sequence with that in Figures 34-36, where Figure 34 shows $A \cap B$, Figure 35 shows $A \cap C$, and Figure 36 shows $(A \cap B) \cup (A \cap C)$.

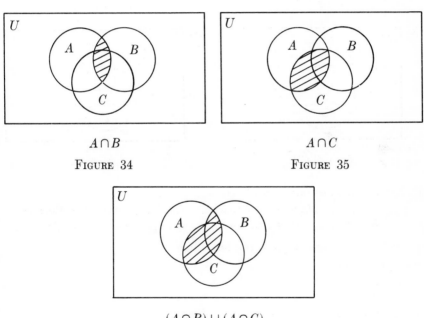

$A \cap B$

FIGURE 34

$A \cap C$

FIGURE 35

$$(A \cap B) \cup (A \cap C)$$

FIGURE 36

Clearly, Figures 33 and 36 show the same shaded region; and our original statement is seen to be true. The operation of forming union and intersection of sets has the property that for sets A, B, and C the statement

$$A \cap (B \cup C) = (A \cap B) \cup (A \cap C)$$

is true. This is known as a distributive property.

Exercise Set 5

1. Make a sequence of Venn diagrams to illustrate that $A \cup (B \cap C) = (A \cup B) \cap (A \cup C)$ is a true statement.

2. Use shading to indicate the following sets.

(a)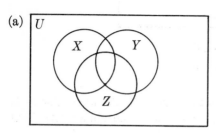

$X \cup (Y \cap Z)$

(c)

$(X \cap Y) \cap Z$

(b)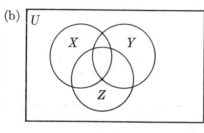

$X \cap (Y \cup Z)$

(d)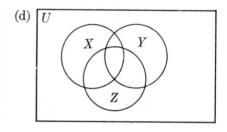

$(X \cup Z) \cap Y$

3. Let $U = \{\text{elementary school teachers}\}$,
   $A = \{\text{elementary school teachers who have traveled in Europe}\}$,
   $B = \{\text{elementary school teachers who have traveled in Mexico}\}$.

   Describe in words each of the following.

   (a) $A \cup B$
   (b) $A \cap C$

4. Let $U = \{80, 81, 82, 83, 84, \ldots, 100\}$,
   $A = \{80, 85, 90, 95, 100\}$,
   $B = \{80, 90, 100\}$,
   $C = \{80, 82, 84, 86, 88, 90\}$,
   $D = \{81, 83, 85, 87, 89\}$.

   List the members of each set.

   (a) $A \cup (B \cap C)$ (c) $(A \cap B) \cup (C \cap D)$
   (b) $(A \cup B) \cap C$ (d) $(A \cap C) \cap (C \cup D)$

Cartesian Products

As a last set operation, we shall consider another binary operation through which we form a new set by operating on two sets, but this operation produces a set not in U. Before discussing this operation, however, we want to establish what is meant by an *ordered pair*.

When objects are paired, the order in which they are paired may or may not be important. For example, the order in which one applies salt and pepper to food seems immaterial, but the order in which one puts a shoe and a stocking on a foot is important. When the order *is* of importance, mathematicians use the symbolism (a, b) (read, "the ordered pair a, b") to denote that a is paired with b, but, more than this, that a is considered first. In the foregoing example, then, we might write (salt, pepper) and (pepper, salt) interchangeably, but we would want to write (stocking, shoe) and mean something quite different from (shoe, stocking). Formally,

> An ordered pair (a, b) *is a pair of objects in which the order in which the objects are considered is first* a, *and second* b.

The symbolism (a, b) is not set notation, and an ordered pair is not a set in the sense in which we have used the term. (It is possible to formulate a definition for an ordered pair entirely in terms of sets; however, we shall not adopt this view, and our ordered pairs are not to be considered sets as such.) The letters a and b used in (a, b) are called the *first* and *second components* (not "members") respectively, of the ordered pair.

We define two ordered pairs to be equal if, and only if, they have identical first components and identical second components: $(a, b) = (c, d)$ if, and only if, $a = c$ and $b = d$. Thus,

$$(a, b) = (a, b) \text{ but } (a, b) \neq (b, a) \text{ unless } a = b.$$

To help in understanding another binary operation on sets, consider this example: "At an ice cream social, devil's food and angel food cakes will be served with these choices of ice cream: vanilla, chocolate, strawberry, and peppermint. How many different combinations of cake and ice cream will be offered?" The choices are

> devil's food cake and vanilla ice cream,
> devil's food cake and chocolate ice cream,
> devil's food cake and strawberry ice cream,
> devil's food cake and peppermint ice cream,

angel food cake and vanilla ice cream,
angel food cake and chocolate ice cream,
angel food cake and strawberry ice cream,
angel food cake and peppermint ice cream.

From our list we can see that we have eight choices.

In our example, devil's food and angel food cakes are members of a set, and the ice creams of different flavors are members of another set. The combinations of cake and ice cream form a set of all possible ordered pairs in which the first component is an element of the set of cakes, and the second component is an element of the set of ice creams of different flavors. All the combinations form a set called the *Cartesian* * *product* of the two sets.

A convenient way to picture the formation of a Cartesian product is by means of an *array* or *lattice*. Figure 37 is an array showing the matchings in the preceding example, in which A is the set of the two kinds of cake and B is the set of the four kinds of ice cream. Each ordered pair consists of one kind of cake and one kind of ice cream. In the array, a dot represents each ordered pair.

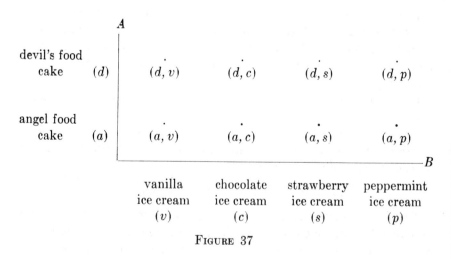

FIGURE 37

Now, let us define the Cartesian product.

> *If* A *and* B *are sets, then the set* A × B *(read "A cross B"), called the Cartesian product of* A *and* B, *is the set of all*

* The word "Cartesian" is derived from the name of René Descartes, a French mathematician who lived in the seventeenth century.

*possible ordered pairs such that the first component of the
ordered pair is an element of* A *and the second component
is an element of* B.

Notice that, for the first time, we are talking about a set whose elements
are not single objects, but ordered pairs. Since the members of the universal set containing A and B are single objects, and the members of the
set $A \times B$ are ordered pairs, the set $A \times B$ is not a subset of U. Hence, the
formation of Cartesian products is not closed in U.

Consider the universal set

$$S = \{a, \; b, \; c, \; d\},$$

and let

$$A = \{a, \; b\},$$

and

$$B = \{b, \; c, \; d\}.$$

Then the Cartesian product $A \times B$ is the set of all possible ordered pairs
whose first components are elements of A and whose second components
are elements of B. Thus,

$$A \times B = \{(a, b), \; (a, c), \; (a, d), \; (b, b), \; (b, c), \; (b, d)\}.$$

Note that the ordered pair (b, b) is a member of $A \times B$. Earlier we agreed
that in set notation, the multiple listing of an element in a set was unnecessary. That is, $\{b, b\} = \{b\}$. However (b, b) is an ordered pair, not a set,
so that it is a legitimate member of $A \times B$.

Continuing with our example, observe that

$$B \times A = \{(b, a), \; (b, b), \; (c, a), \; (c, b), \; (d, a), \; (d, b)\}.$$

By comparing the members of $A \times B$ and $B \times A$, we see that they are not
the same, since the ordered pairs (a, b) and (b, a), for example, are
different ordered pairs. Therefore, we can conclude that in general the
formation of Cartesian products of sets is not commutative.

Figure 38 is an array showing the formation of $A \times B$ in the preceding
example. Note that the vertical axis is associated with set A, and the
letters a, b, which appear to the left of the vertical axis, correspond to the
first components. Similarly, the horizontal axis is associated with set B,
and the letters b, c, d, which appear below the horizontal axis, correspond
to the second components. Using the vertical axis for the first components
is an arbitrary choice, and this may be reversed (in fact it usually is)
when we use Cartesian coordinates to represent points in the plane.

Another way to picture the formation of a Cartesian product is by
means of a *tree graph*. Figure 39 is a tree graph showing the formation of
$A \times B$ in the preceding example.

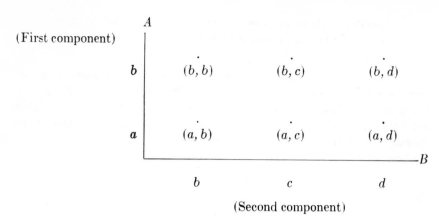

(First component)

Array for $A \times B$

FIGURE 38

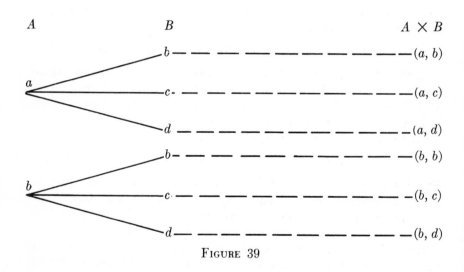

FIGURE 39

Exercise Set 6

1. Let $U = \{$Marie, Nora, Karen, Anne, Bill, Don, Phil, Jim$\}$,
    $A = \{$Marie, Nora, Karen, Anne$\}$,
    $B = \{$Bill, Don, Phil, Jim$\}$.

    Make an array, or lattice, showing the matchings of possible bridge partners, with one partner a member of set A and the other partner a member of set B.

2. Let $U = \{d,\ e,\ f,\ g,\ h\}$,
      $A = \{d,\ e,\ f\}$,
      $B = \{e,\ f,\ g,\ h\}$.

Make an array or lattice showing the formation of $A \times B$.

3. Let $U = \{w,\ x,\ y,\ z\}$,
      $C = \{w,\ x\}$,
      $D = \{x,\ y,\ z\}$.

Make a tree graph showing the formation of $C \times D$.

SUMMARY

It has been our purpose in this booklet to discuss some elementary set concepts and to see how these can be used to help clarify the nature of a number. We have, of course, touched on but a few of the concepts in the enormous field of rich and varied ideas concerning sets and number. The concepts we have introduced are fundamental, however, and are those with which every elementary teacher of modern mathematics will have to be concerned.

It is our design and hope that this short booklet will serve to explain a few of the basic ideas * involved in a modern discussion of sets and numbers, and will, perhaps, serve as a foundation for further study of these ideas in more depth and detail. There are available many excellent expositions of the same matters, expositions both broader and deeper than this. It is our hope that you will explore one or more of them.

SYMBOLS USED IN BOOKLET NO. 1

SYMBOL	WHAT THE SYMBOL SIGNIFIES
$\{\ \}$	Braces: enclosures for members of a set
$A = \{\text{Mary, John}\}$	A is the set whose members are Mary and John.
$\emptyset$	The set with no members, called the "empty set" or "null set." Sometimes it is written $\{\ \}$.
. . .	Follow on in the indicated pattern.
ϵ	"Is a member of"
$\notin$	"Is not a member of"
$=$	"Equals," or "Is equal to," or "Is the same as." For sets: "Contain exactly the same members as"

---

* These ideas will be used in other booklets in this series, especially in Booklet 2: *The Whole Numbers.*

$\neq$	"Is not equal to"
$\sim$	"Is equivalent to"
$<$	"Is less than"
$\nless$	"Is not less than"
$>$	"Is greater than"
$\ngtr$	"Is not greater than"
U	The universal set or universe
$\subseteq$	"Is a subset of"
$\subset$	"Is a proper subset of"
$n(A)$	The cardinal number of the set A
$\cup$	Union
$\cap$	Intersection
(a, b)	The ordered pair: a, b
$A \times B$	The Cartesian product of sets A and B, read: "A cross B."

ANSWERS TO EXERCISE SETS

Exercise Set 1

1. (a) {California, Oregon, Washington, Hawaii, Alaska}
   (b) {January, February, March, April, May, June}
   (c) {Hoover, Truman, Eisenhower}
   (d) $\emptyset$ or { }
   (e) {Michigan, Erie, Huron, Superior, Ontario}
   (f) {a, b, c, d, e}

2. (a) 3   (b) 1   (c) 2

3. (a) $\in$ (d) $\in$ (g) $\notin$
   (b) $\notin$ (e) $\notin$ (h) $\in$
   (c) $\notin$ (f) $\notin$ (i) $\notin$

Exercise Set 2

1. $\emptyset$ {car, airplane}
    {boat}   {car, train}
    {car}   {airplane, train}
    {airplane}   {boat, car, airplane}
    {train}   {boat, car, train}
    {boat, car}   {car, airplane, train}
    {boat, airplane}   {boat, airplane, train}
    {boat, train}   {boat, car, airplane, train}

2. (a) {Los Angeles, Sacramento, San Francisco}
   (b) {Chicago, New York, Detroit, Philadelphia}
   (c) {Sacramento}

3. $\subset$ can be inserted in a, c, d.
   $\subseteq$ can be inserted in all of them.

Exercise Set 3

1. (a) $C \cup O = $ {Colorado, California, Connecticut, Oregon, Oklahoma}
   (b) $C \cup P = $ {Colorado, California, Connecticut, Alaska, Hawaii, Oregon, Washington}
   (c) $O \cup P = $ {Oregon, Oklahoma, Alaska, California, Hawaii, Washington}

2. (a) $S \cup M = $ {Mary, Ellen, Anne, John, Bob, Jimmy, Sue}
   (b) $C \cup W = $ {Don, Mary, Philip, Jimmy, Nora, Anne, Joe}
   (c) $(S \cup C) \cup W = $ {Mary, Ellen, Anne, John, Bob, Joe, Nora, Don, Philip, Jimmy}
   (d) $C \cup (W \cup M) = $ {Mary, Anne, Joe, Nora, John, Bob, Jimmy, Sue, Don, Philip}

3. (a) $A \cup B = $ {1, 2, 3, 4, 5, 6, 7, 8, 9, 10, 11, 12}
   (b) $B \cup C = $ {1, 3, 5, 6, 7, 9, 11, 12}
   (c) $C \cup D = $ {2, 3, 4, 5, 6, 7, 9, 12}
   (d) $(A \cup C) \cup D = $ {2, 3, 4, 5, 6, 7, 8, 9, 10, 12}

Exercise Set 4

1. (a) $B \cap C = $ {Detroit, Lansing}
   (b) $C \cap D = $ {Detroit}
   (c) $C \cap E = \emptyset$ or $C \cap E = \{ \ \}$
   (d) $(B \cap D) \cap C = $ {Detroit}
   (e) $D \cap (C \cap B) = $ {Detroit}
   (f) $(B \cap E) \cap C = \emptyset$ or $(B \cap E) \cap C = \{ \ \}$

2. (a) $A \cap B = \emptyset$ or $A \cap B = \{ \ \}$
   (b) $B \cap C = $ {3, 9, 15}
   (c) $A \cap D = $ {4, 8, 12}
   (d) $(A \cap C) \cap D = $ {12}
   (e) $B \cap (C \cap D) = \emptyset$ or $B \cap (C \cap D) = \{ \ \}$
   (f) $(A \cup D) \cap C = $ {12}

3.

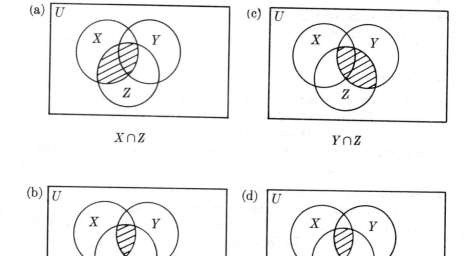

(a) $X \cap Z$

(c) $Y \cap Z$

(b) $(X \cap Z) \cap Y$

(d) $X \cap (Y \cap Z)$

Exercise Set 5

1.

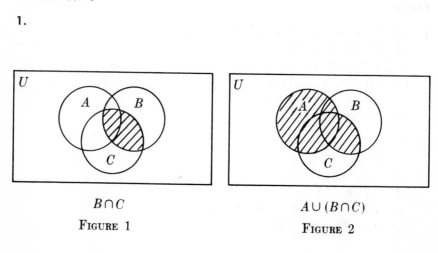

$B \cap C$

FIGURE 1

$A \cup (B \cap C)$

FIGURE 2

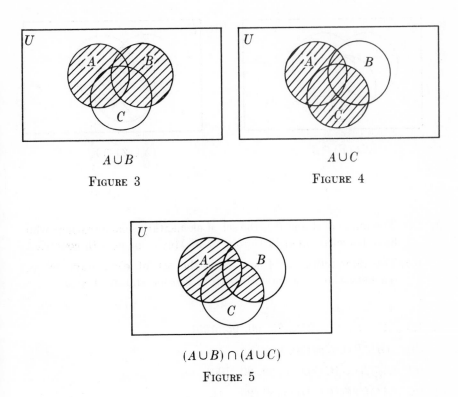

$A \cup B$

FIGURE 3

$A \cup C$

FIGURE 4

$(A \cup B) \cap (A \cup C)$

FIGURE 5

Figures 2 and 5 show that

$A \cup (B \cap C) = (A \cup B) \cap (A \cup C)$ is a true statement.

2.

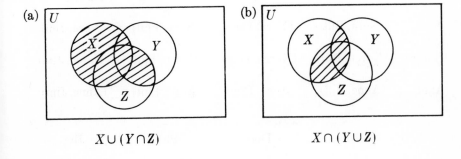

(a)

$X \cup (Y \cap Z)$

(b)

$X \cap (Y \cup Z)$

(c) 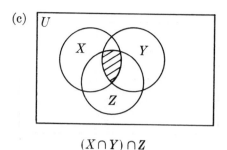   (d)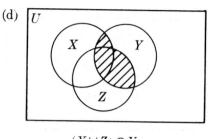

$(X \cap Y) \cap Z$ $(X \cup Z) \cap Y$

3. (a) The union of A and B is the set of elementary school teachers who have traveled either in Europe or in Mexico or in both countries.

    (b) The intersection of A and B is the set of elementary school teachers who have traveled both in Europe and in Mexico.

4. (a) $A \cup (B \cap C) = \{80,\ 85,\ 90,\ 95,\ 100\}$

    (b) $(A \cup B) \cap C = \{80,\ 90\}$

    (c) $(A \cap B) \cup (C \cap D) = \{80,\ 90,\ 100\}$

    (d) $(A \cap C) \cap (C \cup D) = \{80,\ 90\}$

Exercise Set 6

1.

A

Marie	(Marie, Bill)	(Marie, Don)	(Marie, Phil)	(Marie, Jim)
Nora	(Nora, Bill)	(Nora, Don)	(Nora, Phil)	(Nora, Jim)
Karen	(Karen, Bill)	(Karen, Don)	(Karen, Phil)	(Karen, Jim)
Anne	(Anne, Bill)	(Anne, Don)	(Anne, Phil)	(Anne, Jim)
	Bill	Don	Phil	Jim B

2.

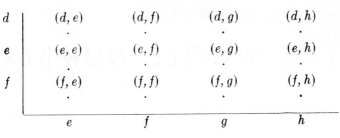

Array for $A \times B$

3.

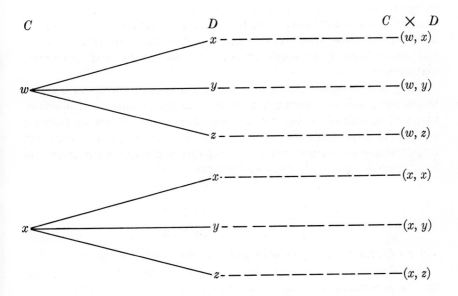

THE WHOLE NUMBERS

INTRODUCTION

It is not necessary to be a mechanic to drive a car, nor is it necessary to study the structure of number systems in order to carry out computations or to teach arithmetic in a rote fashion. This booklet, however, is intended for those who would like to understand arithmetic and use this understanding to teach children to understand and appreciate mathematics.

Many people think that learning arithmetic consists merely of learning to compute, that is, learning how to perform the operations of addition, subtraction, multiplication, and division. Most of us learned methods for performing these operations very early in our lives and have completely forgotten how we learned them. We probably began this learning process by memorizing the basic sums and products:

$$1+1=2 \qquad 1\times1=1$$
$$1+2=3 \qquad 1\times2=2$$
$$1+3=4, \ldots, \qquad 1\times3=3, \ldots;$$

and we drilled until our response to 6×7 was automatically 42.

We ultimately discovered that $5+3=3+5$, that $7+6=6+7$, and that, in general, the sum of two numbers does not depend on the order of the addends. This important property of whole numbers is called the *commutative property of addition.* Similarly, most of us discovered that $3\times(4+7)$ gives the same result as $(3\times4)+(3\times7)$, and that $10\times(8+2)$ gives the same result as $(10\times8)+(10\times2)$. This *distributive property* is also true in general for any three whole numbers.

These are some of the facts that form the basis of the structure of arithmetic. Arithmetic is built on these and other properties, some of which we shall discuss in this booklet.

As the great mathematician Gauss stated: "Mathematics is the Queen of the sciences, and arithmetic is the Queen of mathematics."

48

THE WHOLE NUMBERS

The set of *whole numbers* contains the numbers of the set of *counting numbers* (also called the *natural numbers*)

$$\{1, 2, 3, 4, 5, \ldots\},$$

and zero. That is, the set of whole numbers is

$$\{0, 1, 2, 3, 4, 5, \ldots\}.$$

Notice that this set has a least member, zero, but no greatest member. This set is an *infinite set* because, no matter how many members of the set are listed, there are still other members of the set.

ORDER

Teachers object when their primary pupils count by saying, "One, six, nine, four, two, eight, seven." They object because the *order* in which the number names are given is incorrect. People learn early that there is a correct and an incorrect way to order the whole numbers. This property of whole numbers is called the *order property*.

In Booklet No. 1: *Sets*, it was shown how the whole numbers can be ordered by means of standard sets. Let us review some of the basic concepts developed in that booklet.

Two sets, such as

$$\{a, b, c, d\}$$

and

$$\{\square, \bigcirc, \square, \triangle\}$$

are *equivalent,* since the sets can be placed in one-to-one correspondence.

The ordered sets of numerals

$$\{``1"\}$$

$$\{``1," ``2"\}$$

$$\{``1," ``2," ``3"\}, \text{ etc.,}$$

are called *standard sets.* The set $\{``1," ``2," ``3"\}$ is the standard set for all sets that are equivalent to the set $\{a, b, c\}$; and the *cardinal number* for each of these sets is the number three, named by the last numeral in the standard set $\{``1," ``2," ``3"\}$.

If a standard set, A, is a proper subset of a standard set, B, then the cardinal number of A is defined to be less than the cardinal number of B. For example, $\{``1," ``2"\} \subset \{``1," ``2," ``3," ``4," ``5"\}$; hence, $2 < 5$ (read, "two is less than five"). The number zero, the cardinal number of the empty set, is the least cardinal number.

The elements of the set $\{3, 0, 1, 5\}$ can be ordered $0 < 1 < 3 < 5$ by observing that { } ⊂ {"1"} ⊂ {"1," "2," "3,"} ⊂ {"1," "2," "3," "4," "5"}. Thus we have an ordering for the set of cardinal numbers—or of whole numbers, as we shall call the set of numbers in this booklet.

When the whole numbers are written in the order

$$0, 1, 2, 3, 4, 5, 6, \ldots ,$$

each number is less than any number which comes later in the sequence; thus $1<4$, $0<3$, $5<6$, and so on. The relation $1<4$ can also be written equivalently $4>1$, which is read, "Four is greater than one."

If a is any whole number and b is any whole number, then exactly one of the following three statements is true:

    1. $a=b$ (a is equal to b)

    2. $a<b$ (a is less than b)

    3. $b<a$ (b is less than a)

This is called the *trichotomy principle*.

The number line gives a concrete means of visualizing order in the set of whole numbers. A set of equally spaced points on the line provides a geometric representation for the whole numbers. A point is arbitrarily selected to correspond to zero and labeled 0 as shown in Figure 1. The dots to the right of 0 are next labeled 1, 2, 3, . . ., successively; thus we have a matching of the whole numbers with the equally spaced points, as shown in Figure 2.

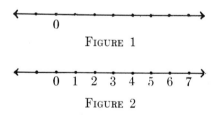

0

FIGURE 1

    0 1 2 3 4 5 6 7

FIGURE 2

Each point is the *graph* of the whole number which it matches, and each whole number is the *coordinate* of the point which it matches.

An examination of the number line should make the following points clear:

    1. To each whole number there corresponds one, and only one, point on the the number line.

    2. A whole number a is less than a whole number b if the point corresponding to a is to the left of the point corresponding to b; a is greater than b if the point corresponding to a is to the right of the point corresponding to b.

3. There is no greatest whole number; the sequence of dots, chosen to correspond to whole numbers, continues indefinitely to the right.

OPERATIONS ON THE SET OF WHOLE NUMBERS

The machine pictured in Figure 3 can be used to illustrate operations on the set of whole numbers. The machine operates on just two numbers at one time; hence, the operation is called a *binary operation.* (The prefix "bi" denotes two, as in "biceps," "bicycle.")

FIGURE 3

Let us choose two whole numbers, for example, 6 and 2. If we put 6 and then 2 into the machine and turn the pointer on the dial to $+$, the symbol for addition, the operation will produce the result 8. Similarly, if we put the same two whole numbers, 6 and 2, into the machine and turn the dial to $-$, the symbol for subtraction, the result will be 4. For the same pair of numbers, the operation of multiplication will give 12 as the result, and the operation of division will give 3.

An operation in mathematics is similar to the operation of this machine. *It is a way of associating an ordered pair of numbers with a specified third number.*

An ordered pair of numbers (a, b) is a pair of numbers such that the order in which the numbers are considered is first a, then b. The number named first is called the *first component,* and the number named second is called the *second component* of the ordered pair.

When we perform the operation of addition, we associate the number 8 with the ordered pair $(6, 2)$. When we think of the same ordered pair of whole numbers, 6 and 2, and perform the operation of multiplication, the result is 12. Subtraction and division are also arithmetical operations. These four operations are called the *four basic operations of arithmetic.* Addition and multiplication are called *primary operations,* while subtraction and division are called *secondary operations.* The choice of these terms is justified by the fact that subtraction is the inverse operation of

addition and division is the inverse operation of multiplication. Inverse
operations will be discussed in a later section of this booklet.

ORDERED PAIR OF NUMBERS	OPERATION	RESULT
(25, 4)	Addition	29
(17, 6)	Subtraction	11
(55, 3)	Multiplication	165
(27, 9)	Division	3
(6, 7)	Addition	13
(75, 25)	Division	3
(16, 9)	Subtraction	7
(8, 4)	Multiplication	32

Exercise Set 1

1. Fill in the blanks in the lists below.

ORDERED PAIR	RESULT	OPERATION USED
(a) (5, 7)	12	_____
(b) (10, 12)	_____	Addition
(c) (5, __)	9	Addition
(d) (__, 9)	7	Subtraction
(e) (10, 2)	8	_____
(f) (3, __)	1	Subtraction
(g) (5, 2)	10	_____
(h) (3, 6)	_____	Multiplication
(i) (8, __)	24	Multiplication
(j) (12, 2)	_____	Division
(k) (25, 5)	_____	Division
(l) (36, __)	9	Division

2. In each of the diagrams in Figure 4, to which operation symbol should
the arrow on the dial be turned?

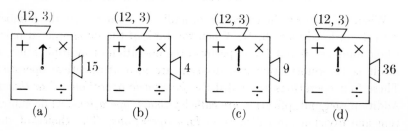

FIGURE 4

3. Write the numeral that represents the result of the indicated operation shown in each diagram of Figure 5.

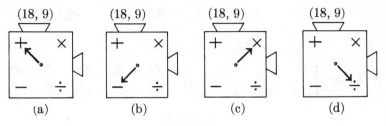

(a)   (b)   (c)   (d)

FIGURE 5

4. Which of the following indicated operations do not have results which are whole numbers?

(a) 4×6 (f) $5 \div 2$

(b) $3 + 8$ (g) $36 \div 9$

(c) $3 - 7$ (h) $4 - 4$

(d) 0×5 (i) $4 \div 8$

(e) $11 - 7$ (j) $0 + 0$

ADDITION

Since number is a property associated with a set of objects, it is natural to go back to the idea of sets * in order to define addition of whole numbers. Let us consider a pair of nonempty sets which have no members in common. Such sets are called *disjoint sets*.

There are standard ways of making new sets out of such a pair of sets. For example, if we have a set of boy-dolls in a classroom exhibit and a set of girl-dolls in the exhibit, we can join these two sets to get the set of dolls in the exhibit. (See Fig. 6.) If X is the set of boy-dolls and Y is the set of girl-dolls, we join the two sets to get a new set consisting of the set of dolls. We call this new set the *union* of X and Y, and denote it by the symbol "$\cup$." Then $X \cup Y$ is read, "the union of X and Y," which means the set obtained when we join set X and set Y to form a new set. The set $X \cup Y$ contains every member which belongs to X and every member which belongs to Y.

---

* For a discussion of sets see Booklet No. 1 in this series.

FIGURE 6

EXAMPLE 1.

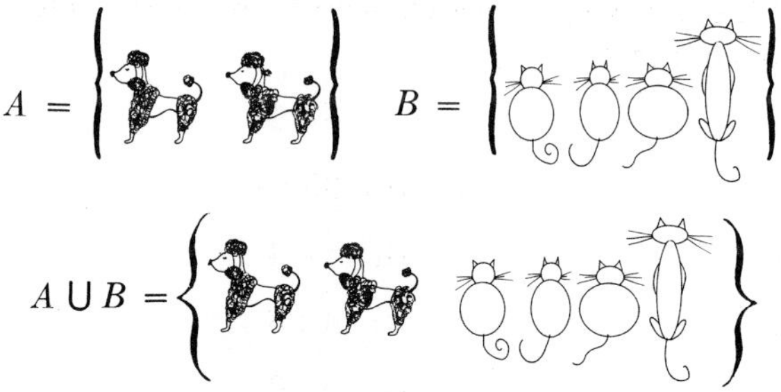

EXAMPLE 2.

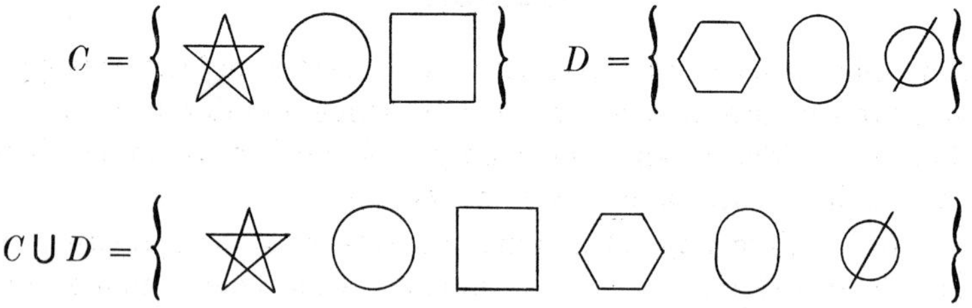

EXAMPLE 3.

$$E = \{1, 2, 3\} \qquad F = \{4, 6, 8\}$$
$$E \cup F = \{1, 2, 3, 4, 6, 8\}$$

Union of *disjoint* sets is used as a basis for the concept of adding whole numbers. There are several basic facts about the union of sets which underlie the operation of addition. If set B is joined to set A, the resulting set is the same as if A were joined to B. For example, let A and B be the sets shown in Figure 7.

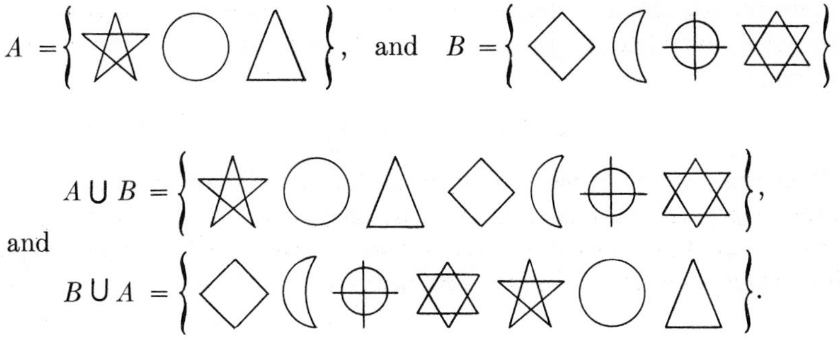

$$A = \left\{ \stackrel{\star}{} \bigcirc \triangle \right\}, \quad \text{and} \quad B = \left\{ \diamondsuit \;(\!(\; \oplus \; \stackrel{\star}{} \right\}$$

and

$$A \cup B = \left\{ \stackrel{\star}{} \bigcirc \triangle \diamondsuit \;(\!(\; \oplus \; \stackrel{\star}{} \right\},$$

$$B \cup A = \left\{ \diamondsuit \;(\!(\; \oplus \; \stackrel{\star}{} \; \stackrel{\star}{} \bigcirc \triangle \right\}.$$

FIGURE 7

Notice that the elements in $A \cup B$ are exactly the same as the elements in $B \cup A$. Hence, $A \cup B = B \cup A$. (See Booket No. 1: *Sets*.)

If we wish to find the union of three sets, we can join only two sets at a time. For example, to find the union of sets A, B, and C (Fig. 8), we can join B to A to get $A \cup B$ and then join C to $A \cup B$; or we can join C to B to get $B \cup C$, and then join this set to A. In either case, the resulting set is the same.

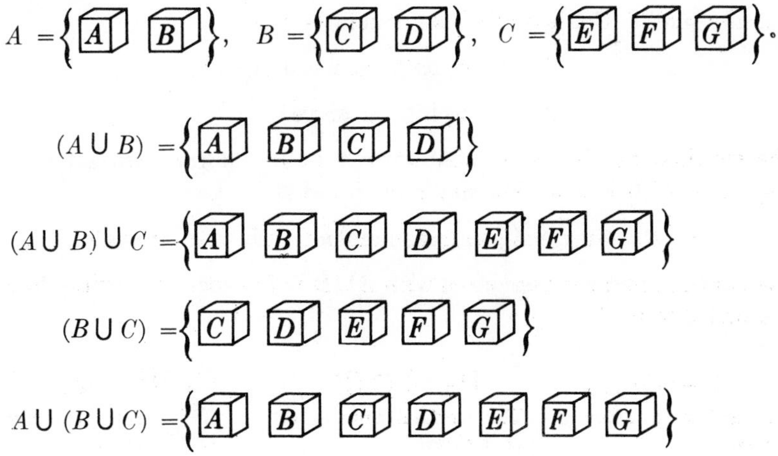

$$A = \left\{ \boxed{A} \; \boxed{B} \right\}, \quad B = \left\{ \boxed{C} \; \boxed{D} \right\}, \quad C = \left\{ \boxed{E} \; \boxed{F} \; \boxed{G} \right\}.$$

$$(A \cup B) = \left\{ \boxed{A} \; \boxed{B} \; \boxed{C} \; \boxed{D} \right\}$$

$$(A \cup B) \cup C = \left\{ \boxed{A} \; \boxed{B} \; \boxed{C} \; \boxed{D} \; \boxed{E} \; \boxed{F} \; \boxed{G} \right\}$$

$$(B \cup C) = \left\{ \boxed{C} \; \boxed{D} \; \boxed{E} \; \boxed{F} \; \boxed{G} \right\}$$

$$A \cup (B \cup C) = \left\{ \boxed{A} \; \boxed{B} \; \boxed{C} \; \boxed{D} \; \boxed{E} \; \boxed{F} \; \boxed{G} \right\}$$

FIGURE 8

The parentheses in the expressions $(A \cup B) \cup C$ and $A \cup (B \cup C)$ mean that the sets named in the parentheses are to be joined first, and the resulting set is to be joined with the third set. Thus, $(A \cup B) \cup C$ means that B is joined to A to form $A \cup B$, and to this set is joined set C.

Similarly, $A \cup (B \cup C)$ means that C is joined to B to form $B \cup C$, then this set is joined to A. In either case, the resulting set is the same. In general,

$$(A \cup B) \cup C = A \cup (B \cup C).$$

Sometimes we have occasion to form the union of two sets, one of which is the *empty set*, that is, a set with ho members. For example, let A be the set of books on a shelf, and let B represent the set of books on a second shelf which contains no books. For example:

$$A = \{\, \square\,\square\,\square\,\square\,\square\,\square\, \}, \qquad B = \{\ \},$$

$$A \cup B = \{\, \square\,\square\,\square\,\square\,\square\,\square\, \}.$$

In general, if B is the empty set,

$$A \cup B = A.$$

We shall use the idea of the union of two disjoint sets to define the operation of addition of whole numbers. Addition is essentially an operation on an ordered pair of numbers. Given two numbers, such as 4 and 3, there is associated with them a third number, 7, which is called the sum of the two numbers. The question is, "What operation suggests that we name 7 as the sum?" Consider the two disjoint sets:

$$B = \{\text{star, ball, square, diamond}\}$$

$$A = \{\text{dish, kite, triangle}\}.$$

The cardinal number associated with A is 4, and the cardinal number associated with B is 3. The union of A and B is

$$A \cup B = \{\text{star, ball, square, diamond, dish, kite, triangle}\}.$$

The cardinal number associated with $A \cup B$ is 7; hence, we define the sum of 4 and 3 to be 7.

$C = \{\triangle\square\}$	$D = \{\lozenge\,\bigcirc\,\square\}$	$C \cup D = \{\triangle\square\,\lozenge\,\bigcirc\,\square\}$
The cardinal number of C is two.	The cardinal number of D is three.	The cardinal number of $C \cup D$ is five.

The sum of 2 and 3 is 5.

$E = \{\text{⌂⃝⌬}\}$	$F = \{⬠⃝\triangle\,\circledcirc\}$	$E \cup F = \{\text{⌂⃝⌬⬠}\triangle\circledcirc\}$
The cardinal number of E is three.	The cardinal number of F is three.	The cardinal number of $E \cup F$ is six.

The sum of 3 and 3 is 6.

*The sum of the cardinal numbers of two disjoint sets is
defined to be the cardinal number of the union of the two
sets.*

Recall that we can form the union of two sets that are not disjoint sets
(that is, sets that have at least one element in common). For example, let

$$A = \{1, \ 3, \ 5, \ 7, \ 9\},$$

$$B = \{1, \ 2, \ 3, \ 4, \ 5\};$$

then

$$A \cup B = \{1, \ 2, \ 3, \ 4, \ 5, \ 7, \ 9\}.$$

Notice that we do not repeat the names of any common members in the
union of two sets. Here the sum of the cardinal numbers of A and B is *not*
the cardinal number of $A \cup B$, because A and B are not disjoint.

When we consider two disjoint sets and form their union, we are operating on sets. When we consider two numbers and get a third, we are operating on numbers. Addition of whole numbers, then, is a binary operation on
the cardinal numbers associated with two disjoint sets. Note that addition
is an operation on numbers representing the cardinality of the two sets,
not an operation on the sets themselves.

There are special names for the numbers operated on in addition. They
are called *addends*, and the result of an addition operation is called the
sum. As you know, the symbol for the operation of addition is "$+$." Thus,
in the sentence

$$16 + 12 = 28,$$

16 and 12 are addends; their sum is 28. The sentence is read,

Sixteen plus twelve equals twenty-eight.

It can also be read,

The sum of sixteen and twelve is twenty-eight.

Exercise Set 2

1. Let $A = \{$dog, cat, cow, pig$\}$,

   $B = \{$duck, horse, elephant$\}$.

   (a) What are the members of $A \cup B$?

   (b) What are the cardinal numbers of A, B, and $A \cup B$?

2. Let $R = \{2, \ 4, \ 6, \ 8, \ 10, \ 12\}$,

   $S = \{1, \ 3, \ 5, \ 7\}$.

   (a) What are the members of $R \cup S$?

   (b) What is the cardinal number of R? of S? of $R \cup S$?

3. If W is the set of all white horses, and L is the set of all lavender horses, what are the members of $W \cup L$?

4. Let $F = \{$dog, cow, horse, pig, turkey$\}$,
   $G = \{$chicken, dog, robin, cat, pig$\}$.

  (a) The number of members in F is _____.

  (b) The number of members in G is _____.

  (c) Name the members of $F \cup G$.

  (d) The number of members in $F \cup G$ is _____.

  (e) Why is the sum of the number of members in F and the number of members in G not the same as the number of members in $F \cup G$?

5. Let $M = \{a,\ b,\ c,\ d,\ e,\ f,\ g\}$,
   $N = \{h,\ i,\ j,\ k\}$.

  (a) What is the number of members in $M \cup N$?

  (b) How did you find your answer?

  (c) Why could you find it in this way?

6. Let $X = \{\bigcirc\square\triangle\bigcirc\}$,
   $Y = \{\quad\}$.
What is the number of elements in X? in Y? in $X \cup Y$?

7. Let $A = \{$hat, coat, purse$\}$, and suppose that
   $A \cup B = \{$hat, coat, purse, gloves$\}$.
If A and B are disjoint sets, what are the members of B?

8. Complete Table I.

TABLE I

	Addend	Addend	Number Sentence	Sum
(a)	5	4	$5+4=n$	9
(b)	9	6		
(c)	7	3		
(d)	2	8		

MULTIPLICATION

Multiplication is an operation which assigns to each ordered pair of whole numbers, such as (4, 5), another whole number, in this case 20. The numbers 4 and 5 are called *factors* of 20, and 20 is called the *product* of the factors 4 and 5. How is this product determined? Since whole numbers were defined in terms of sets, we return to the idea of an operation on sets in order to see how the product of two whole numbers should be defined.

Multiplication may be approached through the *Cartesian product* * of two sets, A and B. This product is formed by pairing each element of A with each element of B. Let A be a set of cups—red, yellow, blue, and green; and let B be a set of saucers—red, yellow, blue, green, and white. Then these can be paired as shown in Figure 9.

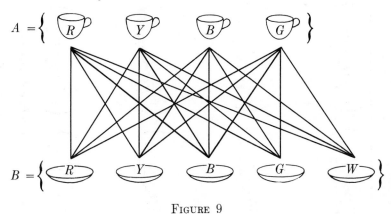

FIGURE 9

The set of all ordered pairs obtained by pairing each element of A with each element of B is called the Cartesian product of sets A and B. The product of the cardinal numbers of A and B is defined to be the cardinal number of the Cartesian product of A and B.

The orderly arrangement of these pairings in rows and columns is called an *array*. Figure 10 depicts an array which shows all the pairs formed by pairing each member of a set of four cups (A) with each member of a set of five saucers (B). There are 20 different matchings, or pairs.

---

* See Booklet No. 1: *Sets.*

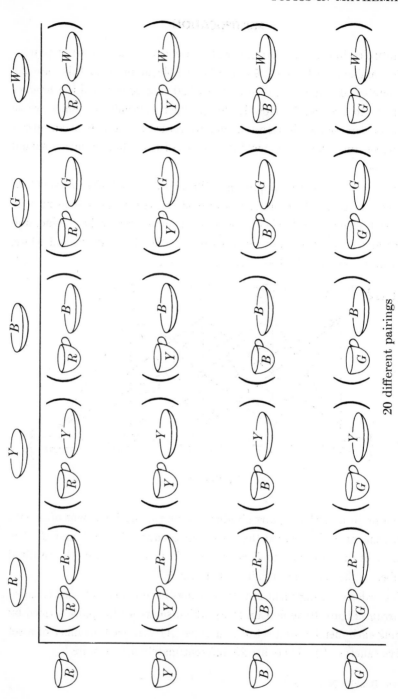

20 different pairings

FIGURE 10

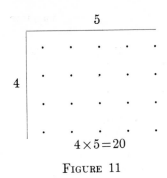

$4 \times 5 = 20$

FIGURE 11

In Figure 11 there are four rows and five columns in the array; each pairing is represented by a dot. The product, written 4×5, and read, "four times five," is defined to be the number of pairings in the array. Thus, given two sets, the product of the cardinal numbers of the sets may be found by counting matchings between the members of the sets. Several of the important properties of multiplication are apparent. We notice in Figures 10 and 11 that a 4 by 5 array is the union of 4 disjoint sets (rows) each having 5 members. Consequently, 4×5 can be obtained from $5+5+5+5$. This way of obtaining the product is sometimes described as *repeated addition;* this repeated-addition description of multiplication is perhaps more familiar than the Cartesian product. It is also true that the array is the union of 5 disjoint sets (columns), each of which has 4 members. Thus, 4×5 can be obtained from $4+4+4+4+4$.

Examples of other arrays are shown in Figures 12 and 13.

ORDERED PAIR	ARRAY	PRODUCT
(2, 3)	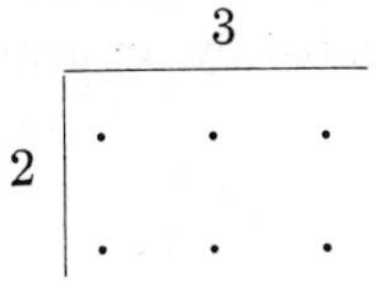	6
(8, 7)	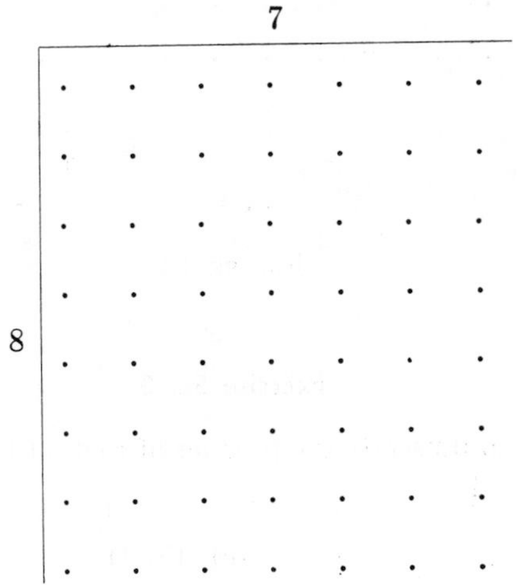	56

FIGURE 12

ORDERED PAIR   ARRAY   PRODUCT

8

(7, 8)   56

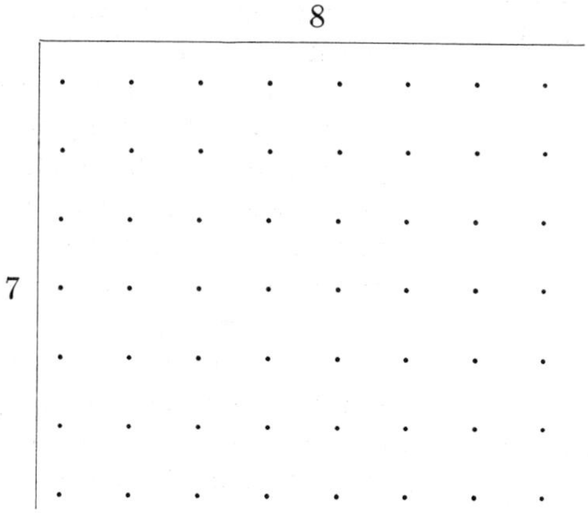

```
    .   .   .   .   .   .   .   .

    .   .   .   .   .   .   .   .

    .   .   .   .   .   .   .   .

7   .   .   .   .   .   .   .   .

    .   .   .   .   .   .   .   .

    .   .   .   .   .   .   .   .

    .   .   .   .   .   .   .   .
```

FIGURE 12 (continued)

Note that the number of rows is written first and the number of columns, second; for example in Figure 12 the product 2×3 is represented by an array of 2 rows and 3 columns. In general, if a and b are whole numbers, the product $a \times b$ is represented by an array with a rows and b columns.

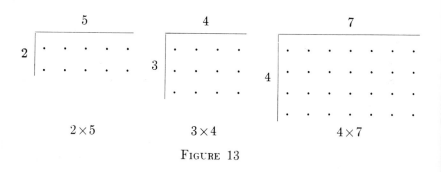

2×5 3×4 4×7

FIGURE 13

Exercise Set 3

1. Draw arrays to illustrate the product of each of the following ordered pairs.

    (a) (4, 2)   (c) (5, 1)

    (b) (3, 9)   (d) (6, 4)

2. Write the multiplication sentence (such as $3 \times 5 = 15$) that describes each of the arrays below.

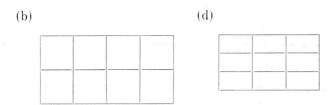

(a)   (c)

(b)   (d)

3. Draw arrays to illustrate each of the following:

    (a) 5×7 (c) 2×4

    (b) 4×2 (d) 3×6

4. Mr. Jackson is buying a two-tone car. The company offers tops in 6 colors and bodies in 8 other colors. Draw an array which shows the number of possible color combinations.

5. Ruth has 5 blouses and 6 skirts. How many "mix-and-match" outfits can Ruth make, assuming each blouse can be worn with each skirt?

6. An ice cream store has 31 flavors of ice cream, and features double-dip cones. From how many different combinations of flavors (including two dips of the same flavor) must you choose when you order a double-dip cone?

7. Fill in the blanks in Table II.

TABLE II

Array	First Factor	Second Factor	Product
(a) • • • • • •	2	3	6
(b) • • • • • • • • • • • •			
(c) • • • • • • • • • • • • • • • • • • • • • • • • • • • • • •			
(d) • • • • • • • • • • • • • • •			
(e) • • • • • • • • • • • • • • • • • • • • • • • • • • • •			

8. Fill in the blanks in Table III.

TABLE III

| Array | | Number Sentence |
rows	columns	
(a) 2	6	$2 \times 6 = 12$
(b) 7	4	$7 \times 4 = \_\_$
(c) 3	7	$\_\_ \times 7 = 21$
(d) 4	6	$4 \times \_\_ = 24$
(e) 8	3	$\_\_ \times \_\_ = \_\_$
(f) __	4	$\_\_ \times \_\_ = 24$
(g) 9	__	$45 = 9 \times \_\_$
(h) 5	n	$\_\_ \times n = 30$
(i) p	3	$p \times \_\_ = 30$

9. Draw rings around subsets to show the following:

(a) $6 \times 5 = 30$

(b) $5 \times 6 = 30$

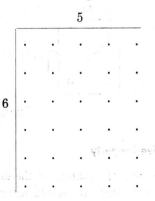

PROPERTIES OF ADDITION

Closure Property

Addition has been defined as an *operation on an ordered pair of numbers, called addends, to produce a specific third number, called their sum.* The addends may be thought of as the cardinal numbers of two disjoint sets; the sum of these numbers is defined to be the *cardinal number of the union of the two disjoint sets.*

The operation of addition is performed on just two numbers, and consequently is called a *binary operation.*

If we add the components of the following ordered pairs of whole numbers, there is in each case an element in the set of whole numbers which is their sum.

$$(4,\ 5) \qquad 4+5=9$$

$$(53,\ 86) \qquad 53+86=139$$

$$(269,\ 406) \qquad 269+406=675$$

$$(1357,\ 2568) \qquad 1357+2468=3825$$

Can you discover any ordered pair of whole numbers whose sum is not a whole number? There is no such pair, for the operation of addition may be performed on any ordered pair of whole numbers to produce another whole number. In mathematical language, we say *the set of whole numbers is closed under the operation of addition.* This property of addition of whole numbers is called the *closure property.*

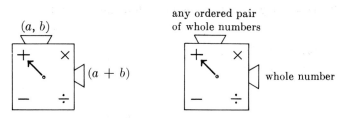

FIGURE 14

Commutative Property

Let us review the concept of the union of two disjoint sets to see if the order in which they are joined affects the result (Fig. 15). Does $A \cup B = B \cup A$? $A \cup B$ and $B \cup A$ are one and the same set. Consequently, the cardinal number of $A \cup B$ is the same as the cardinal number of $B \cup A$ (in the above case, 8).

Let us consider some nonnumerical situations to discover whether or not the order in which some combinations are made affects the result. Does the order in which we add sugar and cream to coffee, or combine blue and yellow paint to make green paint, affect the result?

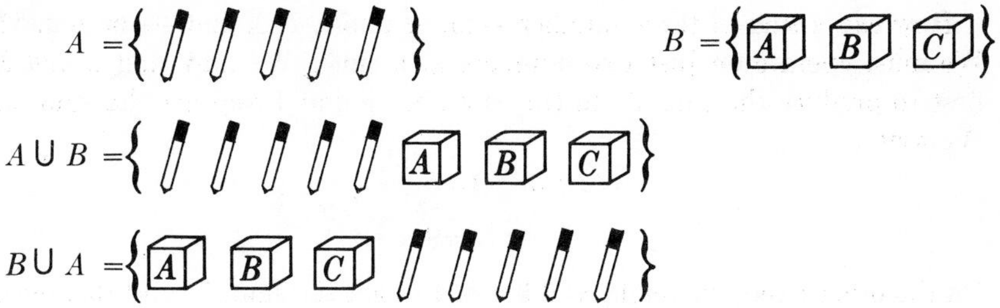

$$A = \left\{ \text{/// // /} \right\} \qquad B = \left\{ \boxed{A} \ \boxed{B} \ \boxed{C} \right\}$$

$$A \cup B = \left\{ \text{// // //} \ \boxed{A} \ \boxed{B} \ \boxed{C} \right\}$$

$$B \cup A = \left\{ \boxed{A} \ \boxed{B} \ \boxed{C} \ \text{// // /} \right\}$$

FIGURE 15

Does each pair of the following sums name the same number?

(a) 7+6, 6+7,

(b) 50+46, 46+50,

(c) 14+32, 32+14.

The property of addition of whole numbers, as illustrated in the previous example, is called the *commutative property of addition*. This property is that the order of the addends may be changed without changing the sum; that is, 7+2=2+7, or, in general, if a and b are any whole numbers, then $a+b=b+a$.

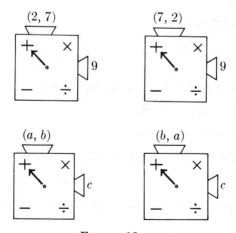

FIGURE 16

Associative Property

It has been emphasized that addition is a binary operation. A binary operation is an operation that can be performed on just two numbers.

How can a sum of three numbers—for example, 2, 3, and 4—be found? We must operate on just two numbers at a time. We may add 2 and 3 first to produce the sum, 5; to this sum, 5, we add 4 and get the sum, 9. We write

$$(2+3) +4=5+4$$

$$=9.$$

On the other hand, we might add 3 and 4 to get the sum, 7; and then add 2 and 7 to get the sum, 9. We write

$$2+ (3+4) =2+7$$

$$=9.$$

In each case the sum is 9. That is,

$$(2+3) +4=2+ (3+4).$$

Study the following statements. Is each statement true? Verify (b) and (c).

(a) $(4+5) +2=4+ (5+2)$,

$(4+5) +2=9+2$,

$=11;$

and

$4+ (5+2) =4+7$,

$=11;$

so

$(4+5) +2=4+ (5+2)$ is a true sentence.

(b) $(8+1) +6=8+ (1+6)$

(c) $(7+5) +9=7+ (5+9)$

In general, if a, b, and c are any whole numbers, then

$$(a+b) +c=a+ (b+c).$$

This grouping property is called the *associative property of addition*. Since

$$(2+3) +4=2+ (3+4)$$

and

$$(6+7) +9=6+ (7+9)$$

and, in general,

$$(a+b) +c=a+ (b+c),$$

it is not necessary to use parentheses in writing the sum of three addends. We may now write $(2+3)+4$ simply as

$$2+3+4.$$

The associative property may be generalized to hold for more than three addends. Thus, we may write

$$2+3+4+5+6,$$

instead of

$$\{[(2+3)+4]+5\}+6.$$

Identity Element

There is one whole number that plays a special role with respect to addition, and that number is zero. The special property of zero arises from the union of two sets, at least one of which is the empty set. Let

$$A=\{x,\ w,\ t\} \qquad \text{and} \qquad B=\{\ \ \},$$

then

$$A \cup B=\{x,\ w,\ t\}.$$

Recall that the cardinal number of B is 0. Thus,

$$3+0=3,$$

$$16+0=16,$$

$$0+43=43,$$

$$0+0=0.$$

Since the sum of zero and any whole number is that whole number, zero is called the *identity element* for addition.

Exercise Set 4

1. Which of the following are commutative?

   (a) To go through a doorway and then open the door

   (b) To put on a coat and hat

   (c) To put on your shoes and socks

   (d) To put on a swimming suit and to jump into the pool

   (e) To cook your dinner and to eat it

   (f) To wash your face and to put on make-up

   (g) To pay the light bill and to pay the gas bill

2. Is the operation of mixing three different colors of paint to produce a new color an associative operation?

3. Which of the following sets are closed under addition?

(a) {2, 3, 6, 8, 10}   (c) {0}

(b) {0, 1}   (d) {0, 2, 4, 6, . . .}

4. What is the identity element for addition in the set of whole numbers?

5. Show that the following statements are true.

(a) $6 + (7+8) = (6+7) + 8$

(b) $(9+10) + 2 = 9 + (10+2)$

(c) $(7+3) + 5 = 7 + (3+5)$

(d) $14 + (6+9) = (14+6) + 9$

6. Name the property illustrated by each of the following statements.

(a) $7 + 13 = 13 + 7$

(b) $9 + 0 = 9$

(c) $(3+4) + 6 = 3 + (4+6)$

7. Complete the chart in Table IV.

TABLE IV

Number Sentence	Name of Property of Addition
(a) $7 + 0 = \underline{\quad}$	
(b) $2 + 4 = 4 + \underline{\quad}$	
(c) $5 + (2+3) = (5+2) + \underline{\quad}$	
(d) $(0+3) + 10 = \underline{\quad} + 10$	
(e) $3 + \underline{\quad} = 5 + 3$	
(f) $0 + \underline{\quad} = 0$	
(g) $(17+7) + n = 17 + (7 + \underline{\quad})$	
(h) $a + b = \underline{\quad} + a$	

PROPERTIES OF MULTIPLICATION

Multiplication is an operation on two numbers, called *factors,* to produce a specific third number, called the *product.* It is a binary operation since we multiply just two numbers.

The product of an ordered pair of whole numbers has been defined as the number of pairings in the Cartesian product of two sets whose cardinal members are the ordered pair formed by pairing each member of the first set with each member of the second set.

An orderly arrangement into rows and columns of the pairings of elements in a Cartesian product is called an *array*. Examples of some arrays are shown in Figure 17.

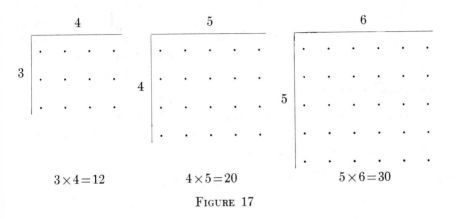

FIGURE 17

The representation of a product by means of an array gives a means of computing a product by counting pairings, or by adding, and makes the important properties of multiplication easy to understand.

We first notice that a 3 by 4 array is the union of 3 disjoint sets (rows), each having 4 members. Consequently, the product, 3×4, can be computed by finding the sum, $4 + 4 + 4$ (Fig. 18). This is the familiar repeated-addition method of multiplication.

FIGURE 18

It is also true that the array (Fig. 18) is the union of 4 disjoint sets (columns), each of which has 3 members. Thus, 3×4 can be alternatively computed by the repeated addition:

$$3+3+3+3=12.$$

Closure Property

The product of every pair of whole numbers is a whole number. If you choose any pair of numbers from the set of whole numbers, their product is a whole number. This property of multiplication is described by saying that the set of whole numbers is *closed* under the operation of multiplication, and it is called the *closure property* of multiplication.

Commutative Property

Study of various arrays reveals another property of the set of whole numbers and the operation of multiplication. Consider the illustrations in Figure 19. Notice that $2 \times 5 = 5 \times 2$ and $3 \times 4 = 4 \times 3$.

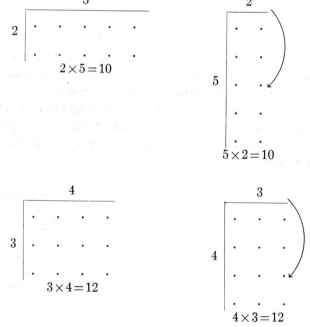

FIGURE 19

In general, as these examples suggest, if a and b are any whole numbers, then $a \times b = b \times a$. This is called the *commutative property of multiplication*. A 2 by 5 array can be changed into a 5 by 2 array by simply turning the array through 90°. A 3 by 4 array can be changed into a 4 by 3 array by simply turning the array through 90°. In general, an a by b array can be changed into a b by a array by turning the array through 90°.

In other words, commuting the order of two factors [changing (3×7) to (7×3)] does not change their product.

Associative Property

Recall that multiplication is a binary operation; that is, it is an operation on two numbers. To find the product of three numbers, for example the numbers 2, 3, and 4, we may multiply 2 and 3 and obtain the product 6, and then multiply 6 and 4. We write this:

$$(2 \times 3) \times 4 = 6 \times 4$$

$$= 24.$$

Or we may multiply 3 and 4 and obtain the product 12, and then multiply 2 and 12:

$$2 \times (3 \times 4) = 2 \times 12$$

$$= 24.$$

In either case, the product is the same. Thus,

$$(2 \times 3) \times 4 = 2 \times (3 \times 4).$$

Study the three examples below. Is each sentence true?

$$(3 \times 5) \times 4 = 3 \times (5 \times 4)$$

$$(2 \times 6) \times 7 = 2 \times (6 \times 7)$$

$$(5 \times 8) \times 9 = 5 \times (8 \times 9)$$

In general, if a, b, and c are any whole numbers,

$$(a \times b) \times c = a \times (b \times c).$$

This property is called the *associative property of multiplication*.

We can illustrate the associativity of multiplication by considering a box which is made up of blocks (Fig. 20). Let the dimension of such a box be 2 by 3 by 4. The number of blocks in the box is $(2 \times 3) \times 4$ and also $2 \times (3 \times 4)$, indicating that it is true that

$$(2 \times 3) \times 4 = 2 \times (3 \times 4).$$

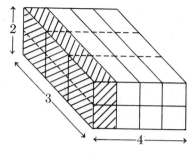

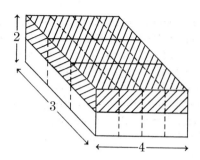

2 × 3 blocks in each
vertical slice

3 × 4 blocks in each
horizontal slice

4 vertical slices

2 horizontal slices

FIGURE 20

In general, these slicings can be done with a box whose dimensions are *a* by *b* by *c*, where *a*, *b*, and *c* are three counting numbers. Since

$$(2 \times 3) \times 4 = 2 \times (3 \times 4),$$

and

$$(6 \times 7) \times 8 = 6 \times (7 \times 8)$$

or, in general,

$$(a \times b) \times c = a \times (b \times c),$$

it is not necessary to use parentheses in writing the product of three factors. We may now write $(2 \times 3) \times 4$ simply as $2 \times 3 \times 4$.

The associative property may be generalized to hold for more than three factors. For example, we may write

$$5 \times 6 \times 7 \times 8 \times 9,$$

instead of

$$\{[(5 \times 6) \times 7] \times 8\} \times 9.$$

Identity Element

The number 1 plays the same role with respect to multiplication as the number 0 plays with respect to addition. Recall that

$$0 + 1 = 1,$$

$$0 + 2 = 2,$$

and, in general, if *n* is any whole number,

$$0 + n = n.$$

We call 0 the *identity element* for addition.

Is there, in similar fashion, an identity element for multiplication? Examine the arrays in Figure 21.

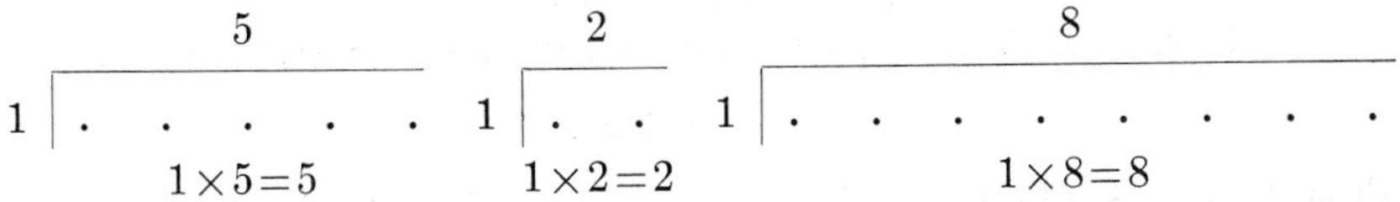

$$1 \times 5 = 5 \qquad 1 \times 2 = 2 \qquad 1 \times 8 = 8$$

FIGURE 21

A 1 by n array consists of one row having n elements; hence, the array has exactly n elements. Thus, if n is any whole number, $1 \times n = n$; and by the commutative property, $n \times 1 = 1 \times n = n$. For this reason, the number 1 is called the *identity element for multiplication.*

The Role of Zero in Multiplication

The number 0 has a special property with respect to multiplication. The number of members in a 5 by 0 array which has 5 rows each with 0 (no) members is clearly 0, because the array is the empty set. Hence,

$$5 \times 0 = 0.$$

Because of the commutative property,

$$0 \times 5 = 5 \times 0,$$
$$= 0.$$

In general, for any whole number, n,

$$n \times 0 = 0 \times n = 0.$$

Distributive Property

The question now arises: Is there a connection between the operations of addition and multiplication?

Consider this problem:

Three boys and two girls are going to the zoo.
The bus fare is 10 cents per person.
How much will it cost for the five children to go to the zoo on the bus?

We can solve this problem in two ways:

1. It will cost 3×10, or 30 cents for the boys.
   It will cost 2×10, or 20 cents for the girls.

It will cost $30+20$, or 50 cents for the boys and the girls.

$$(3 \times 10) + (2 \times 10) = 50$$

2. The number of children is $3+2$, or 5.

It will cost 5×10, or 50 cents, to take the boys and girls.

$$(3+2) \times 10 = 50$$

From this we see that $(3 \times 10) + (2 \times 10) = (3+2) \times 10$. By virtue of the commutative property of multiplication, this sentence can be written

$$10 \times (3+2) = (10 \times 3) + (10 \times 2).$$

Are the following statements true?

$10 \times (3+2) = (10 \times 3) + (10 \times 2)$ $(3+2) \times 10 = (3 \times 10) + (2 \times 10)$

$\qquad 10 \times 5 = 30 + 20 \qquad\qquad\qquad\qquad\qquad 5 \times 10 = 30 + 20$

$6 \times (4+7) = (6 \times 4) + (6 \times 7)$ $(4+7) \times 6 = (4 \times 6) + (7 \times 6)$

$\qquad 6 \times 11 = 24 + 42 \qquad\qquad\qquad\qquad\qquad 11 \times 6 = 24 + 42$

$9 \times (4+3) = (9 \times 4) + (9 \times 3)$ $(4+3) \times 9 = (4 \times 9) + (3 \times 9)$

$\qquad 9 \times 7 = 36 + 27 \qquad\qquad\qquad\qquad\qquad 7 \times 9 = 36 + 27$

In general, if a, b, and c are whole numbers, then

$$a \times (b+c) = (a \times b) + (a \times c), \quad \text{and} \quad (b+c) \times a = (b \times a) + (c \times a).$$

This property is called the *distributive property of multiplication over addition*. Notice that you can distribute from left to right, as in the statements on the left side of the page, and from right to left, as in the statements on the right side of the page. The statement on the left is equivalent to the statement on the right because of the commutative property of multiplication.

It is important that you not only be able to "distribute multiplication over addition," that is, go from the left side to the right side in the statement

$$3 \times (4+6) = (3 \times 4) + (3 \times 6),$$

but that you be able to "undistribute," that is, go from the right side to the left side in the same statement.

We may convince ourselves of the truth of the distributive property by using arrays. For example, let us demonstrate (Fig. 22) that

$$4 \times (2+3) = (4 \times 2) + (4 \times 3).$$

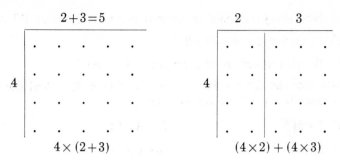

FIGURE 22

The 4 by 5 array can be separated by a vertical line into a 4 by 2 array and a 4 by 3 array, and the number of dots remains the same. Thus, we see that

$$4 \times 5 = (4 \times 2) + (4 \times 3)$$
$$4 \times (2+3) = (4 \times 2) + (4 \times 3).$$

Exercise Set 5

1. Name the property illustrated by each of the following sentences.

(a) $6+0=6$ (e) $5 \times 1 = 5$

(b) $7 \times 4 = 4 \times 7$ (f) $9+5=5+9$

(c) $(13+2)+7=13+(2+7)$ (g) $7 \times 24 = (7 \times 20) + (7 \times 4)$

(d) $8 \times 6 = (8 \times 4) + (8 \times 2)$ (h) $3 \times (4 \times 6) = (3 \times 4) \times 6$

(i) $(11 \times 15) + (11 \times 25) = 11 \times 40$

2. Is the set of whole numbers between 0 and 500 closed under the operation of multiplication? Why?

3. Consider the three arrays of dots, A, B, and C.

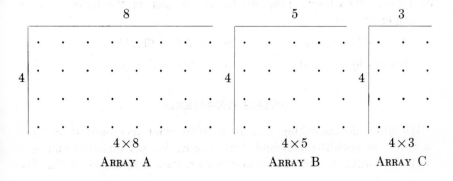

ARRAY A   ARRAY B   ARRAY C

(a) How many elements are there in array A? In array B? Array C?

(b) Is $4 \times 8 = (4 \times 5) + (4 \times 3)$?

(c) Which property is illustrated in (b) above?

4. Show how the distributive property may be used to find the products indicated below. [See Exercise 1 (g).]

(a) 7×24 (c) 8×12

(b) 5×36 (d) 9×57

5. Use the distributive property to rewrite each of the following expressions as the sum of two addends.

(a) $7 \times (90 + 6)$ (c) $(10 + 7) \times 9$ (e) $5 \times (50 + 7)$

(b) $(30 + 8) \times 4$ (d) $(20 + 6) \times 8$

6. In each number sentence in Table V, replace n to make a true statement. Name the property of multiplication that verifies each answer.

TABLE V

Number Sentence	Property
(a) $4 \times 5 = n \times 4$	
(b) $(3 \times 4) \times 5 = 3 \times (4 \times n)$	
(c) $7 \times 1 = n$	
(d) $4 \times 10 = (4 \times 5) + (4 \times n)$	
(e) $7 \times n = 7$	

7. Use the distributive property to rewrite each of the following as a single product.

(a) $(8 \times 2) + (8 \times 4)$ (c) $(9 \times 6) + (9 \times 14)$

(b) $(3 \times 5) + (3 \times 6)$ (d) $(15 \times 2) + (15 \times 8)$

INVERSE OPERATIONS

We often do something and then undo what has been done. For instance, we open the door and then close it. We put on a hat and take it off. We walk four blocks north and then walk four blocks south. The "undoing" activity is called the *inverse* of the "doing" activity. Consider these examples:

ACTIVITY	INVERSE
putting on a coat	taking off a coat
sitting down	standing up
going to sleep	waking up
walking up three flights of stairs	walking down three flights of stairs.

Not every activity has an inverse. For example, scrambling eggs has no inverse. There is no way to unscramble eggs and get them back to their original form.

Arithmetic operations also have inverses. Study the following examples.

$$(4+3)-3=4 \qquad (3\times2)\div2=3$$
$$(7-6)+6=7 \qquad (6\times4)\div4=6$$
$$(7+5)-5=7 \qquad (64\div8)\times8=64$$
$$(8-5)+5=8 \qquad (9\div3)\times3=9$$

The operation of subtraction is the inverse of addition. We add 6 and 4 to get the sum, 10. In order to get back to 6, we subtract 4 from 10. Addition is an operation on two addends to produce a third number, called the *sum*. Subtraction is the operation of finding an unknown addend when the sum and one of the addends are known.

The operation of division is the inverse of multiplication. We multiply 3 by 4 to get the product 12. In order to get back to 3, we divide 12 by 4. Multiplication is an operation on two factors to produce a third number, called the *product*. Division is the operation of finding an unknown factor when the product and one factor are known. The relation between inverse operations may be illustrated by the diagrams in Figure 23.

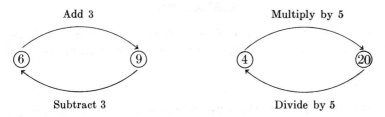

FIGURE 23

Emphasis on the inverse relationship between subtraction and addition, and between division and multiplication, yields a great deal of information concerning subtraction and division facts.

Exercise Set 6

1. What is the inverse operation of each of the following?

(a) adding 3   (d) sitting down

(b) putting on your shoes   (e) walking 3 blocks south

(c) making a pencil mark

2. Which of the following activities have no inverses?

(a) reading a book   (d) cutting the grass

(b) turning on a light   (e) driving from New York to Boston

(c) putting on a coat

3. Apply the "undoing" idea to the following mathematical sentences. Solutions to (a) and (b) are given.

DO	UNDO
(a) $5+2=7$	$7-2=5$
(b) $6-4=2$	$2+4=6$
(c) $36 \div 6=6$	
(d) $4 \times 2=8$	
(e) $18-8=10$	
(f) $25+10=35$	
(g) $42 \div 7=6$	
(h) $9 \times 7=63$	

SUBTRACTION

Now consider the operation of subtraction. If we take the numbers 7 and 3, there are several different ways of determining the number $7-3$.

EXAMPLE 1

Thinking in terms of sets (Figs. 24, 25) we choose a set A with 7 members and a set B with 3 members. Then we hunt for a set C, such that B and C

are disjoint, and such that when B and C are joined, the set $B \cup C$ can be placed in one-to-one correspondence with A.

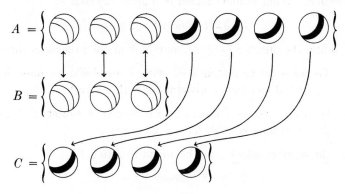

FIGURE 24

There are 4 members in C.

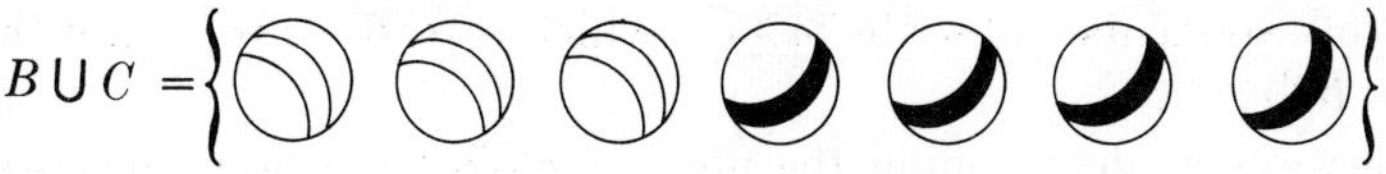

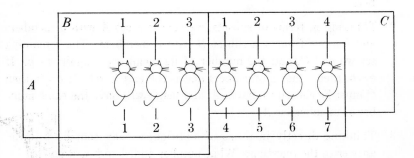

FIGURE 25

EXAMPLE 2

Thinking in terms of subsets (Fig. 26) we choose a set A with 7 members and remove from A a subset B with 3 members. The remainder set we call C, and the number of its members is $7 - 3$, or 4.

FIGURE 26

EXAMPLE 3

Thinking directly in terms of addition, we say that $7-3$ is the answer to the question, "What number added to 3 gives the sum 7?"

$$7-3=4 \quad \text{because} \quad 3+4=7.$$

Then to find the number $7-3$, we may look at the process in three ways:

1. To get a set to match a set with 7 members, we must join to a set with 3 members a disjoint set with 4 members.

2. If, from a set of 7 members, we remove a subset of 3 members, the remaining set will have 4 members.

3. The number which must be added to 3 to get 7 is 4.

$$7-3=4 \quad \text{means} \quad 3+4=7.$$

All three ways of looking at subtraction are important.

In general, suppose that we have two whole numbers a and b, and that a is greater than b or a is equal to b. (We write "a is greater than b" as "$a>b$"; and we write "a is equal to b" as "$a=b$." We sometimes join these two statements and write "$a \geq b$," which is read, "a is greater than or equal to b.")

Three ways of determining the number $a-b$ have been suggested by the previous illustrations:

1. Thinking in terms of sets, we choose a set A with a members and a set B with b members. Then we hunt for a set C, disjoint from B, so that when we join B and C we get a set $B \cup C$ which matches A. The number of members of C is $a-b$. If $a=b$, then the set C chosen is the empty set, which has no members. If $b=0$, then C must be chosen to match A, and hence will have a members.

2. Thinking in terms of subsets, we choose a set A with a members and remove from A a subset B with b members. The remaining set we call C, and the number of its members is again $a-b$. If $a=b$, then C has no members and is the empty set. If $b=0$, then C must be chosen to match A, and hence will have the same number of members as A.

3. Thinking directly in terms of addition, we say that $a-b$ is the answer to the question, "What number added to b will give a?"

$$a-b=c \quad \text{means that} \quad a=c+b.$$

Exercise Set 7

1. From each set below, remove a subset of four members.

   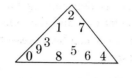

2. Complete the following chart.

	Known Addend	Sum	Number Sentence	Unknown Addend
(a)	15	49	$49 = 15 + n$	34
(b)	9	28		
(c)	35	76		

3. What operation is suggested by each number sentence? In each sentence, does n represent an addend or a sum?

   (a) $n + 61 = 75$ (d) $7 - 1 = n$

   (b) $4 + 6 = n$ (e) $19 = n + 4$

   (c) $35 + n = 47$ (f) $49 = 36 + n$

4. Use the numbers in each addition sentence to write two true subtraction sentences.

   (a) $9 + 8 = 17$ (c) $54 + 26 = 80$

   (b) $6 + 7 = 13$ (d) $37 + 89 = 126$

5. Complete each of the following sentences.

   (a) $3 + 4 = \underline{\quad}$ (d) $\underline{\quad} - 7 = 11$

   (b) $27 - \underline{\quad} = 10$ (e) $15 + \underline{\quad} = 21$

   (c) $\underline{\quad} + 7 = 11$ (f) $36 - 14 = \underline{\quad}$

DIVISION

The operation of division applied to the ordered pair of numbers (20, 4) can be interpreted as determining an unknown factor (in this case, 5) such that the product of 4 and the unknown factor is 20.

Recall that the product, 4×5, can be represented by an array (Fig. 27). Thus, we consider the question:

> If a set containing 20 elements is arranged in 4 rows with the same number of elements in each row, how many elements will there be in each row?

or the question:

> If a set containing 20 elements is arranged in rows with 4 elements in each row, how many rows will there be?

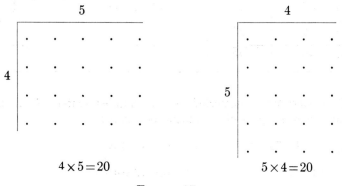

FIGURE 27

The answer to each of these questions is 5. For many ordered pairs of whole numbers, there will be no answer. For example, consider the ordered pair (20, 3). There is no array of 3 rows with the same number of elements in each row that will contain 20 elements. There is no array with 3 elements in each row that will contain 20 elements. Similarly, for (5, 7) there is no array possible. For any ordered pair of whole numbers in which the first component is less than the second component, the operation of division is impossible in the set of whole numbers. Thus, division does not possess the property of closure with respect to the set of whole numbers.

The symbol for division is $\div$. Thus in the sentence $6 \div 2 = n$, n is that unknown factor (if there is one) which when paired with the factor 2 gives the product 6. Considering this sentence in terms of an array, n is the number of columns there are when 6 objects are arranged in an array of 2 rows with the same number of elements in each row, and n is the number of rows there are when 6 objects are arranged in an array of 2 columns with the same number of elements in each column (Fig. 28).

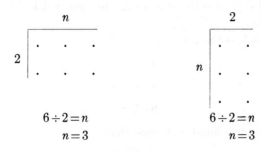

$$6 \div 2 = n \qquad\qquad\qquad 6 \div 2 = n$$
$$n = 3 \qquad\qquad\qquad\qquad n = 3$$

FIGURE 28

Division, then, is described as *finding an unknown factor in a product expression when the product and one factor are known.*

$$2 \times 3 = 6 \rightarrow 6 \div 3 = 2 \qquad 6 \div 2 = 3$$
$$2 \times 9 = 18 \rightarrow 18 \div 9 = 2 \qquad 18 \div 2 = 9$$
$$5 \times 4 = 20 \rightarrow 20 \div 5 = 4 \qquad 20 \div 4 = 5$$

Thus if a and b are whole numbers and n is a whole number.

and if $a \times n = b$, then $b \div n = a$, and $b \div a = n$.

All three number sentences are true for the same number, n.

ZERO IN DIVISION

Zero presents a problem in the operation of division. In the following sentences,

$$0 \div 2 = n,$$

$$0 \div 3 = n,$$

$$0 \div 5 = n,$$

we are looking for a factor n, such that

$$2 \times n = 0,$$

$$3 \times n = 0,$$

and $5 \times n = 0,$ respectively.

These sentences are true if n is zero, and only if n is zero. Thus, zero divided by any counting number (remember that zero is not a counting number) is zero. Zero is the only whole number that is divisible by every counting number.

Now let us look at the sentences:

$$2 \div 0 = r,$$

$$3 \div 0 = r,$$

$$6 \div 0 = r.$$

We are looking for a number, r, such that

$$r \times 0 = 2,$$

$$r \times 0 = 3,$$

and $r \times 0 = 6,$ respectively.

Since the product of zero and any whole number is zero, there is no factor, r, which will make any one of the statements true. Hence, *division of a counting number by zero is not possible.*

There is one other special case to consider, namely,

$$0 \div 0.$$

In this case we are looking for a factor, call it t, such that

$$0 \times t = 0.$$

If we try some whole numbers for t, we have

$$0 \times 5 = 0 \qquad \text{True}$$

$$0 \times 9 = 0 \qquad \text{True}$$

$$0 \times 0 = 0 \qquad \text{True}$$

Since the product of zero and *any* number is zero, the factor t may be any whole number we choose; and the statement

$$0 \times t = 0$$

will be true. Thus, $0 \div 0$ does not indicate a meaningful division. The symbol $0 \div 0$ does not name a number.

Exercise Set 8

1. Complete the following chart.

Array	Number of Rows	Number of Columns	Number of Elements	Multi-plication Sentence	Division Sentence
(a)					
(b)					
(c)					
(d)					

2. Use the array on the right to show that the following sentences are true.

(a) $48 \div 4 = 12$

(b) $48 \div 12 = 4$

3. Write two division sentences for each multiplication sentence given in (b) and (c).

(a) $7 \times 9 = 63$ $63 \div 7 = 9$ $63 \div 9 = 7$

(b) $6 \times 7 = 42$

(c) $9 \times 8 = 72$

4. Name the operation suggested by each of the following number sentences. In each sentence, does n represent a factor, a product, a sum, or an addend?

(a) $7 \times 9 = n$ (f) $n = 12 + 24$

(b) $8 \times n = 40$ (g) $n \times 8 = 32$

(c) $n + 17 = 23$ (h) $13 + 27 = n$

(d) $n = 5 \times 6$ (i) $n + 36 = 40$

(e) $72 = 9 \times n$ (j) $24 \div 3 = n$

5. Draw an array to illustrate the number sentence,

$$21 \div 3 = 7.$$

6. Use the array you drew in Exercise 5 to tell which of the following number sentences are true.

(a) $21 = 3 \times 7$ (d) $21 \div 3 = 7$

(b) $7 \times 3 = 21$ (e) $21 \div 7 = 3$

(c) $3 + 3 + 3 + 3 + 3 + 3 + 3 = 21$ (f) $7 + 7 + 7 = 21$

PROPERTIES OF SUBTRACTION AND DIVISION

Properties of Subtraction

We now inquire whether or not subtraction, the inverse operation of addition, has any of the properties of addition. We found that addition possessed the following properties:

1. *Closure:* The sum of any two whole numbers is a whole number.
2. *Commutativity:* The sum of two whole numbers is not changed when the order of the addends is changed. For example,

$$3 + 2 = 2 + 3.$$

3. *Associativity:* The sum of three numbers does not depend on the way in which the numbers are grouped. For example,

$$(4 + 2) + 6 = 4 + (2 + 6).$$

4. *Identity Element:* Zero is the identity element for addition, that is, the sum of zero and any whole number is that whole number. For example,

$$6 + 0 = 6.$$

Does the operation of subtraction have the same properties as addition? Is the set of whole numbers closed under subtraction? That is to say, if we subtract any whole number from another, is the unknown addend always a whole number? Try $3-7$. Is there a whole number n, such that $n+7=3$? Of course, there is not. Since we have found one pair of whole numbers for which the unknown addend is not a whole number, we conclude that the set of whole numbers is not closed under subtraction.

Is subtraction commutative? Is $4-3$ equal to $3-4$? We know that $4-3=1$, but $3-4$ is not a whole number; there is no whole number n, such that $4+n=3$. Hence, we conclude that subtraction is not commutative.

Is subtraction of whole numbers an associative operation? For example, is $(8-5)-3$ equal to $8-(5-3)$?

$$(8-5)-3=3-3$$
$$=0$$

and

$$8-(5-3)=8-2$$
$$=6.$$

Surely $6 \neq 0$ (the symbol $\neq$ is read, "is not equal to"), so we conclude that subtraction is not associative.

Is there an identity element for subtraction? Try zero, the identity element for addition. For any whole number n, we know that

$$n+0=n.$$

The definition of subtraction then assures us that

$$n=n-0.$$

Thus, zero is the identity element for subtraction.

Properties of Division

What properties does division, the inverse operation of multiplication, have? Does it have the same properties as multiplication? We noted that multiplication has the following properties:

1. *Closure:* The product of any two whole numbers is a whole number.
2. *Commutativity:* The product of any two whole numbers does not depend on the order of the factors. For example,

$$3 \times 2 = 2 \times 3.$$

3. *Associativity:* The product of three numbers does not depend on the way in which the factors are grouped. For example,

$$(2 \times 3) \times 4 = 2 \times (3 \times 4).$$

4. *Identity Element:* One is the identity element for multiplication; that is, the product of one and any number is that number.

$$6 \times 1 = 6$$

Is the set of whole numbers closed under division? Is $7 \div 4$ a whole number? It is not, for there is no whole number, n, for which $4 \times n = 7$ is a true statement. Is $1 \div 2$ a whole number? No. Furthermore, we have seen that division by the whole number zero is impossible. The set of whole numbers is not closed with respect to division.

Is division commutative? Is $6 \div 2$ equal to $2 \div 6$? We know that $6 \div 2 = 3$, because $3 \times 2 = 6$. Is there a whole number, n, such that $6 \times n = 2$? Since there is no whole number, n, which makes the statement true (3 does not), the operation of division is not commutative.

Is division of whole numbers an associative operation? For example, is $(24 \div 6) \div 2 = 24 \div (6 \div 2)$?

$$(24 \div 6) \div 2 = 4 \div 2$$
$$= 2$$
$$24 \div (6 \div 2) = 24 \div 3$$
$$= 8$$

Certainly $8 \neq 2$, so division is not an associative operation.

Is there an identity element for division? We know that for any whole number n,

$$n \times 1 = n.$$

The definition of division then assures us that if

$$n \times 1 = n, \quad \text{then} \quad n = n \div 1.$$

Thus, 1 is the identity element for division.

The primary operations of addition and multiplication have the distributive property of multiplication over addition:

$$3 \times (2 + 6) = (3 \times 2) + (3 \times 6)$$
$$7 \times (8 + 2) = (7 \times 8) + (7 \times 2).$$

In general, if a, b, and c are any whole numbers, then

$$a \times (b + c) = (a \times b) + (a \times c).$$

Multiplication is related to subtraction in the same way. Notice that

$$6 \times (4 - 2) = (6 \times 4) - (6 \times 2)$$
$$6 \times 2 = 24 - 12$$
$$12 = 12,$$
$$3 \times (8 - 5) = (3 \times 8) - (3 \times 5)$$

$$3 \times 3 = 24 - 15$$
$$9 = 9,$$
$$5 \times (7 - 1) = (5 \times 7) - (5 \times 1)$$
$$5 \times 6 = 35 - 5$$
$$30 = 30.$$

In general, if a, b, and c are whole numbers, and if $b-c$ is a whole number (that is, if $b \geq c$), then

$$a \times (b - c) = (a \times b) - (a \times c).$$

Exercise Set 9

1. Which of the following are names for whole numbers?

(a) $23 - 7$ (e) $16 - 20$

(b) $12 + 3$ (f) $15 \div 4$

(c) $56 \div 8$ (g) $2 \div 6$

(d) 5×4 (h) $3 \div 0$

2. Complete the following chart.

Number Sentence	Property
(a) $5 + 6 = 6 + 5$	Commutative (addition)
(b) $36 \times 6 = (30 \times 6) + (6 \times 6)$	
(c) $47 + 0 = 47$	
(d) $3 \times (4 \times 9) = (3 \times 4) \times 9$	
(e) $25 \times 1 = 25$	
(f) $9 \times 38 = (9 \times 30) + (9 \times 8)$	
(g) $7 \times 3 = 3 \times 7$	
(h) $(6 + 8) + 2 = 6 + (8 + 2)$	
(i) $7 \times 99 = (7 \times 100) - (7 \times 1)$	

3. Use the distributive property of multiplication over addition to find n in each of the following sentences.

$$3 \times 57 = (3 \times 50) + (3 \times 7)$$

(a) $7 \times 21 = n$ (c) $43 \times 3 = n$

(b) $93 \times 3 = n$ (d) $125 \times 5 = n$

4. Use the distributive property of multiplication over subtraction to find n.

$$4 \times 49 = (4 \times 50) - (4 \times 1)$$

(a) $8 \times 98 = n$ (c) $6 \times 48 = n$

(b) $5 \times 69 = n$ (d) $7 \times 19 = n$

5. Fill in the blanks to make each of the following statements true.

(a) $(36 \div 6) \div 6 = $ _____ $36 \div (6 \div 6) = $ _____

(b) $48 \div (8 \div 2) = $ _____ $(48 \div 8) \div 2 = $ _____

(c) $(20 - 17) - 3 = $ _____ $20 - (17 - 3) = $ _____

(d) $9 - (6 - 3) = $ _____ $(9 - 6) - 3 = $ _____

6. Are the operations of division and subtraction associative?

7. Perform the indicated operations. Use the commutative property to check each answer.

(a) 9×8 (c) 23×54

(b) $3 + 7$ (d) $19 + 68$

8. Perform the indicated operations. Use the inverse operation to check each answer.

(a) $37 - 24$ (c) 24×3

(b) $135 \div 5$ (d) $45 + 69$

SUMMARY

Whole Numbers

Counting Number:	A member of the set $\{1, 2, 3, 4, \ldots\}$
Whole Number:	A member of the set $\{0, 1, 2, 3, 4, \ldots\}$
Order (Trichotomy Principle):	If a is any whole number and b is any whole number, then one, and only one, of the following statements is true:

$$a = b,$$
$$a > b,$$
$$a < b.$$

Properties of Addition

1. *Closure Property:* The sum of any two whole numbers is a specified whole number.

2. *Commutative Property:* If a and b are any two whole numbers, then $a+b=b+a$.

3. *Associative Property:* If a, b, and c are any whole numbers, then $(a+b)+c=a+(b+c)$.

4. *Identity Element:* Zero is the identity element for addition: for any whole number, n, $n+0=0+n=n$.

Properties of Multiplication

1. *Closure Property:* The product of any two whole numbers is a specified whole number.

2. *Commutative Property:* If a and b are any whole numbers, then $a \times b = b \times a$.

3. *Associative Property:* If a, b, and c are any whole numbers, then $(a \times b) \times c = a \times (b \times c)$.

4. *Identity Element:* One is the identity element for multiplication; for any whole number, n, $n \times 1 = 1 \times n = n$.

5. *Distributive Property of Multiplication over Addition:* If a, b, and c are any whole numbers, then $a \times (b+c) = (a \times b) + (a \times c)$.

6. *Distributive Property of Multiplication Over Subtraction:* If a, b, and c are any whole numbers and $b-c$ is a whole number, then $a \times (b-c) = (a \times b) - (a \times c)$.

Operation

Inverse Operation: An inverse operation is an operation that undoes another operation; subtraction is the inverse operation of addition, and division is the inverse operation of multiplication.

Subtraction: Subtraction is the operation of finding an unknown addend when the sum and one of the addends are known; if a and b are whole numbers and $a \geq b$, then $a-b$ is a whole number c such that $b+c=a$.

Division: Division is the operation of finding an unknown factor when the product and one factor are known; if a and b are whole numbers, $b \neq 0$, then $a \div b$ is a whole number c (when one exists) such that $b \times c = a$.

Operation: An operation is a way of associating an ordered pair of numbers with a specified third number.

Addition: Addition is a binary operation which assigns to an ordered pair of whole numbers a specified whole number; the components of the ordered pair are called addends, and the specified whole number is called their sum.

Multiplication: Multiplication is a binary operation which assigns to each ordered pair of whole numbers a specified whole number; the components of the ordered pair are called factors, and the specified whole number is called their product.

ANSWERS TO EXERCISE SETS

Exercise Set 1

1. (a) Addition   (g) Multiplication

   (b) 22   (h) 18

   (c) 4   (i) 3

   (d) 16   (j) 6

   (e) Subtraction   (k) 5

   (f) 2   (l) 4

2. (a) +   (b) ÷   (c) −   (d) ×

3. (a) 27   (b) 9   (c) 162   (d) 2

4. c, f, i.

Exercise Set 2

1. $A \cup B = \{$dog, cat, cow, pig, duck, horse, elephant$\}$.
   The cardinal number of A is 4; of B, 3; and of $A \cup B$, 7.

2. $R \cup S = \{1, 2, 3, 4, 5, 6, 7, 8, 10, 12\}$.
   The cardinal number of R is 6; of S, 4; and of $R \cup S$, 10.

3. $W \cup L = \{$all white horses$\}$, since L is the empty set.

4. (a) 5

    (b) 5

    (c) $F \cup G = \{$dog, cow, horse, pig, turkey, chicken, robin, cat$\}$.

(d) 8

(e) Because F and G are not disjoint sets

5. (a) 11

    (b) By adding the number of the members of both sets

    (c) Because M and N are disjoint sets

6. 4   0   4

7. $B = \{$gloves$\}$

8. (b) $9+6=n$;   15

    (c) $7+3=n$;   10

    (d) $2+8=n$;   10

Exercise Set 3

1. (a)

    (b)

(c)

(d)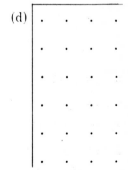

2. (a) $4 \times 5 = 20$

    (b) $2 \times 4 = 8$

(c) $3 \times 2 = 6$

(d) $3 \times 3 = 9$

3. (a)

(c)

(b)

(d)

8

4.

6

$6 \times 8 = 48$

5. $5 \times 6 = 30$

6. 961

7. (b) 4; 3; 12   (c) 5; 6; 30   (d) 3; 5; 15   (e) 7; 4; 28

8. (b) 28   (f) 6; 6; 4

(c) 3   (g) 5; 5

(d) 6   (h) 5

(e) $8 \times 3 = 24$ (i) 3

9. (a)

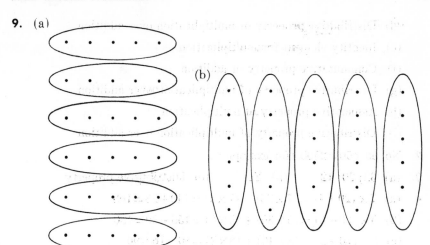

(b)

Exercise Set 4

1. b, g

2. Yes

3. c, d

4. 0

5. (a) $6+15=13+8$ (c) $10+5=7+8$
    $\qquad 21=21$ $15=15$

   (b) $19+2=9+12$ (d) $14+15=20+9$
    $\qquad 21=21$ $29=29$

6. (a) Commutative property of addition
   (b) Identity element for addition
   (c) Associative property of addition

7. (a) 7,   Identity element   (e) 5,   Commutative property
   (b) 2,   Commutative property   (f) 0,   Identity element
   (c) 3,   Associative property   (g) n,   Associative property
   (d) 3,   Identity element   (h) b,   Commutative property

Exercise Set 5

1. (a) Identity element for addition
   (b) Commutative property of multiplication
   (c) Associative property of addition

(d) Distributive property of multiplication over addition

(e) Identity element for multiplication

(f) Commutative property of addition

(g) Distributive property of multiplication over addition

(h) Associative property of multiplication

(i) Distributive property of multiplication over addition

2. No. $50 \times 50 = 2500$ (for example)

3. (a) $32; 20; 12$ (b) Yes   (c) Distributive property

4. (a) $7 \times (20+4) = (7 \times 20) + (7 \times 4) = 140 + 28 = 168$

   (b) $5 \times (30+6) = (5 \times 30) + (5 \times 6) = 150 + 30 = 180$

   (c) $8 \times (10+2) = (8 \times 10) + (8 \times 2) = 80 + 16 = 96$

   (d) $9 \times (50+7) = (9 \times 50) + (9 \times 7) = 450 + 63 = 513$

5. (a) $(7 \times 90) + (7 \times 6)$ (d) $(20 \times 8) + (6 \times 8)$

   (b) $(30 \times 4) + (8 \times 4)$ (e) $(5 \times 50) + (5 \times 7)$

   (c) $(10 \times 9) + (7 \times 9)$

6. (a) 5;   Commutative   (d) 5;   Distributive

   (b) 5;   Associative   (e) 1;   Identity element

   (c) 7;   Identity element

7. (a) 8×6 (b) 3×11 (c) 9×20 (d) 15×10

Exercise Set 6

1. (a) Subtracting 3   (d) Standing up

   (b) Taking off your shoes   (e) Walking 3 blocks north

   (c) Erasing a pencil mark

2. a, d

3. (c) $6 \times 6 = 36$ (f) $35 - 10 = 25;$ $35 - 25 = 10$

   (d) $8 \div 2 = 4;$ $8 \div 4 = 2$ (g) $6 \times 7 = 42$

   (e) $10 + 8 = 18$ (h) $63 \div 7 = 9;$ $63 \div 9 = 7$

Exercise Set 7

1. Answers will vary. One may be

   $\{0, A, +, V\}$ $\{1, 2, 3, 4\}$ $\{$Tom, Mary, Bill, Dick$\}$

2. (b) $28=9+n$;   19   (c) $76=35+n$;   41

3. (a) Subtraction; unknown   (d) Subtraction; unknown
          addend   addend

   (b) Addition; sum   (e) Subtraction; unknown
                                                     addend

   (c) Subtraction; unknown   (f) Subtraction; unknown
          addend   addend

4. (a) $17-8=9$; $17-9=8$ (c) $80-26=54$; $80-54=26$

   (b) $13-7=6$; $13-6=7$ (d) $126-89=37$; $126-37=89$

5. (a) 7   (b) 17   (c) 4   (d) 18   (e) 6   (f) 22

Exercise Set 8

1. (a) 2; 3; 6; $2\times3=6$; $6\div2=3$; $6\div3=2$

   (b) 4; 3; 12; $4\times3=12$; $12\div3=4$; $12\div4=3$

   (c) 4; 4; 16; $4\times4=16$; $16\div4=4$

   (d) 7; 4; 28; $7\times4=28$; $28\div4=7$; $28\div7=4$

2. (a)

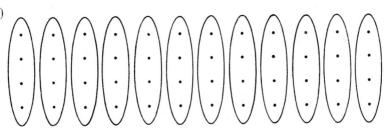

   (b)

3. (b) $42\div6=7$ $42\div7=6$

   (c) $72\div8=9$ $72\div9=8$

4. (a) Multiplication;   product
   (b) Division;   unknown factor
   (c) Subtraction;   unknown addend
   (d) Multiplication;   product
   (e) Division;   unknown factor
   (f) Addition;   sum
   (g) Division;   unknown factor
   (h) Addition;   sum
   (i) Subtraction;   unknown addend
   (j) Division;   unknown factor

5.
```
.   .   .   .   .   .   .          .   .   .

.   .   .   .   .   .   .          .   .   .

.   .   .   .   .   .              .   .   .
                            or
                                  .   .   .

                                  .   .   .

                                  .   .   .
```

6. a, b, c, d, e, f

Exercise Set 9

1. a, b, c, d

2. (b) Distributive property of multiplication over addition
   (c) Identity element for addition
   (d) Associative property of multiplication
   (e) Identity element for multiplication
   (f) Distributive property of multiplication over addition
   (g) Commutative property of multiplication
   (h) Associative property of addition
   (i) Distributive property of multiplication over subtraction

3. (a) $7 \times (20+1) = (7 \times 20) + (7 \times 1) = 140 + 7 = 147$

(b) $(90+3) \times 3 = (90 \times 3) + (3 \times 3) = 270 + 9 = 279$

(c) $(40+3) \times 3 = (40 \times 3) + (3 \times 3) = 120 + 9 = 129$

(d) $(100+25) \times 5 = (100 \times 5) + (25 \times 5) = 500 + 125 = 625$

4. (a) $8 \times (100-2) = (8 \times 100) - (8 \times 2) = 800 - 16 = 784$

(b) $5 \times (70-1) = (5 \times 70) - (5 \times 1) = 350 - 5 = 345$

(c) $6 \times (50-2) = (6 \times 50) - (6 \times 2) = 300 - 12 = 288$

(d) $7 \times (20-1) = (7 \times 20) - (7 \times 1) = 140 - 7 = 133$

5. (a) 1; 36   (b) 12; 3   (c) 0; 6   (d) 6; 0

6. No

7. (a) 72   (b) 10   (c) 1242   (d) 87

8. (a) 13   (b) 27   (c) 72   (d) 114

BOOKLET NUMBER THREE:

NUMERATION SYSTEMS FOR THE WHOLE NUMBERS

ORIGINS OF OUR NUMBER SYSTEM

"Operator, please give me | | | | | | | | | | |-| | | | | | | | | | | |."
"The space capsule is circling the earth every | | | ∩ ∩ ∩ minutes."
| | | ∩ ∩ ∩
∩
"The mileage on my car is MMMCDLXXIV."

Do you recognize these as numerals from numeration systems? Although we might be inclined to smile at these examples, they should help us realize that the numeration system we employ today is not without certain useful features. Indeed, much of the progress man has made over the last few centuries both in science and technology can be attributed in no small part to his development of an efficient means of naming numbers. Our decimal place-value system, as it is called, is the culmination of many centuries of development and contains within its framework contributions from a variety of numeration systems that have been used in the past.

A numeration system is a means of denoting or naming numbers. It involves two things: a set of symbols, and some rules for combining the symbols to denote various numbers. The earliest numeration systems probably employed but a single symbol: a mark on some surface, a notch on a stick, or something similar. Each mark or notch denoted the number one, although the concept of a number as an abstract entity probably played no part in the thoughts of the marker or notcher. Indeed, there is no compelling reason to suppose that a name was attached to the symbol. Marks on a cave wall or notches on a stick simply served as tallies; and if questions involving the idea of "how many" arose, they could easily have been answered by pointing to the marks or notches without recourse to technical terminology such as "one," "two," or the like.

Implicit in a numeration system using a symbol such as | | | | to denote what we now call the number four, however, is a very fundamental and highly intuitive convention, namely, that *the number named is the sum of the numbers denoted by the separate marks.*

A big step for man came when he began to group his single marks to make them more easily understood. The number used as the basis for the grouping usually had some common physical association such as five for the fingers on a hand, ten for the fingers on both hands, twenty for the toes and fingers together. Words we use, such as "score" and "dozen," indicate that numbers other than five or ten have been used as a base at some time in the past.

About the time that man began to group his marks, he became aware of the possibility of developing a set of rules, or a system, for grouping; and he also began to pay attention to the symbols he used. A single tally mark, such as /, was commonly used, even when grouped as *LHT LHT LHT LHT.* Some problems presented themselves, however, when it came to interpreting quickly the amount represented. Thus, it became desirable to have different symbols to represent groups of different sizes, but still to use some particular number as the basis for grouping.

The Egyptian system of numeration used in ancient times indicates these points rather clearly (see Table I). By looking at the examples in Table I, you can see that the number ten was used as the basis for

TABLE I

Ancient Egyptian System of Numerals		
Ancient Egyptian Numeral	Present-Day Name	Decimal Numeral
|	one	1
∩	ten	10
ꝰ	one hundred	100
Ⴟ	one thousand	1,000
⌐	ten thousand	10,000
ꝰ ꝰ ꝰ ∩∩∩|||	three hundred thirty-three	333

grouping, and that different symbols were used to represent groups of different size. By comparing the Egyptian numeral and the decimal place-value numeral, you can see that the Egyptians did not have a place-value system. The meaning of a numeral in the Egyptian system would not have been changed if the order of the symbols had been rearranged. For example in the Egyptian system, thirty-two might have been written in several ways:

$$\cap \cap \cap |\,| \quad \text{or} \quad \cap |\cap| \cap \quad \text{or} \quad \cap |\,| \cap \cap \,;$$

however the first way was the most common. In each case the numeral represented the sum of the numbers represented by the five symbols. It would certainly change the meaning of our numeral 105 if we were to rearrange the symbols to read 501! In the Egyptian system of numeration there was no symbol for zero, because there was no need for it.

Although rather well-developed, the Egyptian system of numeration (and others like it) had several disadvantages. Computation could become very cumbersome. Also, when a symbol was chosen by some person to name a group greater than any that had previously been used, there was no certainty that someone else had not already chosen a different symbol for this group.

Babylonian numeration had several features not present in systems similar to the Egyptian one. It had the beginnings of a place-value system in that the same symbol was used to represent groups of different sizes, depending on its position in the numeral (see Table II). Only two sym-

TABLE II

Babylonian Place Values			
three hundred sixty	sixty	ten	one
<	V	<	V

bols, V and <, were used to write all numerals. Because at first there was no way to indicate the absence of a group of a certain size (for which we use the symbol 0), some problems in interpretation arose. For example, the symbol $\lesseqgtr$ V V might stand for $(2 \times 10) + (2 \times 1)$, or 22. On the other hand, it might stand for $(2 \times 360) + (2 \times 60)$, or 840; or possibly $(2 \times 360) + (2 \times 1)$, or 722. Later, an empty space was used as we use zero; and still later, the symbol ":" was used for the same purpose.

Not until the following developments had taken place did a place-value system such as ours emerge.

    1. A few symbols, which could be written with relative ease, were accepted as symbols for the numbers for which we use the symbols: 1, 2, 3, . . . , 9.

2. These accepted symbols were combined to form numerals for greater numbers; and the position in which the symbol was written, as well as the particular symbol, determined the number represented.

3. The need for a symbol representing zero was recognized, and a symbol was chosen.

Even after these developments, it was some time before the decimal place-value system came into wide-spread use. A story is told that even as late as the 1790's the Bank of London recorded its accounts on tally sticks. Horizontal slashes were made across the stick, and it was then split vertically, half being given to the investor and half kept by the bank. Wishing to improve its accounting system, the bank adopted a modern system and discarded the tally sticks by burning them. Unfortunately, the fire got out of control and the bank itself was burned!

NUMBER AND NUMERAL

Two mathematical terms that are frequently confused are *number* and *numeral*. These terms are not synonymous, and principles of numeration cannot be developed effectively until a distinction is made between the meanings of these two words.

Just what is number? Basically, it is an idea associated with a set* of objects, such as the Set A defined as follows:

$$A = \left\{ \bigcirc, \; \bigstar, \; \boxed{B}, \; \overline{\bowtie}, \; \triangle \right\}.$$

The same number idea can be associated with other sets equivalent to A. (Recall that equivalent sets are sets that can be placed in one-to-one correspondence.) Some such sets are the following examples (Fig. 1).

Now consider all the sets equivalent to any one of these sets in Figure 1. Among them is the standard set:**

$$\{``1", \, ``2", \, ``3", \, ``4", \, ``5"\}.$$

These sets all possess a property in common, namely, that of being equivalent to the same set. This property, which is independent of the nature of the elements in the sets, is called the number five. Note that it is named by the last numeral in the standard set,

$$\{``1", \, ``2", \, ``3", \, ``4", \, ``5"\}.$$

---

*See Booklet No. 1: *Sets*.

**The quotation marks indicate that the symbols themselves, not the numbers they represent, are being considered.

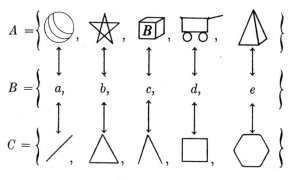

Similarly, {"1"} can be used to identify the property shared by all sets to which it is equivalent, namely the number one; {"1", "2"}, can be used to identify the property shared by all sets to which it is equivalent, namely the number two; etc.

What is a numeral? A numeral is a symbol used to name a number. Numerals, then, provide a means of communicating number ideas.

Let us examine some numerals:

$$5, \quad \cancel{\text{HHT}}, \quad V, \quad 2+3, \quad (2 \times 2)+1, \quad 7-2.$$

These numerals are all names for the same number, five. The fact that the symbol 5 happens to be the simplest symbol (at least, it is for us; perhaps the Romans thought V was the simplest symbol for five!) in no way means that the others are less correct as names for the number idea of five.

A distinction must also be made between a *system of numeration* and a *number system*. A number system is a much broader concept than a system of numeration. A number system, such as the system of whole numbers, is—as the name implies—a system of numbers, irrespective of the symbols used to denote the numbers. A system of numeration, on the other hand, is a means of denoting numbers by symbols in accordance with specified rules, and is not directly concerned with the properties of the numbers.

HINDU-ARABIC SYSTEM OF NUMERATION

All systems of numeration have certain characteristics in common. One of these common characteristics is that only a limited number of symbols is used. Since the set of symbols used is finite and the set of whole numbers is infinite (there is no greatest whole number), it is necessary to use some symbols more than once to represent such numbers.

The Hindu-Arabic system is a place-value system with symbols chosen for zero, one, two, three, etc., up to nine. The next number, ten, plays a special role in this system and is called the *base* of the system. Because ten is the base, the system is called a decimal system, from the Latin word "decem" which means ten.

The symbols in the set

$$\{0, 1, 2, 3, 4, 5, 6, 7, 8, 9\}$$

are frequently called digits; they are numerals for the whole numbers zero through nine. To write a symbol for ten and, in fact, for all numbers greater than nine, we use two or more digits written according to a pattern determined by our system of place values.

Let us look at the numeral for a number requiring several digits and consider what is meant by a place-value system. The number five hundred sixty-nine is written, 569.

$$\overset{\text{②}}{5} \quad \overset{\text{①}}{6} \quad \overset{\text{⓪}}{9}$$

$$569 = \overset{\text{②}}{(\text{five} \times \text{one hundred})} + \overset{\text{①}}{(\text{six} \times \text{ten})} + \overset{\text{⓪}}{(\text{nine} \times \text{one})}.$$

The numerals in the circles indicate that there are three positions involved in writing the numeral. The digit 9 occupies position 0, the digit 6 occupies position 1, and the digit 5 occupies position 2. To each position is assigned a number which is the place value of the position; one is the place value of position 0, ten is the place value of position 1, and one hundred is the place value of position 2, as shown in Table III. The place value assigned to a position in a system with ten as base is ten times as great as the place value assigned to the next position to its right. The

TABLE III

Place Value in Base Ten			
Position 3	Position 2	Position 1	Position 0
one thousand	one hundred	ten	one
$1,000 = 10 \times 100$	$100 = 10 \times 10$	$10 = 10 \times 1$	1

place value is a number assigned to a position, independent of the digit in the position. That is to say, any one of the digits can occupy any one of the positions.

The number represented by the digit 5 in the numeral 569 is a product. It is the product of the number five and the place value assigned to the position 2, which is one hundred. The number represented by the digit 6 is the product of six and the place value assigned to the position 1, which is ten. The 9 represents the product of nine and the place value assigned to the position 0, which is one. The entire numeral represents the sum of the three products:

$$569 = (5 \times 100) + (6 \times 10) + (9 \times 1)$$
$$= \quad 500 \quad + \quad 60 \quad + \quad 9$$
$$= \quad\quad\quad 569.$$

To summarize, the two basic principles of the Hindu-Arabic system are the *place-value principle* and the *additive principle*. The place-value principle includes two ideas:

1. There is a number assigned to each position in the numeral. This number is called the place value of the position.
2. Each digit represents the product of the number it names and the place value assigned to its position.

The additive principle means that the number named is the sum of the products mentioned above.

A place-value system can, of course, have a base other than ten; in fact, any counting number greater than one can be used as base for a place-value system.

Our place-value system is also used to write numerals for numbers that are not whole numbers.* For this purpose, the decimal point is introduced; and place values less than one are assigned to positions to the right of position 0.

Exercise Set 1

1. Give five different names for each of the following.

   (a) seven,   (b) one,   (c) zero.

2. Express the following numbers as sums of products.

   (a) 57   (b) 419   (c) 620   (d) 2,087

3. What is the place value of the position occupied by each of the following?

   (a) "3" in the numeral 637   (c) "2" in the numeral 2146
   (b) "0" in the numeral 490   (d) "5" in the numeral 50,000

─────────

* See Booklet No. 7: *Numeration Systems for the Rational Numbers.*

4. Complete the following statements.

(a) In the numeral 2307, the place value of the position of "3" is _____ times as great as the place value of the position of "0."

(b) In the numeral 2307, the place value of the position of "2" is _____ times as great as the place value of the position of "0."

(c) In the numeral 619,411 the place value of the position of "6" is _____ times as great as the place value of the position of "4."

EXPONENTS

In our decimal (base-ten) system of numeration, we find that 1, 10, 10×10, $10 \times 10 \times 10$, etc., play an important role. With the exception of the first number, all of these specified numbers consist of a single number, used as a factor, and may be written in shorthand form; thus,

$$1 = 10^0,$$
$$10 = 10^1,$$
$$10 \times 10 = 10^2,$$
$$10 \times 10 \times 10 = 10^3,$$
$$10 \times 10 \times 10 \times 10 = 10^4.$$

The numeral 10^4 is called the *exponent form* for the number 10,000.

The number that is repeated as a factor, in this case 10, is called the *base* of the expression. The superscript to the right of the base is used to tell how many times the base has been used as a factor. This superscript is called an *exponent*. Thus, in

$$10^5 = 10 \times 10 \times 10 \times 10 \times 10$$

the base is 10, and the exponent is 5. We read "10^5" as "ten to the fifth power." We read "10^4" as "ten to the fourth power." We read "10^3" as "ten to the third power" or "ten cubed." We read "10^2" as "ten to the second power" or "ten squared." We call the following numbers, 1, $10^2 = 100$, $10^3 = 1000$, etc., the *powers* of ten.

The base of a power can be any counting number, and can be zero if the exponent is not zero. Thus, the third power of five is

$$5^3 = 5 \times 5 \times 5 = 125.$$

The numeral 5^3 is the exponent form for 125.

If the exponent is one, the power is defined to be the base:

$$3^1 = 3$$
$$2^1 = 2$$
$$10^1 = 10.$$

If the exponent is zero, and the base is not zero, the power is defined to be one:

$$5^0 = 1$$
$$10^0 = 1$$
$$4^0 = 1.$$

Consider the numbers:

$$10^0 = 1,$$
$$10^1 = 10,$$
$$10^2 = 10 \times 10 = 100,$$
$$10^3 = 10 \times 10 \times 10 = 1,000,$$
$$10^4 = 10 \times 10 \times 10 \times 10 = 10,000,$$
$$10^5 = 10 \times 10 \times 10 \times 10 \times 10 = 100,000,$$
$$10^6 = 10 \times 10 \times 10 \times 10 \times 10 \times 10 = 1,000,000.$$

Observe that 10^6 is another name for 1,000,000; this numeral consists of "1" followed by six "0's". Similarly,

$$10^7 = 10 \times 10 \times 10 \times 10 \times 10 \times 10 \times 10 = 10,000,000.$$

10^7 may be represented by a numeral which consists of "1" followed by seven "0's".

This is true in general: If n is any counting number, then the number 10^n may be represented by a numeral consisting of "1" followed by n "0's".

$$10^8 = 100,000,000,$$
$$10^{10} = 10,000,000,000.$$

Exercise Set 2

1. Express each of the following using exponents.

(a) $5 \times 5 \times 5$ (d) $3 \times 3 \times 3 \times 3 \times 3 \times 3 \times 3$

(b) 11×11 (e) $9 \times 9 \times 9 \times 9 \times 9$

(c) $2 \times 2 \times 2 \times 2$ (f) $100 \times 100 \times 100$

2. Express each of the following as the product of equal factors.
         Example: $7^3 = 7 \times 7 \times 7$.

(a) 4^3 (d) 13^6

(b) 3^4 (e) 67^2

(c) 10^5 (f) 2^{12}

3. Write each of the following in exponent form.

(a) 27   (d) 10,000,000

(b) 25   (e) 10

(c) 216   (f) 1

EXPANDED NOTATION

For the decimal system of writing numerals, the number ten is used as base. Every position after position 0 has a place value ten times as great as the next position to the right (Fig. 2).

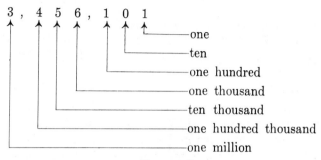

FIGURE 2

The place values of the positions 0, 1, 2, 3, 4, and 5 are shown in Table IV.

TABLE IV

Position	Place Value	Place Value (as a power of ten)
	Place Value in Base Ten	
0	one	$1=1=10^0$
1	ten	$10=10=10^1$
2	one hundred	$10 \times 10=100=10^2$
3	one thousand	$10 \times 10 \times 10=1{,}000=10^3$
4	ten thousand	$10 \times 10 \times 10 \times 10=10{,}000=10^4$
5	one hundred thousand	$10 \times 10 \times 10 \times 10 \times 10=100{,}000=10^5$

Let us see how a whole number can be denoted by an expression involving exponents. Consider, for example, the number whose base-ten numeral is 352.

$$352 = 300 + 50 + 2$$
$$= (3 \times 100) + (5 \times 10) + (2 \times 1)$$
$$= (3 \times 10 \times 10) + (5 \times 10) + (2 \times 1)$$
$$= (3 \times 10^2) + (5 \times 10^1) + (2 \times 10^0) ;$$

similarly,

$$1,684 = 1000 + 600 + 80 + 4$$
$$= (1 \times 1000) + (6 \times 100) + (8 \times 10) + (4 \times 1)$$
$$= (1 \times 10 \times 10 \times 10) + (6 \times 10 \times 10) + (8 \times 10) + (4 \times 1)$$
$$= (1 \times 10^3) + (6 \times 10^2) + (8 \times 10^1) + (4 \times 10^0) ;$$

and

$$34,026 = 30,000 + 4000 + 0 + 20 + 6$$
$$= (3 \times 10,000) + (4 \times 1000) + (0 \times 100) + (2 \times 10) + (6 \times 1)$$
$$= (3 \times 10 \times 10 \times 10 \times 10) + (4 \times 10 \times 10 \times 10) + (0 \times 10 \times 10)$$
$$+ (2 \times 10) + (6 \times 1)$$
$$= (3 \times 10^4) + (4 \times 10^3) + (0 \times 10^2) + (2 \times 10^1) + (6 \times 10^0).$$

This form of expressing a number is called *expanded notation*.

Notice that when a numeral which represents a whole number has three digits, the highest power of ten in the expanded notation is two, $(3-1)$; when the numeral has four digits, the highest power of ten is three, $(4-1)$; when the numeral has five digits, the highest power of ten is four, $(5-1)$. In general, if a numeral representing a whole number has n digits, the highest power of ten is $(n-1)$.

Exercise Set 3

1. Write each of the following in expanded notation.

(a) 607   (d) 14,290
(b) 4800   (e) 4,819,000
(c) 1009   (f) 100

2. Write the ordinary base-ten numeral for the number named by each of the following.

(a) $(2 \times 10^2) + (3 \times 10^1) + (5 \times 10^0)$
(b) $(4 \times 10^4) + (3 \times 10^3) + (0 \times 10^2) + (6 \times 10^1) + (4 \times 10^0)$
(c) $(3 \times 10^6) + (0 \times 10^5) + (2 \times 10^4) + (0 \times 10^3) + (0 \times 10^2) + (6 \times 10^1)$
$+ (0 \times 10^0)$
(d) $(1 \times 10^5) + (0 \times 10^4) + (0 \times 10^3) + (0 \times 10^2) + (0 \times 10^1) + (1 \times 10^0)$

A SYSTEM OF NUMERATION WITH BASE FOUR

We are so familiar with our own decimal (base-ten) system of numeration that we sometimes fail to sense clearly that it is only one of many numeration systems, all of which have the same feature of place value but which use different bases.

A study of numeration systems with bases other than ten reinforces the understanding of our own system, which uses ten as a base. Consider the following example.

Parkview School was planning a play day. Each teacher was asked to let the playground director know how many teams of boys she could supply for the following events:

(1) baseball   9 boys on each team
(2) football   11 boys on each team
(3) four-square   4 boys on each team
(4) basketball   5 boys on each team
(5) relays   10 boys on each team.

TABLE V

Teams For Play Day			
Event	Number of Players on Team	Number of Teams	Number of Substitutes
baseball	nine	1	6
football	eleven	1	4
four-square	four	3	3
basketball	five	3	0
relays	ten	1	5

Miss Barker, who had 15 boys in her room, sent the director the information given in Table V. Let us examine the system of grouping which Miss Barker used in filling out the table.

For baseball she grouped in sets of nine:

(1 × nine) + 6

For football she grouped in sets of eleven:

(1 × eleven) + 4

For four-square she grouped in sets of four:

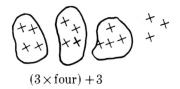

$$(3 \times \text{four}) + 3$$

For basketball she grouped in sets of five:

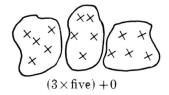

$$(3 \times \text{five}) + 0$$

For relays she grouped in sets of ten:

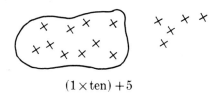

$$(1 \times \text{ten}) + 5$$

Note that in the case of relays (ten on a team), the number fifteen was thought of as

$$(1 \times \text{ten}) + 5.$$

In our system of numeration,

$$(1 \times \text{ten}) + 5$$

can be abbreviated 15.

In the case of baseball (nine on a team), fifteen was thought of in this form:

$$(1 \times \text{nine}) + 6.$$

Can this form be abbreviated? Yes, it can be written as 16 if it is understood that the symbol "1" represents a group of nine instead of a group of ten. A convenient way to write it is

$$16_{\text{nine}},$$

where the word "nine," written as a subscript, indicates that the "1" represents a group of nine (base). The symbol 16_{nine} is read "one, six, base nine."

Examining the rest of the table, you can see that fifteen can also be written as

$$14_{\text{eleven}}, \quad 33_{\text{four}}, \quad 30_{\text{five}}.$$

It is evident that the number of objects in a set remains the same (in this case, fifteen), no matter how the objects are grouped or what numeral is written to indicate the grouping.

In any place-value system of numeration, symbols are chosen for the numbers zero, one, two, etc., up to, but not including, the base. For example, in the decimal system, there are symbols for the numbers zero to nine, inclusive. In the base-four system, there are symbols for the numbers zero, one, two, and three. Each of these represents the number associated with a model set, as shown:

$$\{ \ \ \} \qquad 0$$
$$\{ \times \} \qquad 1$$
$$\{ \times \times \} \qquad 2$$
$$\{ \times \times \times \} \qquad 3.$$

We have now exhausted our symbols. What numeral shall we write for the number of the set

$$\{ \times \times \times \times \}?$$

Using the place-value principle, we write it with two digits: 10_{four}. We read this numeral, "one, zero, base four," meaning one set of four elements and no others. Proceeding we see that the numerals for the numbers associated with the next succeeding sets are the following:

$\{ (\times \times \times \times) \ \times \}$	11_{four}	one four and one
$\{ (\times \times \times \times) \ \times \times \}$	12_{four}	one four and two
$\{ (\times \times \times \times) \ \times \times \times \}$	13_{four}	one four and three
$\{ (\times \times \times \times) (\times \times \times \times) \}$	20_{four}	two fours
$\{ (\times \times \times \times) (\times \times \times \times) \ \times \}$	21_{four}	two fours and one

$$\{ (\times \times \times \times) (\times \times \times \times) (\times \times \times \times) \ \times \times \} \quad 32_{\text{four}} \quad \text{three fours and two}$$
$$\{ (\times \times \times \times) (\times \times \times \times) (\times \times \times \times) \ \times \times \times \} \ 33_{\text{four}} \quad \text{three fours and three.}$$

We have now exhausted the possible two-digit numerals in base four. How, then, shall we write the numeral for the set which has one more member than the last one of those named above, namely,

$$\{ (\times \times \times \times) (\times \times \times \times) (\times \times \times \times) \ \times \times \times \longleftarrow \times \}?$$

When the one more member is added, we have four sets of four:

$$\left\{ \ \boxed{ (\times \times \times \times) (\times \times \times \times) (\times \times \times \times) (\times \times \times \times) } \ \right\}.$$

A new group (enclosed by the rectangle) has been formed and the number associated with it is four fours. When we have four of any group, we form a new group when we are working in base four. The numeral is 100_{four}. This means one set of four fours, no sets of four, and no ones. The numeral 100_{four} is read, "one, zero, zero, base four." Now consider the grouping in this set:

$$\left\{ \boxed{(\times \times \times \times)(\times \times \times \times)(\times \times \times \times)(\times \times \times \times)} \quad (\times \times \times \times) \quad \times \times \right\}.$$

The numeral for the number of this set of objects is 112_{four}. This means one group of four fours, one group of four, and two ones.

The place values in base four (see Table VI) have positions 0, 1, 2, etc.,

TABLE VI

Place Value in Base Four			
Position 3	Position 2	Position 1	Position 0
sixty-four	sixteen	four	one
four × four × four	four × four	four	one
$four^3$	$four^2$	$four^1$	$four^0$

as in base ten, but the place value assigned to each position is different from that in the base-ten system. The position 0, on the right, has place value one, or $four^0$. After that, each place value is four times the place value of the next position to the right. Position 1 has the place value of the base, in this case, four. Position 2 has place value (four × four) or sixteen. Sixty-four (four × four × four) is the place value of position 3, sixteen (four × four) is the place value of position 2, etc.

Let us express the number named by the numeral 312_{four} in expanded notation:

$$\overset{②\,①\,⓪}{3 \;\; 1 \;\; 2} {}_{four} = (\text{three} \times \text{sixteen}) + (\text{one} \times \text{four}) + (\text{two} \times \text{one}).$$

The numerals in the circles indicate that there are three positions in the numeral. The digit 2 occupies position 0, the digit 1 occupies position 1, and the digit 3 occupies position 2. To each position is assigned a number which is the place value of the position. One is the place value of position 0, four is the place value of position 1, and sixteen is the place value of position 2. Any one of the digits 0, 1, 2, 3 in base four can occupy any one of the positions.

To find the base-ten numeral for the number represented by the numeral 312_{four}, we need to apply the principle of place value. The number represented by each digit in this numeral is a product. The number represented by the digit 3 is the product of three and the place value assigned to position 2, sixteen. The number represented by the digit 1 is the product of one and the place value assigned to position 1, four. The number represented by the digit 2 is the product of two and the place value of position 0, one. Finally, the entire numeral represents the sum of the three products:

$$312_{four} = [3 \times (\text{four} \times \text{four})] + (1 \times \text{four}) + (2 \times \text{one}).$$

In base-ten numerals, we write

$$(3 \times 16_{ten}) + (1 \times 4_{ten}) + (2 \times 1_{ten})$$
$$= 48_{ten} + 4_{ten} + 2_{ten}$$
$$= 54_{ten}.$$

Similarly, $323_{four} = 59_{ten}$; that is, 323_{four} and 59_{ten} are numerals naming the same number, fifty-nine.

To write the base-ten numeral for the number represented by 132_{four}, we need first to express the number in expanded notation:

$$132_{four} = [1 \times (\text{four} \times \text{four})] + (3 \times \text{four}) + (2 \times \text{one})$$
$$= (1 \times 4^2{}_{ten}) + (3 \times 4^1{}_{ten}) + (2 \times 4^0{}_{ten})$$
$$= 16_{ten} + 12_{ten} + 2_{ten}$$
$$= 30_{ten}.$$

The following sets (Fig. 3) show that the same number of elements is named by 132_{four} and 30_{ten}.

To write a base-four numeral for a number represented by a given base-ten numeral, think of the objects in model sets regrouped in fours. Thus, if you have forty-six objects (46_{ten}), can you make a set of sixteen objects? Yes, you can make *two* sets of sixteen, and so you place "2" in position 2. (See Table 6.) You have now grouped thirty-two objects and have fourteen left to be grouped. Can you make a set of four objects out of fourteen objects? Yes, you can make three sets of four objects. Write "3" in position 1. You have left two objects, so write "2" in position 0. Accordingly, you have

$$46_{ten} = 32_{ten} + 12_{ten} + 2_{ten}$$
$$= (2 \times 16_{ten}) + (3 \times 4_{ten}) + 2_{ten}$$
$$= (2 \times \text{four}^2) + (3 \times \text{four}^1) + (2 \times \text{four}^0)$$
$$= 232_{four}.$$

Thus, 46_{ten} and 232_{four} name the same number.

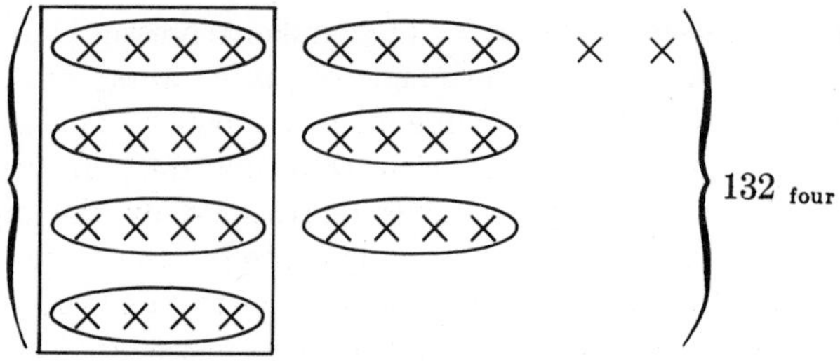

$$132 \text{ four}$$

$$(1 \times \text{four} \times \text{four}) + (3 \times \text{four}) + (2 \times \text{one})$$

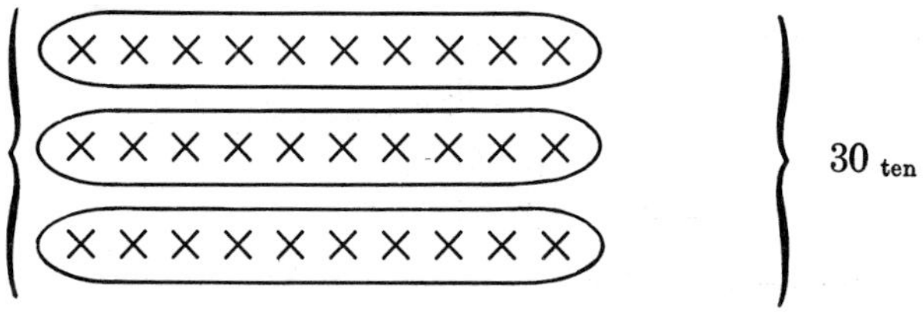

$$30 \text{ ten}$$

$$(3 \times \text{ten}) + \qquad\qquad (0 \times \text{one})$$

FIGURE 3

Exercise Set 4

1. Write the base-four numerals for the numbers from one to twenty-five.

2. What numbers are represented by the numerals 132_{four}? 200_{four}?

3. What is the greatest number that can be represented by a 3-digit numeral in base four? Can you write the base-four numeral? The decimal numeral?

4. Write each of the following in expanded notation.

EXAMPLE: $321_{\text{four}} = (3 \times \text{four}^2) + (2 \times \text{four}^1) + (1 \times \text{four}^0)$.

(a) 30_{four} (d) 330_{four}
(b) 201_{four} (e) 233_{four}
(c) 33_{four} (f) 1000_{four}

THE DUODECIMAL SYSTEM

We have seen how to construct a numeration system with a base other than ten. Although we used base four, which is less than ten, we could also have used a base greater than ten.

It would be convenient to have a base that is related to our common units of measure. Many of our units of measure are based on twelve.

There are twelve inches in one foot, twelve hours on the face of the clock, and twelve eggs in a dozen.

A system of numeration in base twelve is called the *duodecimal system*. In the duodecimal system we have twelve symbols, and we form groups of twelves (dozen), twelve-twelves (gross), twelve-twelve-twelves (great gross), etc. We need two new symbols. The symbols T and E are often used for ten and eleven, respectively. Our twelve digits are

$$\{0, 1, 2, 3, 4, 5, 6, 7, 8, 9, T, E\}.$$

In the duodecimal system we group in sets of one dozen. Then the numeral for this collection

$$\{\times \times \times \times \times \times \times \times \times \times \times \times \quad \times \times \times\}$$

TABLE VII

Decimal Notation	Duodecimal Grouping	Duodecimal Notation
0		0
1	×	1
2	× ×	2
3	× × ×	3
4	× × × ×	4
5	× × × × ×	5
6	× × × × × ×	6
7	× × × × × × ×	7
8	× × × × × × × ×	8
9	× × × × × × × × ×	9
10	× × × × × × × × × ×	T
11	× × × × × × × × × × ×	E
12	× × × × × × × × × × × ×	10
13	(×××××××××××) ×	11
14	(×××××××××××) × ×	12
.	.	.
.	.	.
.	.	.
24	(×××××××××××) (×××××××××××)	20
.	.	.
.	.	.
.	.	.
35	(×××××××××××) × × × × × × × × × × ×	2E
	(×××××××××××)	

is 13_{twelve} (read, "one, three, base twelve," or "one dozen and three") because we have a dozen (twelve) and three ones.

Table VII shows numerals in the decimal and the duodecimal systems.

When the symbols T and E are used for ten and eleven in the duodecimal system, we have some interesting numerals, such as

$$TOE_{twelve}$$
$$TOO_{twelve}$$
$$TEE_{twelve}$$
$$ET_{twelve}.$$

What is the decimal numeral for the number TOE_{twelve}?

We use the same method to change from base-ten to base-twelve
numerals as we did to change from base-ten to base-four numerals. For
example,

$$35_{ten} = 24_{ten} + 11_{ten}$$
$$= (2 \times twelve^1) + (E \times twelve^0)$$
$$= 2E_{twelve},$$
$$148_{ten} = 144_{ten} + 4_{ten}$$
$$= (1 \times twelve^2) + (0 \times twelve^1) + (4 \times twelve^0)$$
$$= 104_{twelve}.$$

Exercise Set 5

1. Write the decimal numerals for the numbers named by these numerals.

   (a) TO_{twelve} (b) $3T_{twelve}$ (c) ET_{twelve} (d) $1TT_{twelve}$

2. Write duodecimal numerals for the numbers named by these decimal
   numerals.

   (a) 37_{ten} (b) 34_{ten} (c) 131_{ten}

3. Write the following duodecimal numerals in exponential notation.

   (a) 132_{twelve} (b) TOE_{twelve} (c) 64_{twelve}

THE BINARY SYSTEM

From a practical standpoint the most important place-value system of
numeration, except for the decimal system, is probably the base-two
system, called the *binary system* of numeration. The work of the modern
electronic computer is based on binary notation for numbers. It seems
important, then, that special attention be given to this system of numeration.

The binary system requires only two symbols, 0 and 1. The place values in this system are the powers of two, which are one, two, two×two, two×two×two, and so on. The binary numeral for two is 10_{two}, since

$$10_{two} = (1 \times two) + (0 \times one).$$

Binary numerals are based on groups of two, just as the decimal system is based on groups of ten. Table VIII shows how base-two numerals and base-ten numerals are related.

TABLE VIII

Base-Ten Notation	Binary Grouping	Binary Notation
0		0
1	×	1
2	⊗⊗	10
3	⊗⊗ ×	11
4	⊗⊗ ⊗⊗	100
5	⊗⊗ ⊗⊗ ×	101
6	⊗⊗ ⊗⊗ ⊗⊗	110
7	⊗⊗ ⊗⊗ ⊗⊗ ×	111
8	⊗⊗ ⊗⊗ ⊗⊗ ⊗⊗	1000

The place values for the binary system of numeration are shown in Table IX.

TABLE IX

Place Value in Base Two						
Position 6	Position 5	Position 4	Position 3	Position 2	Position 1	Position 0
sixty-four	thirty-two	sixteen	eight	four	two	one
two×two ×two× two×two ×two	two×two ×two× two×two	two×two ×two× two	two×two ×two	two×two	two	one
two^6	two^5	two^4	two^3	two^2	two^1	two^0

Let us look at some binary numerals:

$$1101_{two} = (1 \times two^3) + (1 \times two^2) + (0 \times two^1) + (1 \times two^0)$$
$$= (1 \times eight) + (1 \times four) + (0 \times two) + (1 \times one)$$
$$= (1 \times 8_{ten}) + (1 \times 4_{ten}) + (0 \times 2_{ten}) + (1 \times 1_{ten})$$
$$= 8_{ten} + 4_{ten} + 0 + 1_{ten}$$
$$= 13_{ten},$$

$$11011_{two} = (1 \times two^4) + (1 \times two^3) + (0 \times two^2) + (1 \times two^1)$$
$$+ (1 \times two^0)$$
$$= (1 \times sixteen) + (1 \times eight) + (0 \times four) + (1 \times two) + 1$$
$$= (1 \times 16_{ten}) + (1 \times 8_{ten}) + (0 \times 4_{ten}) + (1 \times 2_{ten}) + (1 \times 1_{ten})$$
$$= 16_{ten} + 8_{ten} + 0 + 2_{ten} + 1_{ten}$$
$$= 27_{ten},$$

$$111111_{two} = (1 \times two^5) + (1 \times two^4) + (1 \times two^3) + (1 \times two^2)$$
$$+ (1 \times two^1) + (1 \times two^0)$$
$$= (1 \times thirty\text{-}two) + (1 \times sixteen) + (1 \times eight)$$
$$+ (1 \times four) + (1 \times two) + (1 \times one)$$
$$= (1 \times 32_{ten}) + (1 \times 16_{ten}) + (1 \times 8_{ten}) + (1 \times 4_{ten})$$
$$+ (1 \times 2_{ten}) + (1 \times 1_{ten})$$
$$= 32_{ten} + 16_{ten} + 8_{ten} + 4_{ten} + 2_{ten} + 1_{ten}$$
$$= 63_{ten}.$$

We can change decimal numerals to binary numerals by the same methods we used to change base-ten numerals to base-four numerals; for example, let us find the binary numeral for 12_{ten}:

$$12_{ten} = 8_{ten} + 4_{ten}$$
$$= (1 \times 8_{ten}) + (1 \times 4_{ten}) + (0 \times 2_{ten}) + (0 \times 1_{ten})$$
$$= (1 \times two^3) + (1 \times two^2) + (0 \times two^1) + (0 \times two^0)$$
$$= 1100_{two}.$$

Here are two more examples:

$$27_{ten} = 16_{ten} + 8_{ten} + 2_{ten} + 1_{ten}$$
$$= (1 \times 16_{ten}) + (1 \times 8_{ten}) + (0 \times 4_{ten}) + (1 \times 2_{ten}) + (1 \times 1_{ten})$$
$$= (1 \times two^4) + (1 \times two^3) + (0 \times two^2) + (1 \times two^1) + (1 \times two^0)$$
$$= 11011_{two},$$

$$31_{ten} = 16_{ten} + 8_{ten} + 4_{ten} + 2_{ten} + 1_{ten}$$
$$= (1 \times 16_{ten}) + (1 \times 8_{ten}) + (1 \times 4_{ten}) + (1 \times 2_{ten}) + (1 \times 1_{ten})$$
$$= (1 \times two^4) + (1 \times two^3) + (1 \times two^2) + (1 \times two^1) + (1 \times two^0)$$
$$= 11111_{two}.$$

Exercise Set 6

A simple computer to illustrate binary numerals may be made using a cardboard box and a string of Christmas tree lights. When a light is on,

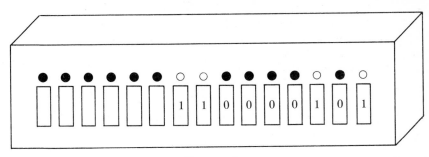

FIGURE 4

indicated in Figure 4 by ○, it corresponds to the numeral 1 in the binary system. When a light is off, indicated in Figure 4 by ●, it corresponds to the numeral 0. The binary numeral indicated in Figure 4 is 110000101_{two}.

1. Write the binary numerals for the following signals shown on the "computer" in Figure 4.

   (a) ○ ○ ○ ● ● ●   (d) ○ ● ●

   (b) ○ ● ○ ● ○ ○ ● ●   (e) ○ ○ ○ ○ ○ ● ○ ● ○

   (c) ○ ○ ○ ○ ○ ○ ●

2. Write the numerals in Exercise 1 in binary exponent notation.

3. What decimal numerals name the same numbers as the binary numerals found in Exercise 1?

THE OCTAL SYSTEM

It was mentioned earlier that use of the binary system is essential in working with electronic computers. The reason is that an electric circuit can be open, or it can be closed—these are only the two possibilities. The binary system has just two symbols, 0 and 1. By matching the members of these two sets

open circuit⟷0

closed circuit⟷1,

we obtain a correspondence whereby the open circuit on the computer represents 0 and the closed circuit represents 1.

The large number of digits required to write binary numerals makes the system cumbersome. For example, while the decimal numeral for the number forty-five has only two digits, the binary numeral has six digits.

$$45_{ten} = 101101_{two}.$$

The numerals 1023_{ten} and 1111111111_{two} represent the same number.

Binary numerals are easily converted to octal (base-eight) numerals, and octal numerals require fewer digits than the corresponding binary numerals. For example,

$$132_{eight} = 1011010_{two}.$$

In the octal system there are eight symbols,

$$\{0,\ 1,\ 2,\ 3,\ 4,\ 5,\ 6,\ 7\}.$$

The place values are eight^0, eight^1, eight^2, and so on. The numeral 15_{eight} represents $(1 \times eight^1) + (5 \times eight^0)$, or thirteen.

What number does 132_{eight} represent?

$$
\begin{aligned}
132_{eight} &= (1 \times eight^2) + (3 \times eight^1) + (2 \times eight^0) \\
&= (1 \times 64_{ten}) + (3 \times 8_{ten}) + (2 \times 1_{ten}) \\
&= 64_{ten} + 24_{ten} + 2_{ten} \\
&= 90_{ten}.
\end{aligned}
$$

So 132_{eight} names the number ninety.

Let us see how to write the octal numeral for 1110101_{two}. First insert commas so the digits are in groups of three, starting from the right,

$$1,110,101_{two}.$$

This numeral can be converted to an octal numeral as follows:

$$
\begin{aligned}
1,110,101_{two} = &\ [\,(1 \times two^6)\,] + [\,(1 \times two^5) + (1 \times two^4) + (0 \times two^3)\,] \\
&+ [\,(1 \times two^2) + (0 \times two^1) + (1 \times two^0)\,].
\end{aligned}
$$

Notice that the first bracket encloses the number represented by "1," in position 6, the second bracket the number represented by "110," and the third bracket the number represented by "101."

Look at the three expressions enclosed in brackets:

$$
\begin{aligned}
1 \times two^6 &= sixty\text{-}four \\
&= 1 \times eight^2,
\end{aligned}
$$

$$
\begin{aligned}
(1 \times two^5) + (1 \times two^4) + (0 \times two^3) &= thirty\text{-}two + sixteen + zero \\
&= 32_{ten} + 16_{ten} + 0 \\
&= 48_{ten} \\
&= 6 \times eight^1,
\end{aligned}
$$

$$(1 \times two^2) + (0 \times two^1) + (1 \times two^0) = four + zero + one$$
$$= 4_{ten} + 0_{ten} + 1_{ten}$$
$$= 5 \times one$$
$$= 5 \times eight^0.$$

Putting this together, we have

$$1{,}110{,}101_{two} = (1 \times eight^2) + (6 \times eight^1) + (5 \times eight^0)$$
$$= 165_{eight}.$$

This example may suggest that the process needed to convert the numeral $1{,}110{,}101_{two}$ to the numeral 165_{eight} is not simple. There is, however, a very direct relationship between the two numerals. Look again at

$$1{,}110{,}101_{two}.$$

There are three groups of digits: 1, 110, 101. Consider each group standing alone as a numeral written in base two. What numbers are named by these binary numerals?

> "1" names one;
> "110" names six;
> "101" names five.

Table X shows the pattern that is involved; as can be seen, we have a kind of algorithm, or special process, for converting binary to octal numerals.

TABLE X

Converting Binary to Octal Numerals			
Binary Numeral	1	110	101
Number Named	one	six	five
Octal Numeral	1	6	5

The binary numeral $11{,}001{,}100{,}101{,}011{,}111_{two}$ converted to octal would become 3 1 4 5 3 7_{eight}. Here the binary numeral has *seventeen* digits, whereas the octal numeral has only *six*. A certain computer can handle 36-digit binary numerals. These can be recorded as 12-digit octal numerals.

Of course, when an octal numeral is taken out of "cold storage" it must be converted to a binary numeral if it is to be fed into the computer. As an example, take octal numeral 4167_{eight}. Consider each digit as a separate base-eight numeral and write it in binary notation, as shown in Table XI.

TABLE XI

Converting Octal to Binary Numerals				
Octal Numeral	4	1	6	7
Number Named	four	one	six	seven
Binary Numeral	100	001	110	111

$$4167_{eight} = 100,001,110,111_{two}$$

PLACE-VALUE SYSTEMS

Table XII suggests a number of features common to all place-value

TABLE XII

Place-Value Systems of Numeration					
Place Value of Position in Numeral					
Position 3	Position 2	Position 1	Position 0	Symbols	Base
. . . two^3	two^2	two^1	two^0	{0, 1}	two
. . . $three^3$	$three^2$	$three^1$	$three^0$	{0, 1, 2}	three
.	.	.	.	.	.
.	.	.	.	.	.
.	.	.	.	.	.
. . . $eight^3$	$eight^2$	$eight^1$	$eight^0$	{0, 1, 2, 3, 4, 5, 6, 7}	eight
. . . $nine^3$	$nine^2$	$nine^1$	$nine^0$	{0, 1, 2, 3, 4, 5, 6, 7, 8}	nine
. . . ten^3	ten^2	ten^1	ten^0	{0, 1, 2, 3, 4, 5, 6, 7, 8, 9}	ten
. . . $twelve^3$	$twelve^2$	$twelve^1$	$twelve^0$	{0, 1, 2, 3, 4, 5, 6, 7, 8, 9, T, E}	twelve
. . . $base^3$	$base^2$	$base^1$	$base^0$	Vary	Any whole number greater than one

numeration systems. It can best be read from right to left. Note the following features:

1. Every place-value system of numeration has a base which may be any whole number greater than one. A place-value numeration system with base one is impossible because the place value of each position would be a power of one, and every power of one is one. We observe, also, that the only numeral in a numeration system with base one would be 0.

2. The number of different symbols is the same number as the base. These symbols, also called digits, are the numerals for the whole numbers less than the base. Thus, to write the numerals in base seven, the set of symbols used is

$$\{0, 1, 2, 3, 4, 5, 6\}.$$

3. Each position in a numeral is assigned a place value which is a power of the base. The place value assigned to position 0 is $base^0 = 1$, the place value assigned to position 1 is $base^1$, the place value assigned to position 2 is $base^2$, etc. Note that the exponent is the same as the corresponding position number.

TABLE XIII

Place Value in Base Seven			
Position 3	Position 2	Position 1	Position 0
three hundred forty-three	forty-nine	seven	one
seven × seven × seven	seven × seven	seven	one
$seven^3$	$seven^2$	$seven^1$	$seven^0$

When writing numerals in a place-value system, we observe the following requirements and conventions:

1. More than one digit must be used when writing a numeral for the base or for any number greater than the base. *Whatever base is used, the symbol 10 always stands for the base.* The numeral 10 means $(1 \times base) + 0$.

2. The base of the system in which a numeral is written is indicated by a subscript to the right of the numeral. The subscript is written in words.

3. Each digit in a numeral represents a number. This number is the product of the number named by the digit and the place value assigned to the position of the digit in the numeral (see Table XIII). For example, consider the numeral 546_{seven}: The digit 5 is in position 2 of the numeral; the place value assigned to position 2 is $seven^2$; thus the digit 5 represents the number (five × $seven^2$). Similarly, the digit 4 in the numeral 546_{seven} represents the product (four × $seven^1$), and the digit 6 in the numeral represents the product (six × $seven^0$), or (six × one).

4. The number named by the numeral 546_{seven} is the sum of the products mentioned above. Thus, the numeral 546 in base seven names the sum

$$546_{seven} = (\text{five} \times \text{seven} \times \text{seven}) + (\text{four} \times \text{seven}) + (\text{six} \times \text{one}),$$

or the number two hundred seventy-nine.

Exercise Set 7

1. Write in expanded notation.

(a) 325_{six} (b) 2102_{three} (c) 875_{ten} (d) 413_{five}

2. Express the numbers named by these numerals in decimal notation.

(a) 212_{three} (b) 561_{seven} (c) 1001_{two} (d) 208_{twelve}

3. What number is represented by the digit 2 in each numeral?

(a) 238_{ten} (b) 432_{five} (c) 2010_{three} (d) 526_{seven}

4. What number is represented by n?

$$n_{four} + 2_{four} = 11_{four}$$

5. Fill in the blanks.

(a) $42_{five} = $ _____ $_{three}$
(b) $54_{seven} = $ _____ $_{eight}$

6. Use the symbol "$=$", "$>$", or "$<$" in each blank, so that the resulting sentence is true.

(a) 100_{three} _____ 21_{four} (b) 54_{six} _____ 201_{four} (c) 106_{seven} _____ 63_{ten}

SUMMARY

1. Every place-value system of numeration has a base which may be any whole number greater than one. The numeration system we use most commonly has base ten.

2. A set of symbols is used to write a numeral for any whole number. These symbols (also called digits) are the numerals for the whole numbers less than the base. Thus, the number of different symbols used in a particular numeration system is the same number as the base. For example, to write numerals in base seven, the set of symbols used is

$$\{0, 1, 2, 3, 4, 5, 6\}.$$

3. To write a numeral for the base or any number greater than the base, more than one digit must be used. In this case, three conditions determine the number which the digit represents:

   (a) the digit itself,
   (b) the base of the numeration system,
   (c) the position of the digit in the numeral, which determines a *place value*.

4. A place value is a number which is a power of the base. The place value assigned to the right-hand position in a numeral for a whole number is base^0. (Recall that the zero power of any counting number is one.) The place value assigned to the second position from the right is base^1; to the third position is base^2, or (base $\times$ base); to the fourth position is base^3, or (base $\times$ base $\times$ base); and so on. For example, the digits in the numeral 213 in a system with base four occupy positions which have the following place values:

2	four^2, or (four $\times$ four);
1	four^1, or four;
3	four^0, or one.

5. The number represented by a digit in a numeral is the product of two numbers:

   (a) the number represented by the digit considered as a single numeral (and thus less than the base),
   (b) the place value assigned to the position in which the digit is written.

   Thus, in the illustration above:

   2 represents the number (two $\times$ four^2) or (two $\times$ four $\times$ four),
   1 represents the number (one $\times$ four^1) or (one $\times$ four),
   3 represents the number (three $\times$ four^0) or (three $\times$ one).

6. The number named by the complete numeral is the sum of these products. Thus, the numeral 213 in a system with base four names the sum

$$(\text{two} \times \text{four} \times \text{four}) + (\text{one} \times \text{four}) + (\text{three} \times \text{one}),$$

in other words, the number thirty-nine.

7. The base of the system in which a numeral is written is indicated by a subscript to the right of the numeral: for example,

$$213_{four}, \quad 528_{ten}, \quad 513_{eight}.$$

The number for the base is written *in words* in each case because in *any* place-value system of numeration the numeral for the base is written "10." Thus, if we write 213_{10} this does not tell us what the particular base is.

ANSWERS TO EXERCISES

Exercise Set 1

1. There are many correct answers. Some are
   (a) $6+1$, $\quad 0+7$, $\quad$ VII, $\quad$ ⫲⫲ //, $\quad$ $56 \div 8$.
   (b) I, $\quad 2-1$, $\quad 3-2$, $\quad 4 \div 4$, $\quad$ etc.
   (c) $1-1$, $\quad 2-2$, $\quad 0 \times 6$, $\quad 4 \times 0$, $\quad$ etc.
2. (a) $(5 \times 10) + (7 \times 1)$
   (b) $(4 \times 100) + (1 \times 10) + (9 \times 1)$
   (c) $(6 \times 100) + (2 \times 10) + (0 \times 1)$
   (d) $(2 \times 1000) + (0 \times 100) + (8 \times 10) + (7 \times 1)$
3. (a) ten $\quad$ (b) one $\quad$ (c) one thousand $\quad$ (d) ten thousand
4. (a) ten $\quad$ (b) one hundred $\quad$ (c) one thousand

Exercise Set 2

1. (a) 5^3 $\quad$ (b) 11^2 $\quad$ (c) 2^4 $\quad$ (d) 3^7 $\quad$ (e) 9^5 $\quad$ (f) 100^3
2. (a) $4 \times 4 \times 4$
   (b) $3 \times 3 \times 3 \times 3$
   (c) $10 \times 10 \times 10 \times 10 \times 10$
   (d) $13 \times 13 \times 13 \times 13 \times 13 \times 13$
   (e) 67×67
   (f) $2 \times 2 \times 2 \times 2 \times 2 \times 2 \times 2 \times 2 \times 2 \times 2 \times 2 \times 2$
3. (a) 3^3 $\quad\quad$ (b) 5^2 $\quad\quad$ (c) 6^3
   (d) 10^7 $\quad\quad$ (e) 10^1 $\quad\quad$ (f) n^0, where n represents any number except zero.

Exercise Set 3

1. (a) $(6 \times 10^2) + (0 \times 10^1) + (7 \times 10^0)$
   (b) $(4 \times 10^3) + (8 \times 10^2) + (0 \times 10^1) + (0 \times 10^0)$
   (c) $(1 \times 10^3) + (0 \times 10^2) + (0 \times 10^1) + (9 \times 10^0)$
   (d) $(1 \times 10^4) + (4 \times 10^3) + (2 \times 10^2) + (9 \times 10^1) + (0 \times 10^0)$

(e) $(4\times10^6)+(8\times10^5)+(1\times10^4)+(9\times10^3)+(0\times10^2)$
$+(0\times10^1)+(0\times10^0)$
(f) $(1\times10^2)+(0\times10^1)+(0\times10^0)$

2. (a) 235   (b) 43,064   (c) 3,020,060   (d) 100,001

Exercise Set 4

1. (All numerals in base four.) 1, 2, 3, 10, 11, 12, 13, 20, 21, 22, 23, 30, 31, 32, 33, 100, 101, 102, 103, 110, 111, 112, 113, 120, 121.

2. 30_{ten}, 32_{ten}.

3. Sixty-three, 333_{four}, 63_{ten}.

4. (a) $(3\times four^1)+(0\times four^0)$
(b) $(2\times four^2)+(0\times four^1)+(1\times four^0)$
(c) $(3\times four^1)+(3\times four^0)$
(d) $(3\times four^2)+(3\times four^1)+(0\times four^0)$
(e) $(2\times four^2)+(3\times four^1)+(3\times four^0)$
(f) $(1\times four^3)+(0\times four^2)+(0\times four^1)+(0\times four^0)$

Exercise Set 5

1. (a) 120   (b) 46   (c) 142   (d) 274

2. (a) 31_{twelve} (b) $2T_{twelve}$ (c) TE_{twelve}

3. (a) $(1\times twelve^2)+(3\times twelve^1)+(2\times twelve^0)$
(b) $(T\times twelve^2)+(0\times twelve^1)+(E\times twelve^0)$
(c) $(6\times twelve^1)+(4\times twelve^0)$

Exercise Set 6

1. (a) $111,000_{two}$ (d) 100_{two}
(b) $10,101,100_{two}$ (e) $111,110,101_{two}$
(c) $1,111,110_{two}$

2. (a) $(1\times two^5)+(1\times two^4)+(1\times two^3)+(0\times two^2)+(0\times two^1)$
$+(0\times two^0)$
(b) $(1\times two^7)+(0\times two^6)+(1\times two^5)+(0\times two^4)+(1\times two^3)$
$+(1\times two^2)+(0\times two^1)+(0\times two^0)$
(c) $(1\times two^6)+(1\times two^5)+(1\times two^4)+(1\times two^3)+(1\times two^2)$
$+(1\times two^1)+(0\times two^0)$
(d) $(1\times two^2)+(0\times two^1)+(0\times two^0)$
(e) $(1\times two^8)+(1\times two^7)+(1\times two^6)+(1\times two^5)+(1\times two^4)$
$+(0\times two^3)+(1\times two^2)+(0\times two^1)+(1\times two^0)$

3. (a) $32+16+8+0+0+0=56$
   (b) $128+0+32+0+8+4+0+0=172$
   (c) $64+32+16+8+4+2+0=126$
   (d) $4+0+0=4$
   (e) $256+128+64+32+16+0+4+8+1=501$

Exercise Set 7

1 (a) $(3 \times \text{six}^2) + (2 \times \text{six}^1) + (5 \times \text{six}^0)$
   (b) $(2 \times \text{three}^3) + (1 \times \text{three}^2) + (0 \times \text{three}^1) + (2 \times \text{three}^0)$
   (c) $(8 \times \text{ten}^2) + (7 \times \text{ten}^1) + (5 \times \text{ten}^0)$
   (d) $(4 \times \text{five}^2) + (1 \times \text{five}^1) + (3 \times \text{five}^0)$

2. (a) 23   (b) 288   (c) 9   (d) 296

3. (a) 2×100, or 200   (b) 2×1, or 2   (c) 2×27, or 54   (d) 2×7, or 14

4. $n = 3$

5. (a) 211_{three} (b) 47_{eight}

6. (a) "$=$"   (b) "$>$"   (c) "$<$"

ALGORITHMS FOR OPERATIONS WITH WHOLE NUMBERS

INTRODUCTION

The original of an important book on the use of Hindu-Arabic numerals, written by Al Khowarizmi about 825 A.D., was lost; but a Latin translation was found which, when put into English, began: "Spoken has Algorithmi." Thus, in translation the name Al Khowarizmi became Algorithmi, from which is derived our present word *algorithm,* or algorism, meaning a convenient procedure for finding the result of an operation on two numbers when the result is not immediately apparent.

When we perform operations with numbers named by single digit numerals, we recall the basic sums and products from memory (or perhaps resort to counting). On the other hand, when we are faced with a computation involving a number whose numeral has two or more digits, we usually use an algorithm, or special process.

Since the result of the operation of addition, subtraction, multiplication, or division is a number, and numbers can be pictured by model sets, the number sought might always be found by the simple process of counting. While this theoretically constitutes a valid method, computation by counting, except for very simple cases, is not very practical. Evidence of this is seen in the fact that in the ancient civilizations, whenever computation with large numbers was involved, the computer resorted to an aid such as the counting board or abacus.

Until the Hindu-Arabic place-value system came into use, mechanical aids such as the abacus were universally employed. With the use of the Hindu-Arabic system, computation no longer depended upon the availability of mechanical devices; the computer could manipulate the symbols themselves. Under the Hindu-Arabic system, the computer could write down the numerals involved in the problem, follow a pattern, and ultimately get the correct result. These patterns of procedure are called algorithms.

The algorithms we know and use are by-products of and closely related

to the place-value system of notation. The place-value system of notation and the properties of the number system (in this booklet, the system
of whole numbers) make the algorithms possible.

The algorithms presented in this booklet are not the only possible ones.
There have been changes over the centuries and there may be more in the
future. Improvements in the algorithms lead to more efficient use of the
system of numeration.

Terms Used

In order to facilitate reading and understanding of the material in this
booklet, it is strongly recommended that the reader first read Booklet
No. 2: *The Whole Numbers*, and Booklet No. 3: *Systems of Numeration
for the Whole Numbers*.

In mathematics it is essential that each term used be clearly understood.
To be sure that the reader will understand the exact meanings of terms
used, the following summary is presented with illustrations.

BINARY OPERATION

A binary operation associates a definite number with an ordered
pair of numbers. Addition and multiplication are binary operations. They are called the primary operations of arithmetic, and
they are defined for *all* ordered pairs of whole numbers. Subtraction and division, called the secondary operations of arithmetic, are also binary operations, but they are not defined for all
ordered pairs of whole numbers. For example, neither subtraction
nor division associates a whole number with the ordered pair
$(4, 15)$.

Operation	Ordered Pair	Associated Number
Addition	(84, 42)	126
Multiplication	(84, 42)	3528
Subtraction	(84, 42)	42
Division	(84, 42)	2

NUMERAL

A numeral is a symbol, or combination of symbols, that names
a number. The number ten, for example, has many different
names, or numerals, some of which are

$$10, \quad 5 \times 2, \quad 8+2, \quad 20-10, \quad \frac{30}{3}, \quad (2 \times 3)+4, \quad 2 \times (3+2).$$

The equality symbol, $=$, is commonly used to indicate that two numerals name the same number. Thus, the fact that the numerals 5×2 and $(2 \times 3) + 4$ name the same number is expressed as follows:

$$5 \times 2 = (2 \times 3) + 4.$$

SYSTEMS OF NUMERATION

A system of numeration is a way of building numerals for numbers through the use of a set of symbols and a set of rules for combining these symbols. Our decimal (from the Latin word *decem* for ten), or base-ten, system of numeration makes use of just ten symbols:

$$\{0, 1, 2, 3, 4, 5, 6, 7, 8, 9\}.$$

This is a place-value system, which means that the number represented by each digit in a numeral is determined by the particular digit and its position in the numeral. In our decimal system the place value of each position is ten times the place value of the position immediately to the right of it, the place value of the position at the extreme right of the numeral (for a whole number) being one.

EXPANDED NOTATION

The number 4036, for example, is expressed in expanded notation when it is represented by any of the following forms:

$$4036 = (4 \times 1000) + (0 \times 100) + (3 \times 10) + (6 \times 1)$$
$$= (4 \times 10 \times 10 \times 10) + (0 \times 10 \times 10) + (3 \times 10) \times (6 \times 1)$$
$$= (4 \times 10^3) + (0 \times 10^2) + (3 \times 10) + (6 \times 1).$$

PROPERTIES OF ADDITION

Closure. The set of whole numbers,

$$\{0, 1, 2, 3, 4, 5, \ldots\},$$

is closed under the operation of addition. By this, we mean that the sum of any two whole numbers is a whole number.

Associative Property. Addition in a binary operation; that is, it is performed on only two numbers at a time. The associative property of addition concerns the sum of three numbers. According to this property, for example,

$$(2 + 6) + 7 = 2 + (6 + 7);$$

that is, the numerals $(2 + 6) + 7$ and $2 + (6 + 7)$ name the same number. In the first of these numerals, the parentheses indicate that $(2+6)$ is to be thought of as a name for one number, 8; while in the second, the parentheses indicate that $(6+7)$ is to be thought of as a name for one number, 13. Thus,

$$(2+6)+7=8+7$$
$$=15,$$

and

$$2+(6+7)=2+13$$
$$=15.$$

In both cases the sum is 15.

The associative property can be applied to sums of more than three numbers. We can show, for example, that

$$[(2+3)+4]+5=2+[(3+4)+5]$$

as follows:

$$[(2+3)+4]+5=[5+4]+5$$
$$=9+5$$
$$=14,$$

and

$$2+[(3+4)+5]=2+[7+5]$$
$$=2+12$$
$$=14.$$

The associative property of addition, then, is the property that allows one to change the grouping of the addends without changing the sum.

Commutative Property. The commutative property of addition allows one to change the order of two addends without changing their sum. Thus,

$$8+3=3+8,$$

and

$$182+11=11+182.$$

Identity Element. The identity element for addition is the number zero. This means that the sum of any number and zero is the number itself. Thus,

$$5+0=5$$
$$0+27=27.$$

Closure. The set of whole numbers is closed under the operation of multiplication. In other words, the product of any two whole numbers is a whole number.

Associative Property. Multiplication, like addition, is a binary operation; that is, it is performed on only two numbers at a time. The associative property of multiplication concerns the product of three numbers. According to this property, for example,

$$(8 \times 9) \times 6 = 8 \times (9 \times 6).$$

In the numeral on the left, (8×9) is to be thought of as a name for one number, 72; and in the numeral on the right, (9×6) is to be thought of as a name for one number, 54. Thus,

$$(8 \times 9) \times 6 = 72 \times 6$$
$$= 432,$$

and

$$8 \times (9 \times 6) = 8 \times 54$$
$$= 432.$$

Commutative Property. Multiplication of whole numbers is commutative; that is, the product of two whole numbers remains unchanged if the order of the two numbers is reversed. For example,

$$9 \times 7 = 7 \times 9.$$

Identity Element. The identity element for multiplication is the number, 1. This means that the product of any number and 1, is the number itself. Thus,

$$6 \times 1 = 6$$
$$1 \times 497 = 497$$
$$1 \times 1 = 1.$$

Distributive Property. The distributive property of multiplication over addition, or simply the distributive property, involves both multiplication and addition. According to this property, for example,

$$5 \times (12 + 7) = (5 \times 12) + (5 \times 7).$$

The expression $5 \times (12 + 7)$ indicates first the addition of 12 and 7, then the multiplication of the sum by 5:

$$5 + (12 + 7) = 5 \times 19$$
$$= 95.$$

The expression $(5 \times 12) + (5 \times 7)$ indicates first the multiplication of 12 by 5 and the multiplication of 7 by 5, then the addition of the two products:

$$(5 \times 12) + (5 \times 7) = 60 + 35$$
$$= 95.$$

Thus, the same number is named by $5 \times (12 + 7)$ and by $(5 \times 12) + (5 \times 7)$.

In the foregoing example, multiplication (by 5) was distributed from left-to-right (over the sum $12 + 7$). Because of the commutative property of multiplication, we can also distribute from right-to-left, as illustrated in the following example:

$$(7 + 20) \times 6 = (7 \times 6) + (20 \times 6).$$

Multiplication is distributed over sums of three or more addends:

$$5 \times (4 + 8 + 3) = (5 \times 4) + (5 \times 8) + (5 \times 3).$$

Multiplication is distributive also over subtraction. The following example illustrates this fact:

$$25 \times (12 - 8) = (25 \times 12) - (25 \times 8),$$

for

$$25 \times (12 - 8) = 25 \times 4$$
$$= 100,$$

and

$$(25 \times 12) - (25 \times 8) = 300 - 200$$
$$= 100.$$

ADDITION AND SUBTRACTION AS INVERSE OPERATIONS

Subtraction is the inverse operation of addition and vice versa. Examine the following examples:

$$(12 - 7) + 7 = 12,$$
$$(39 + 14) - 14 = 39.$$

Notice that in the first example the addition of 7 to $(12 - 7)$ has the effect of "undoing" the subtraction of 7 from 12. In the second example the subtraction of 14 from $(39 + 14)$ has the effect of "undoing" the addition of 14 to 39.

MULTIPLICATION AND DIVISION AS INVERSE OPERATIONS

Division is the inverse operation of multiplication and vice versa. Examine the following examples:

$$(12 \times 7) \div 7 = 12,$$
$$(42 \div 7) \times 7 = 42.$$

Recall, however, that division by 0 is undefined. It is true that $(0 \times 12) \div 12 = 0$, but $(12 \times 0) \div 0$ and $(12 \div 0) \times 0$ are meaningless expressions.

SYMBOLS USED FOR GROUPING (MATHEMATICAL PUNCTUATION MARKS)

The numeral

$$\{[(6+2)+7]+8\} + (4 \times 10)$$

names a number as the sum of two numbers. We know that

$$(4 \times 10) = 40.$$

Let us find a simple name for the other number:

$$\{[(6+2)+7]+8\} = \{[8+7]+8\}$$
$$= \{15+8\}$$
$$= 23;$$

therefore, the number represented by

$$\{[(6+2)+7]+8\} + (4 \times 10)$$

is

$$23+40,$$

or 63. Notice that in the process of finding the number represented by $\{[(6+2)+7]+8\}$, the innermost grouping symbol, in this case ( ), was considered first, then the next grouping symbol [ ], and finally { }. The simplification is effected by starting from the inside and moving outward.

ALGORITHMS AND OPERATIONS

It is important to distinguish between a binary operation and the algorithm for the operation. A binary operation associates with an ordered pair of numbers a definite number. An algorithm is a device or pattern used to find the number that the operation associates with the given pair of numbers.

The operation of addition associates with the number-pair 84 and 42, the number 126. The operation of multiplication associates with the same number pair, the number 3528. The operation of subtraction associates with the same pair, the number 42. The operation of division associates with that pair, the number 2. The procedures used to find the numbers 126, 3528, 42, and 2 are called algorithms.

In many cases (for example, when both numbers have single-digit numerals) a table of elementary facts recalled from memory or written down is all that is necessary to find the number which an operation associates with the given pair. More generally, one uses an algorithm that is based on (a) the properties of whole numbers, and (b) the properties of a place-value system of number notation.

ADDITION ALGORITHM

We are now assuming that we have at our disposal (a) the sum of any pair of members from the set {0, 1, 2, 3, 4, 5, 6, 7, 8, 9}, (b) the properties of the set of whole numbers, and (c) the properties of our numeration system.

Let us see what properties are used when we find the simplest name for the sum of two numbers. In other words, let us see how the algorithm for addition can be justified.

As our first example, let us consider the addition of 23 and 45. We know, of course, that the sum is 68, but let us see how we can arrive at this result by virtue of the commutative and associative properties (of addition) and the distributive property.

$$
\begin{aligned}
23+45 &= [(2\times10)+(3\times1)]+[(4\times10)+(5\times1)] & \text{Expanded notation} & \quad(1)\\
&= [(2\times10)+(3\times1)]+[(5\times1)+(4\times10)] & \text{Commutative property} & \quad(2)\\
&= \{[(2\times10)+(3\times1)]+(5\times1)\}+(4\times10) & \text{Associative property} & \quad(3)\\
&= \{(2\times10)+[(3\times1)+(5\times1)]\}+(4\times10) & \text{Associative property} & \quad(4)\\
&= (4\times10)+\{(2\times10)+[(3\times1)+(5\times1)]\} & \text{Commutative property} & \quad(5)\\
&= [(4\times10)+(2\times10)]+[(3\times1)+(5\times1)] & \text{Associative property} & \quad(6)\\
&= [(4+2)\times10]+[(3+5)\times1] & \text{Distributive property} & \quad(7)\\
&= (6\times10)+(8\times1) & \text{Basic sums} & \quad(8)\\
&= 68 & \text{Place-value notation} & \quad(9)
\end{aligned}
$$

Notice that the steps numbered (2), (3), (4), (5), and (6), justified by the commutative and associative properties of addition, serve the purpose of getting (2×10) and (4×10) next to each other, and getting (3×1) and (5×1) next to each other. Then in step (7) the distributive property is used to "combine" (2×10) and (4×10), and to "combine" (3×1) and (5×1).

When we write

$$
\begin{aligned}
23 &= (2\times10)+(3\times1)\\
45 &= (4\times10)+(5\times1)\\
&= [(2+4)\times10]+[(3+5)\times1] & \text{Distributive property}\\
&= (6\times10)+(8\times1)\\
&= 68,
\end{aligned}
$$

commutativity and associativity of addition are taken for granted, and only the application of the distributive property is explicitly shown.

Now we are ready to see what goes on "behind the scenes" when we write the algorithm for the addition of 23 and 45 as follows:

$$\begin{array}{r} 23 \\ 45 \\ \hline 68 \end{array}$$

In writing the numbers 23 and 45 in the vertical array $\begin{array}{r}23\\45\\\hline\end{array}$, we are indicating that we are ready to apply the distributive property. Next, we write the numeral 8, shown circled below.

$$\begin{array}{r} 23 \\ 45 \\ \hline ⑧ \end{array}$$

In doing this we are recognizing that $(3 \times 1) + (5 \times 1) = (3 + 5) \times 1$, or in more traditional terms, that 3 ones plus 5 ones equals 8 ones. The basis for this step is the distributive property. Finally, we write the numeral 6, shown circled below.

$$\begin{array}{r} 2\,3 \\ 4\,5 \\ \hline ⑥8 \end{array}$$

This step is also justified by the distributive property:

$$(2 \times 10) + (4 \times 10) = (2 + 4) \times 10 = 6 \times 10.$$

Let us consider the problem of adding 18 and 9. Again the associative and commutative properties justify our starting directly with the vertical form:

$$
\begin{array}{rll}
18 = & (1 \times 10) + (8 \times 1) & \\
9 = & \underline{ (9 \times 1)} & \\
18 + 9 = & (1 \times 10) + [\,(8 + 9) \times 1\,] & \text{Distributive property} \\
= & (1 \times 10) + (17 \times 1) & \text{Basic sum} \\
= & (1 \times 10) + [\,(1 \times 10) + (7 \times 1)\,] & \text{Expanded notation} \\
= & [\,(1 \times 10) + (1 \times 10)\,] + (7 \times 1) & \text{Associative property} \\
= & [\,(1 + 1) \times 10\,] + (7 \times 1) & \text{Distributive property} \\
= & (2 \times 10) + (7 \times 1) & \text{Basic sum} \\
= & 27. & \text{Place-value notation}
\end{array}
$$

Below, we show these steps contracted even more:

$$
\begin{array}{ll}
18 = 10+8 & \qquad \qquad \textcircled{1} \\
\underline{9 = 9} & \qquad \qquad 18 \\
 = 10+17 \qquad \text{or} & \qquad \qquad \underline{9} \\
 = 10+(10+7) & \qquad \qquad 27. \\
 = (10+10)+7 & \\
 = 20+7 & \\
 = 27 &
\end{array}
$$

The illustration above shows the carrying of one ten. The same method is used to carry hundreds, thousands, etc.

In vertical form, we may abbreviate still further. Here are three abbreviated forms showing the addition of 67 and 48.

$$
\begin{array}{ll}
67 & \\
\underline{48} & \\
15 & (8+7) \\
\underline{100} & (40+60) \\
115 &
\end{array}
$$

$$
\begin{array}{ll}
\textcircled{10} & \\
67 & \\
\underline{48} & \\
5 & \left[\begin{array}{l} 8+7 = 15 = (1\times 10)+5 \\ \text{``carry''} \quad (1\times 10) \end{array}\right] \\
\underline{110} & (40+60+10) \\
115 &
\end{array}
$$

$$
\begin{array}{l}
\textcircled{1} \\
67 \\
\underline{48} \\
115
\end{array}
$$

An abacus can be a valuable aid to develop understanding of the addition algorithm. Each wire of the abacus corresponds to a position in the numeral. The place value of the position is shown on the abacus pictured in Figure 1. The number of beads on each wire shows the number named by the digit in that position.

The addition of 723 and 248 on an abacus is shown in Figure 1.

The explanation of the algorithm for addition with numerals in base ten is the same as with numerals in any other number base. This will be shown by using base four.* The addition table and the place-value chart in base four numerals are shown in Tables I and II.

---

*For a detailed explanation of the numeration system in base four, see Booklet No. 3: *Systems of Numeration for the Whole Numbers.*

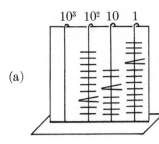

(a)

The beads have been placed to show the addends **723** (upper) and **248** (lower).

Small clothespins separate the sets of beads for the two addends.

Addends

$(7 \times 10^2) + (2 \times 10) + (3 \times 1)$

$(2 \times 10^2) + (4 \times 10) + (8 \times 1)$

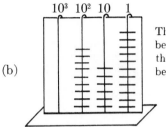

(b)

The clothespins have been removed to permit the joining of the sets of beads.

Sum

$(9 \times 10^2) + (6 \times 10) + (11 \times 1)$

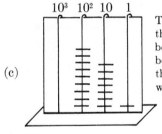

(c)

Ten of the beads on the right-hand wire have been removed, and one bead has been added to the group on the next wire.

Sum renamed

$(9 \times 10^2) + (7 \times 10) + (1 \times 1) = 971$

FIGURE 1

TABLE I

Base-Four Addition Chart				
+	0	1	2	3
0	0	1	2	3
1	1	2	3	10
2	2	3	10	11
3	3	10	11	12

TABLE II

Place Value in Base Four		
four² or sixteen	four or four	four⁰ or one

Consider the sum $21_{four} + 12_{four}$:

$$21_{four} + 12_{four} = [\,(2 \times four) + (1 \times one)\,] + [\,(1 \times four) + (2 \times one)\,]$$

If the commutative and associative properties are applied, we obtain

$[\,(2 \times four) + (1 \times four)\,] + [\,(1 \times one) + (2 \times one)\,]$
$= [\,(2+1) \times four\,] + [\,(1+2) \times one\,]$ Distributive property
$= (3 \times four) + (3 \times one)$ Basic sums
$= 33_{four}.$ Place-value notation

So $21_{four} + 12_{four} = 33_{four}$.

Since the base-four numeral for the number four is 10_{four}, we could have written the addition given above, using base-four numerals, as follows:

$$21_{four} + 12_{four} = [\,(2 \times 10_{four}) + (1 \times 1_{four})\,] + [\,(1 \times 10_{four}) + (2 \times 1_{four})\,]$$

and by repeated use of the commutative and associative properties,

$= [\,(2 \times 10_{four}) + (1 \times 10_{four})\,] + [\,(1 \times 1_{four}) + (2 \times 1_{four})\,]$
$= [\,(2+1) \times 10_{four}\,] + [\,(1+2) \times 1_{four}\,]$ Distributive property
$= (3 \times 10_{four}) + (3 \times 1_{four})$ Basic sums
$= 33_{four}.$ Place-value notation

The familiar vertical form would then be

$$\begin{array}{r} 21_{four} \\ 12_{four} \\ \hline 33_{four}. \end{array}$$

Adding 21_{four} and 12_{four} is simple because it involves only the basic sums and place value; but the properties justify the addition of 2 fours and 1 four to obtain the sum 3 fours.

Let us consider an example of adding in base four which involves carrying. Try to identify the properties that justify carrying a number in renaming an indicated sum.

$$\begin{array}{l} 12_{four} + 13_{four} = \,? \\ 12_{four} = 10_{four} + 2_{four} \\ 13_{four} = 10_{four} + 3_{four} \\ \hline \quad 20_{four} + 11_{four} \end{array}$$

The preceding example has shown the justification for adding the columns as shown. We now rename $20_{four} + 11_{four}$:

$$20_{four} + 11_{four} = [\,(2 \times four) + (0 \times one)\,] + [\,(1 \times four) + (1 \times one)\,].$$

By applying the associative and commutative properties, we obtain

$$[\,(2 \times \text{four}) + (1 \times \text{four})\,] + [\,(0 \times \text{one}) + (1 \times \text{one})\,]$$

$$= [\,(2+1) \times \text{four}\,] + [\,(0+1) \times \text{one}\,] \quad \text{Distributive property}$$
$$= (3 \times \text{four}) + (1 \times \text{one}) \qquad\qquad \text{Basic sums}$$
$$= 31_{\text{four}} \qquad\qquad\qquad\qquad\qquad \text{Place-value notation}$$

so $12_{\text{four}} + 12_{\text{four}} = 31_{\text{four}}.$

This example suggests that carrying can proceed with base-four numerals in the familiar fashion. Thus,

$\textcircled{1}$ $\textcircled{1}$

12_{four} 23_{four} $3+3=12_{\text{four}}$ (from the

13_{four} and 33_{four} addition

$\overline{31_{\text{four}}}$ $\overline{122_{\text{four}}}$ $1+2+3=12_{\text{four}}.$ chart)

The addition of 23_{four} and 33_{four} on an abacus is pictured in Figure 2.

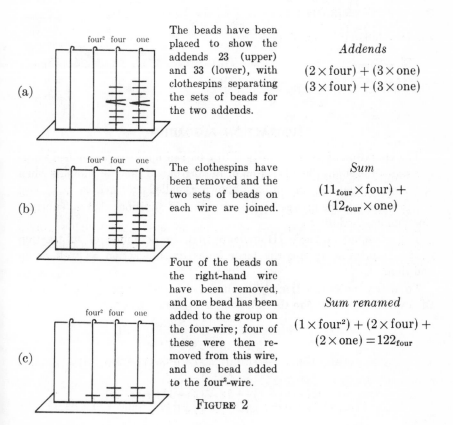

(a)   The beads have been placed to show the addends 23 (upper) and 33 (lower), with clothespins separating the sets of beads for the two addends.

Addends

$(2 \times \text{four}) + (3 \times \text{one})$
$(3 \times \text{four}) + (3 \times \text{one})$

(b)   The clothespins have been removed and the two sets of beads on each wire are joined.

Sum

$(11_{\text{four}} \times \text{four}) +$
$(12_{\text{four}} \times \text{one})$

(c)   Four of the beads on the right-hand wire have been removed, and one bead has been added to the group on the four-wire; four of these were then removed from this wire, and one bead added to the four²-wire.

Sum renamed

$(1 \times \text{four}^2) + (2 \times \text{four}) + (2 \times \text{one}) = 122_{\text{four}}$

FIGURE 2

Exercise Set 1

Most people know that you can check an addition problem such as

$$\begin{array}{r} 3 \\ 4 \\ 5 \\ \hline 12 \end{array}$$

by adding down the column after you have added up the column. Below is a proof of the fact that

$$(5+4)+3 = (3+4)+5.$$
(adding up)   (adding down)

Fill in the blanks giving the reason for reach step in the proof.

1. $(5+4)+3 = 5+(4+3)$ _____

2. $= (4+3)+5$ _____

3. $= (3+4)+5$ _____

Find the following sums in base four.

4. 32_{four}
        21_{four}

5. 31_{four}
        23_{four}

6. 12_{four}
        23_{four}
        33_{four}

SUBTRACTION ALGORITHM

The operation of *addition* assigns to a pair of numbers a specified number called the sum. The operation of finding one of the two addends when the other addend and the sum are known, is called *subtraction*.

Subtraction is the inverse of the operation of addition; that is, subtraction "undoes" addition.

The examples in Table III indicate that the definition of subtraction makes it possible to use the basic sums in subtraction as well as in addition.

To justify the subtraction algorithm, we observe a property suggested by the examples below. Are the following statements true?

$$\begin{array}{ll} \text{(a)} & (8+6)-(3+2) = (8-3)+(6-2) \\ & \qquad 14-5 = 5+4 \\ \text{(b)} & (7+11)-(6+9) = (7-6)+(11-9) \\ & \qquad 18-15 = 1+2 \\ \text{(c)} & (25+8)-(14+8) = (25-14)+(8-8) \\ & \qquad 33-22 = 11+0 \end{array}$$

TABLE III

Addition			Subtraction		
Addend	Addend	Sum	Sum	Addend	Unknown Addend
$6 + 4 = 10$			$\begin{cases}10 & - & 4 & = & 6\\10 & - & 6 & = & 4\end{cases}$		
$9 + 6 = 15$			$\begin{cases}15 & - & 9 & = & 6\\15 & - & 6 & = & 9\end{cases}$		
$a + b = c$			$\begin{cases}c & - & b & = & a\\c & - & a & = & b\end{cases}$		

In general, the fact which may be observed by studying the preceding sentences may be written:

If $a \geq c^*$ and $b \geq d$, then $(a+b) - (c+d) = (a-c) + (b-d)$.

We shall call this a statement of the subtraction property. We will accept this subtraction property as true. It can be proved, but the proof is beyond the scope of this booklet. This property is used in almost every example of subtraction. Notice its use in the following examples.

$$
\begin{aligned}
76 - 23 &= (70+6) - (20+3)\\
&= (70-20) + (6-3)\\
&= 50+3\\
&= 53
\end{aligned}
$$

Now let us consider the way in which this property and other properties of whole numbers and the numeration system assure us that the familiar algorithm for subtraction is reasonable. We wish to find $(78-32)$.

$$
\begin{aligned}
78 - 32 &= [\,(7 \times 10) + (8 \times 1)\,] - [\,(3 \times 10) + (2 \times 1)\,]\\
&= [\,(7 \times 10) - (3 \times 10]\, + [\,(8+1) - (2 \times 1)\,] \quad \text{Subtraction property}\\
&= [\,(7-3) \times 10] + [\,(8-2) \times 1] \quad\quad\;\; \text{Distributive property}\\
&= (4 \times 10) + (6 \times 1) \quad\quad\quad\quad\quad\quad\;\; \text{of multiplication}\\
&= 46 \quad\quad\quad\quad\quad\quad\quad\quad\quad\quad\quad\quad\;\; \text{over subtraction}
\end{aligned}
$$

In the next example we have a situation in which the process sometimes called *borrowing*, or *regrouping*, is required. If we attempt to use the method of the last example to find $(88-49)$, we encounter difficulty be-

---

* $a \geq c$ is read "a is greater than c or a is equal to c." The sentence $6 \geq 5$ is true because $6 > 5$. The sentence $5 \geq 5$ is true because $5 = 5$.

cause we cannot subtract 9 ones from 8 ones. The number 88 can be renamed, however, as 7 tens and 18 ones, as shown below:

$$88 = (8 \times 10) + (8 \times 1)$$
$$= [(7+1) \times 10] + (8 \times 1)$$
$$= [(7 \times 10) + (1 \times 10)] + (8 \times 1) \qquad \text{Distributive property}$$
$$= (7 \times 10) + [(1 \times 10) + (8 \times 1)] \qquad \text{Associative property}$$
$$= (7 \times 10) + [(10 \times 1) + (8 \times 1)] \qquad \text{Commutative property of multiplication}$$
$$= (7 \times 10) + [(10+8) \times 1] \qquad \text{Distributive property}$$
$$= (7 \times 10) + (18 \times 1).$$

The subtraction of 49 from 88 now proceeds as follows:

$$88 - 49 = [(7 \times 10) + (18 \times 1)] - [(4 \times 10) + (9 \times 1)]$$
$$= [(7 \times 10) - (4 \times 10)] + [(18 \times 1) - (9 \times 1)] \quad \text{Subtraction property}$$
$$= [(7-4) \times 10] + [(18-9) \times 1] \qquad \text{Distributive property}$$
$$= (3 \times 10) + (9 \times 1) \qquad\qquad\qquad \text{of multiplication}$$
$$= 39. \qquad\qquad\qquad\qquad\qquad\qquad \text{over subtraction}$$

As we work through the steps, we can see that we are renaming a number in a form in which there are enough ones and enough tens to meet the condition that $(a \geq c)$ and $(b \geq d)$. The old term "borrowing a ten" implies that we will pay it back, but we never pay back the ten; we are really renaming the number in the most convenient manner for the computation. The distributive property allows us to subtract tens from tens and ones from ones. The illustration above shows renaming of one ten. The same method is used in renaming hundreds, thousands, etc.

As a second example, consider the subtraction of 67 from 324. It is clear that we cannot subtract 7 ones from 4 ones; hence we rename 324 initially as 3 hundreds + 1 ten + 14 ones. Now we notice that we cannot subtract 6 tens from 1 ten, so we rename 324 again; this time as 2 hundreds + 11 tens + 14 ones. The subtraction can now proceed:

$$324 = (2 \times 10^2) + (11 \times 10) + (14 \times 1)$$
$$\underline{67 = \qquad\qquad\quad (6 \times 10) + (7 \times 1)}$$
$$(2 \times 10^2) + [(11-6) \times 10] + [(14-7) \times 1]$$
$$= (2 \times 10^2) + (5 \times 10) + (7 \times 1)$$
$$= 257.$$

The abacus can be employed to picture the renaming of the sum in subtraction. In Figure 3, the subtraction of 42 from 69 is shown.

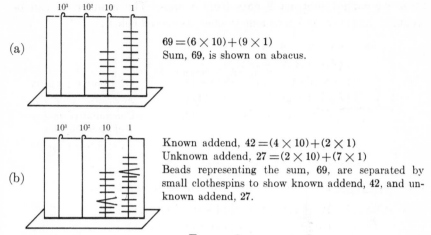

(a) $69 = (6 \times 10) + (9 \times 1)$
Sum, 69, is shown on abacus.

(b) Known addend, $42 = (4 \times 10) + (2 \times 1)$
Unknown addend, $27 = (2 \times 10) + (7 \times 1)$
Beads representing the sum, 69, are separated by small clothespins to show known addend, 42, and unknown addend, 27.

FIGURE 3

Now let us consider $328 - 49 = n$ (Fig. 4, p. 18).

To subtract numbers named by numerals in another base involves the same definition of subtraction and the same number properties that we use with numerals in the decimal system. When subtracting numbers named by base-four numerals, we need to refer to the basic sums written in numerals in base four shown in Table IV.

TABLE IV

+	0_{four}	1_{four}	2_{four}	3_{four}
0_{four}	0_{four}	1_{four}	2_{four}	3_{four}
1_{four}	1_{four}	2_{four}	3_{four}	10_{four}
2_{four}	2_{four}	3_{four}	10_{four}	11_{four}
3_{four}	3_{four}	10_{four}	11_{four}	12_{four}

We must also know the relation between the basic sums and subtraction. For example,

$$2_{four} + 3_{four} = 11_{four} \begin{cases} 11_{four} - 3_{four} = 2_{four} \\ 11_{four} - 2_{four} = 3_{four} \end{cases}$$

$$3_{four} + 1_{four} = 10_{four} \begin{cases} 10_{four} - 3_{four} = 1_{four} \\ 10_{four} - 1_{four} = 3_{four}. \end{cases}$$

Let us find $33_{four} - 21_{four}$. Since all numerals are in base four, we will

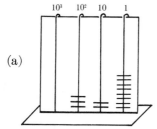

(a)

Sum, 328, is shown as $(3 \times 10^2)+(2 \times 10)+(8 \times 1)$.

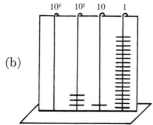

(b)

Sum, 328, is renamed as $(3 \times 10^2)+(1 \times 10)+(18 \times 1)$ to meet the condition that $b \geq d$.

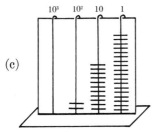

(c)

Sum, 328, is again renamed as $(2 \times 10^2)+(11 \times 10)+(18 \times 1)$ to meet the condition that $a \geq c$ and $b \geq d$.

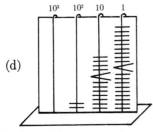

(d)

Sum is separated. Known addend $49 =(4 \times 10)+(9 \times 1)$.
Unknown addend $(2 \times 10^2)+(7 \times 10)+(9 \times 1)= 279$.

FIGURE 4

omit the subscripts to simplify the notation. Remember 10 is the symbol for four in base four.

$$33 - 21 = [\,(3 \times 10) + (3 \times 1)\,] - [\,(2 \times 10) - (1 \times 1)\,]$$
$$= [\,(3 \times 10) - (2 \times 10)\,] + [\,(3 \times 1) - (1 \times 1)\,] \quad \text{Subtraction property}$$
$$= [\,(3-2) \times 10\,] + [\,(3-1) \times 1\,] \quad \text{Distributive property}$$
$$= (1 \times 10) + (2 \times 1) \quad \text{of multiplication}$$
$$= 12. \quad \text{over subtraction}$$

In the next example, subtracting 13_{four} from 32_{four} involves the renaming of a number to meet the condition in the subtraction property that $a \geq c$ and $b \geq d$. Since all numerals are in base four, we shall again omit the subscripts.

The number 32 can be renamed as $(2 \times 10) + (12 \times 1)$, since

$$32 = (3 \times 10) + (2 \times 1)$$
$$= [\,(2+1) \times 10\,] + (2 \times 1)$$
$$= [\,(2 \times 10) + (1 \times 10)\,] + (2 \times 1) \quad \text{Distributive property}$$
$$= (2 \times 10) + [\,(1 \times 10) + (2 \times 1)\,] \quad \text{Associative property}$$
$$= (2 \times 10) + [\,(10 \times 1) + (2 \times 1)\,] \quad \text{Commutative property}$$
$$\qquad\qquad\qquad\qquad\qquad\qquad\qquad \text{of multiplication}$$
$$= (2 \times 10) + (12 \times 1). \quad \text{Distributive property}$$

The subtraction of 13_{four} from 32_{four} then proceeds as follows:

$$32 - 13 = [\,(2 \times 10) + (12 \times 1)\,] - [\,(1 \times 10) + (3 \times 1)\,]$$
$$= [\,(2 \times 10) - (1 \times 10)\,] + [\,(12 \times 1) - (3 \times 1)\,] \quad \text{Subtraction property}$$
$$= [\,(2-1) \times 10\,] = [\,(12-3) \times 1\,] \quad \text{Distributive property}$$
$$\qquad\qquad\qquad\qquad\qquad\qquad\qquad \text{of multiplication}$$
$$\qquad\qquad\qquad\qquad\qquad\qquad\qquad \text{over subtraction}$$
$$= (1 \times 10) + (3 \times 1) \quad 12 - 3 = 3, \text{ since in}$$
$$\qquad\qquad\qquad\qquad\qquad\qquad\qquad \text{base-four numerals}$$
$$\qquad\qquad\qquad\qquad\qquad\qquad\qquad 3 + 3 = 12.$$
$$= 13.$$

Now we can look at the problem in the next stage:

$$32 = 20 + 12$$
$$\underline{13 = 10 + 3}$$
$$10 + 3$$
$$= 13.$$

The process of renaming a number and showing the computation in base four can also be shown on an abacus, just as in base ten, but the place values of the positions represented by the wires are changed.

Let us consider the subtraction, $33_{four} - 21_{four}$ (Fig. 5):

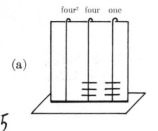

(a)   Sum 33_four is shown as $(3 \times \text{four}) + (3 \times 1)$.

-5

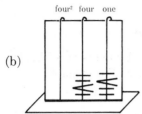

(b)   Sum 33_four is separated to show the known addend, $(2 \times \text{four}) + (1 \times 1)$, and the unknown addend, $(1 \times \text{four}) + (2 \times 1)$.

FIGURE 5

Now let us consider the example, $32_\text{four} - 13_\text{four} = n$ (Fig. 6):

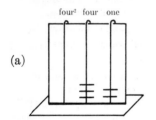

(a)   Sum 32_four is shown as $(3 \times \text{four}) + (2 \times 1)$.

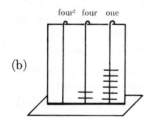

(b)   Sum 32_four is renamed $(2 \times \text{four}) + (\text{six} \times 1)$ to meet the condition $a \geq c$ and $b \geq d$.

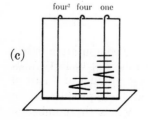

(c)   Sum is separated into known addend, 13_four, and unknown addend, 13_four.

FIGURE 6

Exercise Set 2

Subtract the following using base-four numerals.

1. 32_{four}
21_{four}

2. 31_{four}
12_{four}

3. 301_{four}
122_{four}

4. 100_{four}
23_{four}

5. 200_{four}
33_{four}

MULTIPLICATION ALGORITHM

The algorithm for the multiplication of a number by ten is very simple: annex a zero to the base-ten numeral of the number. For example,

$$10 \times 319 = 3190.$$

This convenient algorithm can be justified by the properties of the whole numbers and the properties of the place-value system of notation. Let us use the example 10×319:

$10 \times 319 = 319 \times 10$	Commutative property of multiplication
$= [\,(3 \times 10^2) + (1 \times 10) + (9 \times 1)\,] \times 10$	Expanded notation
$= [\,(3 \times 10^2) \times 10\,] + [\,(1 \times 10) \times 10\,] + [\,(9 \times 1) \times 10\,]$	Distributive property
$= [\,3 \times (10^2 \times 10)\,] + [\,1 \times (10 \times 10)\,] + [\,9 \times (1 \times 10)\,]$	Associative property of multiplication
$= (3 \times 10^3) + (1 \times 10^2) + (9 \times 10)$	$10^2 \times 10 = 10^3;\ 10 \times 10 = 10^2$
$= (3 \times 10^3) + (1 \times 10^2) + (9 \times 10) + (0 \times 1)$	$0 \times 1 = 0$, and zero is the identity element for addition
$= 3190.$	Place-value notation

Multiplication of a number by one hundred is accomplished by annexing two zeros to the base-ten numeral of the number. Three zeros are annexed to the numeral of a number when multiplying the number by one thousand, and so on. Thus,

$$10 \times 319 = 3190,$$
$$100 \times 319 = 31,900,$$
$$1000 \times 319 = 319,000,$$

etc.

We are now going to use the properties of multiplication to justify the multiplication algorithm that is employed to find the product of a pair of whole numbers when these numbers are such that their product is not stored in our memory. Obviously, knowing that $a \times b$ is the number of elements in an a by b array is of little help if we are asked to compute 68×23. There are just too many elements to count conveniently. But we can make use of the commutative and associative properties of multiplication and addition, the distributive property, the special properties of 0 as an addend and as a factor, and of 1 as a factor, and the basic sums and products to help us in our computation. If you have ever tried to multiply two numbers, even fairly small ones, which are written as numerals in the Roman system, you will appreciate, more than ever, our own place-value system. Try $(\text{XVII}) \times (\text{DCXI})$. The properties of numbers do not depend on the numeration system we use for naming them, but facility in computation does lean heavily on it.

The commonly used algorithm for multiplication often disguises what is happening mathematically behind the scenes. Let us see what is really involved in finding the simplest name for the product 6×29.

$$
\begin{aligned}
6 \times 29 &= 6 \times [\,(2 \times 10) + (9 \times 1)\,] \\
&= [\,6 \times (2 \times 10)\,] + [\,6 \times (9 \times 1)\,] && \text{Distributive property} \\
&= [\,(6 \times 2) \times 10\,] + [\,(6 \times 9) \times 1\,] && \text{Associative property} \\
&= (12 \times 10) + (54 \times 1) && \text{Basic products} \\
&= 120 + (54 \times 1) && \text{Multiplication of 12 by ten} \\
&= 120 + 54 && \text{Multiplication of 54 by one} \\
&= 174. && \text{Addition algorithm}
\end{aligned}
$$

Let us now examine what happens when we find the product of two two-digit numbers:

$$
\begin{aligned}
36 \times 79 &= (30 + 6) \times 79 \\
&= (30 \times 79) + (6 \times 79) && \text{Distributive property} \\
&= [\,(10 \times 3) \times 79\,] + (6 \times 79) \\
&= [\,10 \times (3 \times 79)\,] + (6 \times 79) && \text{Associative property} \\
&= (10 \times 237) + (6 \times 79) && 3 \times 79 = 237* \\
&= 2370 + 474 && \text{Multiplication by ten} \\
&&& 6 \times 79 = 474* \\
&= 2844. && \text{Addition algorithm}
\end{aligned}
$$

It is instructive to look at this procedure in a vertical form:

$$
\begin{array}{r|l}
79 & \\
36 & \\
\hline
474 & = 6 \times 79 \\
2370 & = 30 \times 79 \\
\hline
2844 & = (30 + 6) \times 79.
\end{array}
$$

---

*Multiplication by a number which has a single-digit numeral was justified in a previous example involving the product 6×29. The justification here would be entirely similar and hence is not given.

If you erase everything to the right of the vertical line, that which remains is the commonly used algorithm, except that the digit 0 is sometimes omitted from the numeral 2370.

Another way of looking at the product 36×79 is as follows:

$$
\begin{aligned}
36 \times 79 &= (30+6) \times (70+9) \\
&= [30 \times (70+9)] + [6 \times (70+9)] \qquad \text{Distributive property} \\
&= (30 \times 70) + (30 \times 9) + (6 \times 70) + (6 \times 9) \qquad \text{Distributive property} \\
&= 2100 + 270 + 420 + 54 \\
&= 2844.
\end{aligned}
$$

Notice that there are four products involved, namely, the products of each of the numbers 70 and 9 by each of the numbers 30 and 6. In vertical form these products can be shown as follows.

$$
\begin{array}{r}
79 \\
\underline{36} \\
54 = 6 \times 9 \\
420 = 6 \times 70 \\
270 = 30 \times 9 \\
\underline{2100} = 30 \times 70 \\
2844
\end{array}
$$

It is easy to verify that $6 \times 70 = 420$ and that $30 \times 70 = 2100$. Let us examine the latter of these two products.

$$
\begin{aligned}
30 \times 70 &= (3 \times 10) \times (7 \times 10) \\
&= [(3 \times 10) \times 7] \times 10 \qquad \text{Associative property} \\
&= [7 \times (3 \times 10)] \times 10 \qquad \text{Commutative property} \\
&= [(7 \times 3) \times 10] \times 10 \qquad \text{Associative property} \\
&= 21 \times (10 \times 10) \qquad \text{Associative property} \\
&= 2100 \qquad \text{Multiplication by one hundred}
\end{aligned}
$$

It is interesting to go back to the definition of the product of 15×12 as the number of elements in an array of 15 rows with 12 elements in each row and see how our algorithm is reflected in the array (Fig. 7). We separate it into several smaller arrays (Fig. 8).

The four arrays shown in Figure 8 are the four partial products resulting from application of the distributive property.

$$
\begin{array}{r l l}
12 \\
\underline{15} \\
10 & (5 \times 2) & \left.\vphantom{\begin{array}{c}a\\b\end{array}}\right\} (5 \times 12) \\
50 & (5 \times 10) & \\
20 & (10 \times 2) & \left.\vphantom{\begin{array}{c}a\\b\end{array}}\right\} (10 \times 12) \\
\underline{100} & (10 \times 10) & \\
180
\end{array}
$$

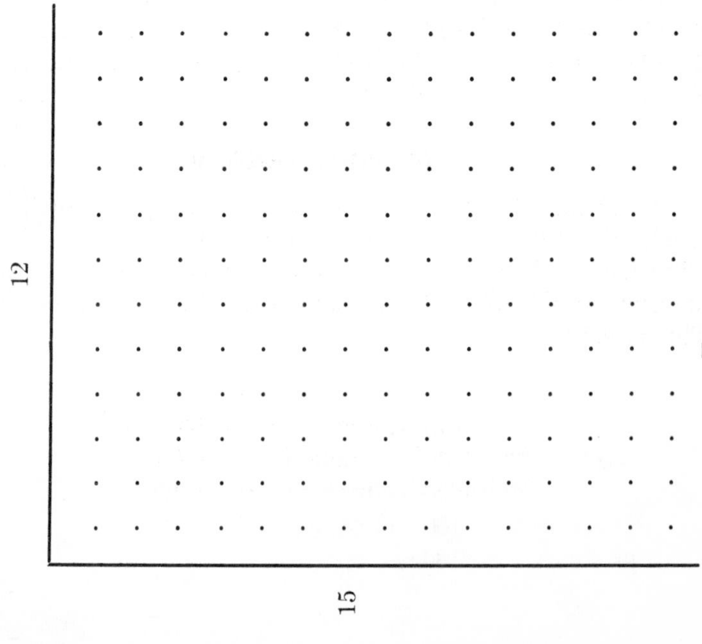

10 × 2 = 20

5 × 2 = 10

2

10

10

10 × 10
= 100

5

5 × 10
= 50

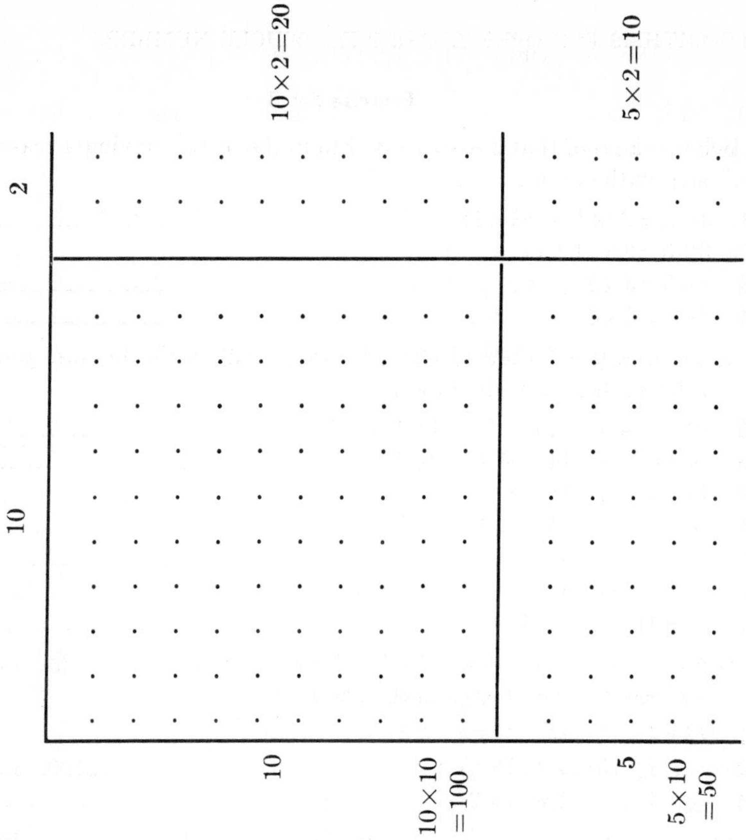

FIGURE 8

12

15

FIGURE 7

Exercise Set 3

Below is a proof that $3+3=2\times3$. Fill in the blanks, giving a reason for each step in the proof.

1. $3+3=(3\times1)+(3\times1)$ _____
2. $3+3=3\times(1+1)$ _____
3. $3+3=3\times2$ _____
4. $3+3=2\times3$ _____

Below is a proof that $(4+4)+4=3\times4$. Fill in the blanks, giving a reason for each step in the proof.

5. $(4+4)+4=[(4\times1)+(4\times1)]+4$ _____
6. $(4+4)+4=[4\times(1+1)]+4$ _____
7. $(4+4)+4=(4\times2)+4$ _____
8. $(4+4)+4=(4\times2)+(4\times1)$ _____
9. $(4+4)+4=4\times(2+1)$ _____
10. $(4+4)+4=4\times3$ _____
11. $(4+4)+4=3\times4$ _____

Below is the proof that $(3\times4)\times5=4\times(5\times3)$. Fill in the blanks, giving a reason for each step in the proof.

12. $(3\times4)\times5=(4\times3)\times5$ _____
13. $(3\times4)\times5=4\times(3\times5)$ _____
14. $(3\times4)\times5=4\times(5\times3)$ _____

Below is a proof that $(2\times6)+(6\times4)=6\times(4+2)$. Fill in the blanks, giving a reason for each step in the proof.

15. $(2\times6)+(6\times4)=(6\times2)+(6\times4)$ _____
16. $(2\times6)+(6\times4)=6\times(2+4)$ _____
17. $(2\times6)+(6\times4)=6\times(4+2)$ _____

DIVISION ALGORITHM

The algorithm for division is the most complex and usually the most troublesome of the basic computational procedures.

The four fundamental operations of addition, subtraction, multiplication, and division are related in many ways. Figure 9 shows some of the relationships.

$$\text{Addition} \xleftrightarrow{\text{inverse}} \text{Subtraction}$$
$$\text{repeated} \uparrow \qquad \text{inverse} \qquad \uparrow \text{repeated}$$
$$\text{Multiplication} \xleftrightarrow{} \text{Division}$$

FIGURE 9

The horizontal relationship indicated in Figure 9 is the inverse relationship. (See Booklet No. 2: *The Whole Numbers.*) Thus,

$2+3=5$ is equivalent to $5-3=2$ and to $5-2=3$,
$2\times3=6$ is equivalent to $6\div3=2$ and to $6\div2=3$.

A product may be thought of as the sum of equal addends. Consider the product,

$$2\times3=(1+1)\times3 \qquad \text{Basic sum}$$
$$=(1\times3)+(1\times3) \qquad \text{Distributive property}$$
$$=3+3.$$

There is a similar parallel relationship existing between subtraction and division. Starting with 6, three successive subtractions of 2 are required to obtain a remainder of 0.

$$
\begin{array}{c}
6 \\
-\,2 \underline{\qquad\qquad}1 \\
\overline{4} \\
-\,2 \underline{\qquad\qquad}1 \\
\overline{2} \\
-\,2 \underline{\qquad\qquad}1 \\
\overline{0}
\end{array}
\Bigg\} 3
\qquad
\begin{array}{l}
6=(1\times2)+4 \\[1.5em]
6=(1\times2)+[(1\times2)+2] \\[1.5em]
6=(1\times2)+(1\times2)+(1\times2)+0
\end{array}
$$

The division operation can be applied only to certain ordered pairs of whole numbers. For example $6\div2$ is the whole number 3 because $2\times3=6$, but $8\div3$ does not represent a whole number because there is no whole number which when multipled by 3 gives the product 8.

We can say something, however, about any ordered pair of whole numbers (if the second number is not zero) and the operation of division. For example, given the whole numbers 15 and 7, we can express 15 as a multiple of 7 plus a remainder 1:

$$15=(7\times2)+1.$$

This mathematical statement illustrates the *division property of numbers*. The property (or algorithm) can be deduced from basic assumptions about whole numbers, but we shall accept it here without proof.

In general, the division property expresses the fact that for any two whole numbers a and b, there is a unique pair of whole numbers q and r, such that

$$a=(b\times q)+r,$$

where $r\geq0$ but $r<b$. We say that q is the quotient and r is the remainder when the number a is divided by the number b.

The division property of numbers is illustrated in Table V for the given pairs of whole numbers.

TABLE V

Ordered Pair (a, b)	$a = (b \times q) + r$	q	r
(12, 5)	$12 = (5 \times 2) + 2$	2	2
(26, 4)	$26 = (4 \times 6) + 2$	6	2
(81, 7)	$81 = (7 \times 11) + 4$	11	4
(26, 13)	$26 = (13 \times 2) + 0$	2	0
(125, 15)	$125 = (15 \times 8) + 5$	8	5
(7, 18)	$7 = (18 \times 0) + 7$	0	7

Let us examine an example to illustrate this division property. Suppose we want to find $40 \div 5$. Since $5 \times 8 = 40$, we know that $40 \div 5 = 8$. To illustrate using arrays, we can arrange 40 elements in an array with 5 rows (or columns) with equal number of elements in each row (or column).

Now, suppose we want to find n for which the sentence $42 \div 5 = n$ is true. We know there is no whole number n, such that $5 \times n = 42$. We see that we can arrange 5 rows with 1 element in each row using 5 elements, then 2 elements in each row using 10 elements, and so on until we have 5 rows with 8 elements in each row using 40 elements, and we have 2 elements left over; thus we have an array as in Figure 10.

$$42 = (5 \times 8) + 2$$

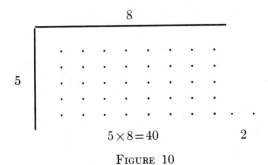

$5 \times 8 = 40$ 2

FIGURE 10

Suppose we try $98 \div 15$. We find we can use 15 elements, placing 1 in each of 15 rows, and have 83 left. Again we use 15 elements, 1 in each of the 15 rows (we have used 30 in all), and have 68 left. We continue in this fashion having 53 left, then 38, then 23, then 8 left. Thus, we have

$$98 = (15 \times 6) + 8.$$

In other words, when 98 is divided by 15, the quotient is 6 and the remainder is 8.

Notice that we can regard this division as consisting of repeated subtractions of the number 15, starting with the number 98.

$$
\begin{array}{rl}
98 & \\
-15 \underline{\qquad\qquad} 1 & \\
\hline
83 & \qquad 98 = (15 \times 1) + 83 \\
-15 \underline{\qquad\qquad} 1 & \\
\hline
68 & \qquad 98 = (15 \times 2) + 68 \\
-15 \underline{\qquad\qquad} 1 & \\
\hline
53 & \qquad 98 = (15 \times 3) + 53 \\
-15 \underline{\qquad\qquad} 1 & \\
\hline
38 & \qquad 98 = (15 \times 4) + 38 \\
-15 \underline{\qquad\qquad} 1 & \\
\hline
23 & \qquad 98 = (15 \times 5) + 23 \\
-15 \underline{\qquad\qquad} 1 & \\
\hline
8 & \qquad 98 = (15 \times 6) + 8.
\end{array}
$$

This, of course, is the *repeated subtraction* process for division.

Instead of doing this repeated subtraction of the number 15, we might try to see how great a multiple of 15 we could subtract from 98.

If we guess 7, we find that $7 \times 15 = 105$ and we cannot subtract 105 from 98. If we guess 5, we have $5 \times 15 = 75$

$$
\begin{aligned}
98 &= 75 + 23 \\
&= (15 \times 5) + 23.
\end{aligned}
$$

But $23 > 15$ so we can write

$$
\begin{aligned}
98 &= (15 \times 5) + [(15 \times 1) + 8] \\
&= [(15 \times 5) + (15 \times 1)] + 8 \\
&= (15 \times 6) + 8.
\end{aligned}
$$

This form of the division algorithm may look unfamiliar to you. The vertical form as shown below may be more familiar.

$$
\begin{array}{r}
6 \\
15 \overline{)\ 98} \\
\underline{90} \leftarrow (15 \times 6) \qquad 98 = (15 \times 6) + 8 \\
8
\end{array}
$$

Let us consider the division indicated by $4387 \div 32$. What multiple of 32 can be subtracted from 4387? The answer is any multiple that is not greater than 4387. We usually consider first the products that have 10, 100, or 1000, and so on, as factors because their products can be found easily. First we see that 32×100 equals 3200, which is less than 4387. Hence, 32×100 can be subtracted from 4387, the result being 1187. Can 32×100 be subtracted again? Obviously, it can not, since 3200 is greater than 1187. Next we use the products 32×10 and 32×1. We subtract 32×10 as many times as possible before proceeding to 32×1.

$$
\begin{array}{r|l}
32\overline{)\ 4387} & \\
3200 & 32 \times 100 \\
\hline
1187 & \\
320 & 32 \times 10 \\
\hline
867 & \\
320 & 32 \times 10 \\
\hline
547 & \\
320 & 32 \times 10 \\
\hline
227 & \\
32 & 32 \times 1 \\
\hline
195 & \\
32 & 32 \times 1 \\
\hline
163 & \\
32 & 32 \times 1 \\
\hline
131 & \\
32 & 32 \times 1 \\
\hline
99 & \\
32 & 32 \times 1 \\
\hline
67 & \\
32 & 32 \times 1 \\
\hline
35 & \\
32 & 32 \times 1 \\
\hline
3 & \overline{32 \times 137}
\end{array}
$$

Thus,

$$
\begin{aligned}
4387 &= [\,(32 \times 100) + (32 \times 10) + (32 \times 10) + (32 \times 10) + (32 \times 1) + \\
&\quad (32 \times 1) + (32 \times 1) + (32 \times 1) + (32 \times 1) + (32 \times 1) + (32 \times 1)\,] + 3 \\
&= 32 \times [\,100 + 10 + 10 + 10 + 1 + 1 + 1 + 1 + 1 + 1 + 1\,] + 3 \\
&= (32 \times 137) + 3.
\end{aligned}
$$

Let us do the same example in a more familiar form.

$$32\overline{\smash{\big)}4387}$$

We see that $32 \times 1000 = 32{,}000$ is too great a multiple and that 32×100, which is 3200, is the best basic multiple to use. What is the greatest multiple of 3200 which can be subtracted from 4387? Notice that

$$1 \times 3200 = 3200,$$
$$2 \times 3200 = 6400.$$

We see that 6400 is too great; therefore, the greatest multiple of 3200 we can subtract from 4387 is (1×3200) with the remainder 1187.

$$
\begin{array}{r}
1 \\
32\overline{\smash{\big)}4387} \\
3200 = 32 \times 100 \qquad 4387 = (32 \times 100) + 1187 \\
\hline
1187
\end{array}
$$

The next basic multiple is $32 \times 10 = 320$. Now,

$$1 \times 320 = 320,$$
$$2 \times 320 = 640,$$
$$3 \times 320 = 960,$$
$$4 \times 320 = 1280.$$

The greatest multiple of 320 we can subtract from 1187 is 3×320. The remainder is 227.

$$
\begin{array}{r}
13 \\
32\overline{\smash{\big)}4387} \\
3200 \\
\hline
1187 \\
960 = 32 \times 30 \qquad 1187 = (32 \times 30) + 227 \\
\hline
227
\end{array}
$$

Now,

$$1 \times 32 = 32,$$
$$2 \times 32 = 64,$$
$$3 \times 32 = 96,$$
$$4 \times 32 = 128,$$
$$5 \times 32 = 160,$$
$$6 \times 32 = 192,$$
$$7 \times 32 = 224,$$
$$8 \times 32 = 256.$$

The greatest multiple of 32 we can subtract from 227 is $7 \times 32 = 224$.

```
        137
32/ 4387
     3200
     ‾‾‾‾
     1187
      960
      ‾‾‾
      227
      224 = 32 × 7
      ‾‾‾
        3              227 = (32 × 7) + 3
```

The remainder is 3, which is less than 32. The quotient is

$$100 + 30 + 7 = 137.$$

Thus,

$$4387 = (137 \times 32) + 3.$$

In the familiar division form we have the following:

```
        137
32/ 4387
     3200 = 32 × 100
     ‾‾‾‾
     1187                    4287 = (32 × 100) + 1187
      960 = 32 × 30
      ‾‾‾
      227                    4287 = (32 × 100) + (32 × 30) + 227
      224 = 32 × 7
      ‾‾‾
        3                    4287 = (32 × 100) + (32 × 30) + (32 × 7) + 3.
```

So, $4387 = (32 \times 100) + 1187$
$= (32 \times 100) + [(32 \times 30) + 227]$
$= [(32 \times 100) + (32 \times 30)] + 227$ Associative property
$= [32 \times (100 + 30)] + 227$ Distributive property
$= (32 \times 130) + 227$
$= (32 \times 130) + [(32 \times 7) + 3]$
$= [(32 \times 130) + (32 \times 7)] + 3$ Associative property
$= [32 \times (130 + 7)] + 3$ Distributive property
$= (32 \times 137) + 3.$

In teaching the division algorithm, developing the idea of the basic multiple is most important and gives meaning to the position of digits in the quotient.

We now look at our division problem worked in the usual form and we break it down into parts to see how each step of the computation involves basic multiples. The quotient is computed first because the explanation involves working backward. One would not ordinarily give children this explanation, but it is done here to illuminate what is actually happening in the familiar form of the division algorithm.

$$
\begin{array}{r}
137 \\
32\overline{)4387} \\
3200 \\
\hline
1187 \\
960 \\
\hline
227 \\
224 \\
\hline
3
\end{array}
$$

Notice that

$$
\begin{aligned}
4387 &= 3200 + 960 + 224 + 3 \\
&= (32 \times 100) + (32 \times 30) + (32 \times 7) + 3 \\
&= [\,(100 + 30 + 7) \times 32\,] + 3 \\
&= (137 \times 32) + 3.
\end{aligned}
$$

As stated earlier, division is a difficult algorithm to understand. In teaching this algorithm, it is helpful always to write the result of a division in the form $a = (b \times q) + r$. For example, in the problem $74 \div 8$ we can write the computation in the usual way,

$$
\begin{array}{r}
9 \\
8\overline{)74} \\
72 \\
\hline
2
\end{array}
$$

and then rewrite the result:

$$
74 = (8 \times 9) + 2.
$$

To prepare children for division by larger numbers, time is needed for working with multiples of 10, 100, and 1000, so that the placing of the numeral in the quotient does not involve mere guessing, but rather an understanding of the particular basic multiple being used in each step of the computation. Emphasis on estimation of products, to develop judgment as to whether or not the solution is a reasonable one, is also important in the teaching of long division.

To see how confusing the use of long division with base-ten numerals can seem to the learner, try the algorithm using numerals in another base, for example, base-four numerals.

Exercise Set 4

Fill in the blanks in Table VI.

TABLE VI

Ordered Pair (a, b)	$a = (b \times q) + r$	q	r
1. (18, 7)	$18 = (7 \times 2) + 4$		
2. (29, 9)			
3. (59, 12)			
4. (127, 23)			
5. (300, 25)			

6. What is the greatest multiple of 48 that can be subtracted from 9835?
7. What is the greatest multiple of 96 that can be subtracted from 12,307?

ANSWERS TO EXERCISE SETS

Exercise Set 1

1. Associative property of addition
2. Commutative property of addition
3. Commutative property of addition

4. 113_{four}
5. 120_{four}
6. 200_{four}

Exercise Set 2

1. 11_{four}
2. 13_{four}
3. 113_{four}

4. 11_{four}
5. 101_{four}

Exercise Set 3

1. Identity for multiplication
2. Distributive property
3. Basic sums
4. Commutative property of multiplication
5. Identity of multiplication
6. Distributive property
7. Basic sums
8. Identity for multiplication
9. Distributive property
10. Basic sums
11. Commutative property of multiplication

12. Commutative property of multiplication
13. Associative property of multiplication
14. Commutative property of multiplication
15. Commutative property of multiplication
16. Distributive property
17. Commutative property of addition

Exercise Set 4

1. $2, 4$
2. $29 = (9 \times 3) + 2,$ $3, 2$
3. $59 = (12 \times 4) + 11$ $4, 11$
4. $127 = (23 \times 5) + 12$ $5, 12$
5. $300 = (25 \times 12) + 0$ $12, 0$
6. $204 \times 48 = 9792$
7. $128 \times 96 = 12,288$

BOOKLET NUMBER FIVE:

NUMBERS AND THEIR FACTORS

INTRODUCTORY REMARKS

When a fire drill is signaled, each pupil marches out with a partner. Miss Smith, who has thirty-two pupils, notes immediately, without counting, that at least one of her pupils is missing. How does she know?

Instructions for arranging pupils for class pictures read: "Arrange your pupils in rows, with the same number in each row and at least two in each row. Make rows as short as possible." If the enrollments in various rooms in the school range from 27 to 38, inclusive, will the largest class have the longest rows? Why?

If a new pupil were added to one of the classes, might shorter rows be possible? Under what circumstances would this be the case?

Is there a quick way to tell whether or not the number 5,678,901,234 is divisible by three? Suppose the digits were rearranged: 5,768,901,324. If one of the numbers is divisible by three, is the other one also?

The answers to the foregoing questions are related to certain properties of the counting numbers. In the following pages, these and other properties will be explored.

This booklet deals primarily with factorization of counting numbers (that is, expressing counting numbers as products of counting numbers) and topics related to it. The set of whole numbers, W, as you recall from Booklet No. 2: *The Whole Numbers*, is the set:

$$W = \{0, 1, 2, 3, 4, \ldots\}.$$

Note that W is the union of the set of counting numbers

$$\{1, 2, 3, 4, \ldots\}$$

with the set

$$\{0\}.$$

For the sake of review, some of the properties of the whole numbers are illustrated here by examples:

$3+6=6+3$ (Commutative property of addition)

167

$4 \times 11 = 11 \times 4$	(Commutative property of multiplication)
$(2+5) + 43 = 2 + (5+43)$	(Associative property of addition)
$(4 \times 8) \times 12 = 4 \times (8 \times 12)$	(Associative property of multiplication)
$3 \times (12+7) = (3 \times 12) + (3 \times 7)$	(Distributive property of multiplication over addition)
$5+0 = 0+5 = 5$	(Identity element for addition)
$8 \times 1 = 1 \times 8 = 8$	(Identity element for multiplication)
$0 \times 7 = 7 \times 0 = 0$	(Property of multiplication by zero)

The set of whole numbers, W, can be expressed as the union of disjoint subsets in many different ways. Recall that two nonempty sets are disjoint if they have no members in common.
If

$A = \{$all whole numbers less than 80$\}$,

and

$B = \{$all whole numbers greater than or equal to 80$\}$;

then

$W = A \cup B$.

Every whole number is a member of either A or B, but not both. Let us consider next an important pair of disjoint subsets of W, the even numbers and the odd numbers.

EVEN NUMBERS AND ODD NUMBERS

A whole number that is the product of the number 2 and a whole number is called an *even number*. To obtain the even numbers, first multiply 2 by 0, then by 1, then by 2, then by 3, 4, 5, etc. The first five even numbers are

$$0 = 2 \times 0,$$
$$2 = 2 \times 1,$$
$$4 = 2 \times 2,$$
$$6 = 2 \times 3,$$
$$8 = 2 \times 4.$$

If n is any whole number, then $(2 \times n)$ is an even number.

Even numbers can also be defined, alternatively, in terms of division by 2, as follows:

A whole number is an even number if, when the number is divided by 2, the remainder is 0. We say, in this instance, that the original number is divisible by 2. For example, 18 is divisible by 2, and 95 is divisible by 5.

If E denotes the set of all even numbers, we can write,

$$E = \{0, 2, 4, 6, \ldots\}.$$

When a whole number is divided by 2, the remainder is either 0 or 1. As we have agreed, the number is even if the remainder is 0. If the remainder is 1, we call the original number an *odd number*. The number 29 is odd, for when 29 is divided by 2 the resulting quotient is 14 with remainder 1. The numbers 1, 3, 5, 7, 9, and 11 are the first six odd numbers.

If we examine the following true sentences,

$$1 = (2 \times 0) + 1$$
$$3 = (2 \times 1) + 1$$
$$5 = (2 \times 2) + 1$$
$$7 = (2 \times 3) + 1$$
$$9 = (2 \times 4) + 1,$$

we see that each of the numbers 1, 3, 5, 7, and 9 is expressed as the sum of an even number and the number 1. Any odd number, in fact, can be expressed in the form,

$$(2 \times \text{a whole number}) + 1.$$

We have seen that $(2 \times n)$ is an even number, where n is any whole number. We now see, that

$$(2 \times n) + 1 \text{ is an odd number.}$$

If F represents the set of odd numbers, we can write,

$$F = \{1, 3, 5, 7, 9, \ldots\}.$$

Since every whole number is either even or odd, but not both, the set of even numbers and the set of odd numbers are disjoint sets whose union is the set of whole numbers:

$$W = E \cup F.$$

Properties of Even Numbers and Odd Numbers

Previous work with even numbers and odd numbers has probably convinced you of the following:

1. The sum of two even numbers is an even number.
2. The product of two even numbers is an even number.

For example, choose the numbers 8 and 14:

$$8+14=22 \qquad \text{(22 is an even number)},$$
$$8 \times 14 = 112 \qquad \text{(112 is an even number)}.$$

How can we show conclusively that given *any* two even numbers, their sum is an even number? Let the two even numbers be $2 \times k$ and $2 \times m$, where k and m are whole numbers (k and m might be the same whole number, or they might not). We want to show that $(2 \times k) + (2 \times m)$ is an even number. By the distributive property,

$$(2 \times k) + (2 \times m) = 2 \times (k+m).$$

Since $(k+m)$ is a whole number, $[2 \times (k+m)]$, the product of 2 and a whole number, is an even number. (Why?) The fact that the sum of any two even numbers is an even number is expressed by saying, that the set of even numbers, E, is *closed under addition*.

Now let us show that the product of any two even numbers is an even number. This time, let the two even numbers be $2 \times r$ and $2 \times s$, where r and s are whole numbers. Is $(2 \times r) \times (2 \times s)$ an even number? By the associative property of multiplication, we have

$$(2 \times r) \times (2 \times s) = 2 \times [r \times (2 \times s)].$$

Now, $r \times (2 \times s)$, the product of two whole numbers, is a whole number. Hence $2 \times [r \times (2 \times s)]$ is two times a whole number and therefore is an even number. Thus, E is also *closed under multiplication*.

The set F of odd numbers is not closed under addition; in fact, the sum of any two odd numbers is an even number. The set F is closed under multiplication; that is, the product of any two odd numbers is an odd number.

It can also be shown that the sum of an even number and an odd number is in every case an odd number, and that the product of an even number and an odd number is always an even number.

Tables I and II summarize symbolically the various facts we have noted about sums and products of even and odd numbers.

Since addition and multiplication are commutative, each table would

TABLE I

+	even	odd
even	even	odd
odd	(odd)	even

TABLE II

×	even	odd
even	even	even
odd	(even)	odd

need to have only three entries instead of four. The circled entry in each table is superfluous.

Exercise Set 1

1. (a) Write the set of even numbers that are greater than 10 but less than 30.
   (b) Write the set of odd numbers that are greater than 81 but less than 87.

2. (a) Which of the following numbers are multiples of 2? 11,   29, 402,   1001.
   (b) Which of the numbers in part (a) of this exercise are odd numbers?

3. Express each of the following even numbers in the form $(2 \times n)$.
   (a) 36   (c) 328
   (b) 142   (d) 1000

4. Express each of the following odd numbers in the form $(2 \times n) + 1$.
   (a) 17   (c) 121
   (b) 39   (d) 1363

5. Which of the following numbers are divisible by 2? by 3? by 5?
   (a) 8   (d) 30
   (b) 12   (e) 49
   (c) 25

6. When a whole number is divided by 3, the remainder is 0, 1, or 2. Let A, B, and C be the sets of whole numbers for which the remainders, after division by 3, are 0, 1, and 2, respectively. Then the first four members of A are 0, 3, 6, and 9.
   (a) What are the first four members of B?
   (b) What are the first four members of C?
   (c) Are the sets A, B, and C disjoint sets?
   (d) Is $A \cup B \cup C = W$ (the set of whole numbers)?
   (e) Verify, by using numerical examples, that the sum of a member of B and a member of C is a member of A.

7. Show that the sum of any even number and any odd number is an odd number. Let the even number be $(2 \times n)$ and the odd number $(2 \times k) + 1$.

8. Show that the sum of any two odd numbers is an even number.

9. Show that the product of any even number and any odd number is an even number.

FACTORS AND MULTIPLES

The *multiples* of a counting number are obtained by multiplying it by 1, 2, 3, 4, and so on. Naming the multiples of a counting number in increasing order is the same as "counting" by that number. Thus the multiples of 3 are

$$3, 6, 9, 12, \ldots;$$

and the multiples of 7 are

$$7, 14, 21, 28, \ldots.$$

In general,

> *if* n *is a counting number and* k *is a counting number, then* (k×n) *is called a multiple of* n.

The product expression "5×6" is a name for the number 30. The numbers 5 and 6 are said to be *factors* of the number 30. Saying that 5 is a factor of 30 is the same as saying that 30 is a multiple of 5. Is 2 a factor of 30? Yes, because 30 is the product 15×2 and is, therefore, a multiple of 2. The numbers 1, 3, 10, 15, and 30 are also factors of 30.

What are the factors of 25? The numbers 2, 3, and 4 are not factors, since 25 is not a multiple of any of these. But 5 is a factor, since 5×5=25. The only other factors of 25 are 1 and 25. Notice that any counting number has itself and one as factors. We restrict our attention, of course, to factors that are counting numbers.

The definition of factor can be formalized as follows:

> *A counting number*, f, *is called a factor of a counting number*, n, *if* n *is a multiple of* f, *that is, if* n *is divisible by* f.

Examining the list of factors of a counting number enables us to find product expressions for the number. The number 12 has the following factors: 1, 2, 3, 4, 6, 12. From this list, various product expressions can be formed, not all involving the same number of factors. The following are all product expressions for 12:

$$1 \times 12$$
$$2 \times 6$$
$$3 \times 4$$
$$1 \times 2 \times 6$$
$$1 \times 3 \times 4$$
$$2 \times 2 \times 3$$
$$1 \times 2 \times 2 \times 3.$$

In fact, this list includes all of the product expressions that are essentially different, except that of course the factor 1 could be repeated any number of times. To be sure, other expressions can be obtained by rearranging the factors in the given expressions. For example, the factors in $1 \times 3 \times 4$ can be rearranged to give us $1 \times 4 \times 3$, or $3 \times 1 \times 4$, or $4 \times 3 \times 1$; all of these, however, will be regarded as being essentially the same, in the sense that each of them gives us the same set of factors.

It is interesting to note that in order to write all possible product expressions involving exactly two factors for a counting number, it is only necessary to list all of the factors of the number in increasing order, and then to pair the first factor with the last one, the second factor with the second from the last, and so on. To illustrate this, let us find all possible two-factor product expressions for the number 105. The factors of 105, listed in increasing order, and the pairing of factors are given in Figure 1.

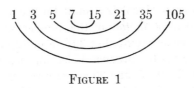

FIGURE 1

The desired product expressions for 105 are

$$1 \times 105, \quad 3 \times 35, \quad 5 \times 21, \quad 7 \times 15.$$

Exercise Set 2

1. List all of the factors of each of the following numbers.

(a) 14   (b) 19   (c) 42   (d) 36   (e) 16

2. Write three essentially different product expressions for each of the following numbers.

(a) 18   (b) 24   (c) 50   (d) 27

3. Find all possible product expressions involving only two factors for each of the following numbers.

(a) 8   (b) 18   (c) 100

PRIME NUMBERS AND COMPOSITE NUMBERS

We have seen that any whole number is either an even number or an odd number, but not both. In other words, the set of even numbers and the set of odd numbers are disjoint sets whose union is the set of all whole numbers, W.

Now we shall focus our attention on a decomposition of W into four disjoint sets. One of these sets will have 1 as its only member, and another set will have 0 as its only member. In order to describe the other two sets, it is necessary to give some definitions.

First consider these sets:

$A = \{x\}$　　　$B = \{x\,x\,x\,x\,x\,x\}$　　　$C = \{x\,x\,x\,x\,x\,x\,x\}$
$D = \{x\,x\,x\,x\,x\,x\,x\,x\,x\,x\,x\,x\,x\,x\,x\}$　　　$E = \{x\,x\,x\,x\,x\,x\,x\,x\,x\,x\,x\,x\}$

We wish to arrange the elements of each set in rows, with the same number of elements in each row. In how many ways can we do this?

A:　　　　.

　　　1 by 1

B:　　　. . .　　　　　　. .　　　　　　. . . . . .　　　　　.

　　　. . .　　　　　　. .　　　　　　1 by 6　　　　　.

　　　2 by 3　　　　　. .　　　　　　　　　　　　　　.

　　　　　　　　　3 by 2　　　　　　　　　　　　　　.

　　　　　　　　　　　　　　　　　　　　　　　　　.

　　　　　　　　　　　　　　　　　　　　　　　　　6 by 1

C:　　　　. . . . . . .　　　　　.

　　　　　1 by 7　　　　　　　.

　　　　　　　　　　　　　　　.

　　　　　　　　　　　　　　　.

　　　　　　　　　　　　　　　.

　　　　　　　　　　　　　　　.

　　　　　　　　　　　　　　　.

　　　　　　　　　　　7 by 1

D: . . . . .　　. . .　　. . . . .

　　　. . . . .　　. . .　　1 by 15　　　　　　.

　　　. . . . .　　. . .　　　　　　　　　　.

　　　3 by 5　　　. . .　　　　　　　　　　.

　　　　　　　. . .　　　　　　　　　　.

　　　　　5 by 3　　　　　　　　　　　.

　　　　　　　　　　　　　　　　　.

　　　　　　　　　　　　　　　　　.

　　　　　　　　　　　　　　　　　.

　　　　　　　　　　　　　　　　　.

　　　　　　　　　　　　　　　　　.

　　　　　　　　　　　　　　　　　.

　　　　　　　　　　　　　　　　　.

　　　　　　　　　　　　　　　　　.

　　　　　　　　　　　　　　　　15 by 1

E: . . . .

       1 by 11   .

                                    .

                                    .

                                    .

                                    .

                                    .

                                    .

                                    .

                                    .

                                    .

                         11 by 1

What do these arrays suggest about the set of factors of each of the numbers associated with these sets?

Recall that every counting number greater than 1 has itself and the number 1 as factors. The number 7 has only 7 and 1 as factors; whereas the number 15 has factors other than 15 and 1, namely, 5 and 3. In the preceding paragraph we saw that for the set C associated with 7, the 7 by 1 array and the 1 by 7 array were the only possible arrays; whereas for the set D associated with 15, there were arrays other than 1 by 15 and 15 by 1.

We have a special interest in these counting numbers, greater than 1, that have only themselves and 1 as factors. The numbers 2, 5, 11, and 19 are such numbers, and we call them *prime numbers*, or *primes*. The numbers 6, 10, and 25 are not primes; for $6=2\times3$, $10=2\times5$, and $25=5\times5$. A prime number, or prime, then, is defined to be a *counting number greater than 1 that has only itself and 1 as factors*. We emphasize that, although the only factor of 1 is 1, by the above definition the number 1 is not a prime number.

Counting numbers greater than 1 that are not prime numbers are called *composite numbers*. These are numbers, such as 6 and 25, that do have factors other than themselves and 1.

Composite numbers are in a sense "composed" or "built" of prime numbers as factors.

$$6=2\times3$$
$$25=5\times5$$

The prime numbers 2 and 3 are used as factors to build the number 6. The prime number 5 is used as a factor twice to build the number 25.

The set of whole numbers, therefore, is the union of the following four disjoint sets:

1. The set having 0 as its only member,
2. The set having 1 as its only member,
3. The set of prime numbers,
4. The set of composite numbers.

The Sieve of Eratosthenes

A scheme for finding the prime numbers, or primes, among the counting numbers from 1 to 50 inclusive is shown in Figure 2. The scheme, called a sieve, is named after the Greek mathematician, Eratosthenes.

~~1~~	2	3	~~4~~	5	~~6~~	7	~~8~~	~~9~~	~~10~~
11	~~12~~	13	~~14~~	~~15~~	~~16~~	17	~~18~~	19	~~20~~
~~21~~	~~22~~	23	~~24~~	~~25~~	~~26~~	~~27~~	~~28~~	29	~~30~~
31	~~32~~	~~33~~	~~34~~	~~35~~	~~36~~	37	~~38~~	~~39~~	~~40~~
41	~~42~~	43	~~44~~	~~45~~	~~46~~	47	~~48~~	~~49~~	~~50~~

FIGURE 2

The object is to strike out all those numbers that are not primes. The number 1 is not a prime, so we strike it out. The next number we encounter in the list is the prime number 2. All numbers greater than 2 having 2 as a factor are struck out. These are multiples of 2. As we start the next strike-out process the prime number 3 is encountered first, we cross out all numbers greater than 3 that are divisible by 3 (some of these were crossed out on the first trip). These are multiples of 3. The next time, the prime number 5 appears first; and we cross out all numbers greater than 5 that are divisible by 5 (actually all but 25 and 35 were already crossed out). Now the number 7 appears first, and all numbers greater than 7 and divisible by 7 are crossed out (49 is the only multiple of 7 that was not already crossed out). The numbers that are left, 2, 3, 5, 7, 11, 13, 17, 19, 23, 29, 31, 37, 41, 43, and 47, are the prime numbers between 1 and 50.

You may wonder why we could stop the repetitive crossing-out process with the number 7. Why did we not repeat it with the next prime, 11? The reason is this: Any composite number less than or equal to 50, having 11 as a factor, must have a prime factor that is smaller than 11. (Why?) This means that this composite number would already have been struck out when this smaller prime was used.

Exercise Set 3

1. Construct a sieve like the one in Figure 2 for the counting numbers from 1 to 100, inclusive.
2. Explain why 2 is the only even prime number.
3. The number 385 is the product of three prime factors. What are these factors?
4. Why is it impossible for the sum of two odd prime numbers to be a prime number?

DIVISIBILITY TESTS

Is 1071 divisible by 9? This question can be answered by dividing 1071 by 9, using the division algorithm.

$$
\begin{array}{r}
119 \\
9\overline{)1071} \\
900 \\
\hline
17 \\
90 \\
\hline
81 \\
81 \\
\hline
0 \longrightarrow
\end{array}
$$

Since the remainder is zero, 1071 is divisible by 9.

Since long division can be a tedious chore, the development of tests for divisibility by certain counting numbers as a substitute for long division would perhaps seem to be desirable.

The divisibility tests to be presented here depend directly on our base-ten system of notation. On the other hand, the answer to the question, "Is 27 divisible by 9?", does not depend on the numeration system used. The answer is "yes," if the numbers 27 and 9 are represented by the numerals 27_{ten} and 9_{ten} in the base-ten system, the numerals 102_{five} and 14_{five} in the base-five system, or by numerals in any place-value system. The tests for divisibility, however, are applied to numerals, and so they depend on the system of numeration used.

The justification of these tests (that is, the reason why they work) depends on a rather basic fact concerning the divisibility of a sum of two numbers by a number. Suppose that we ask, "Is the number named by $24+60$ divisible by 6?" The answer is "yes"; and our reasoning is as follows:

$$
\begin{aligned}
24+60 &= (6 \times 4) + (6 \times 10) \\
&= 6 \times (4+10)
\end{aligned}
$$

(Distributive property)

Thus $24 + 60$ is divisible by 6, because 24 and 60 are both divisible by 6.

Is the sum $(35 + 19)$ divisible by 5?

The answer would be yes, provided there were a counting number n such that $19 = 5 \times n$, for then we could write:

$$35 + 19 = (5 \times 7) + (5 \times n)$$
$$= 5 \times (7 + n),$$

and $(35 + 19)$ would be a multiple of 5. There is, however, no counting number n such that $5 \times n$ is equal to 19. Therefore, $(35 + 19)$ is not divisible by 5.

Consider two more examples:

$11 + 18$ is not divisible by 3; $(29 \div 3$ is not a whole number).
$14 + 35$ is divisible by 7; $(49 \div 7 = 7)$.

In the first example, one of the addends is divisible by 3, the other is not, and the sum is not. In the second example, each addend is divisible by 7, and the sum of the addends is also divisible by 7.

What we have observed in these examples can be verbalized as follows: If one addend in the sum of two addends is divisible by a number, c, then the sum is divisible by c if, and only if, the other addend in the sum is divisible by c. This can be stated more concisely using letters:

Let a be divisible by c. Then, $a + b$ is divisible by c if, and only if, b is divisible by c.*

For convenience, we shall refer to this as the *property of the divisibility of a sum.*

Divisibility by 2, 5, 10

Even numbers were defined earlier as whole numbers that are divisible by 2. The numerals representing even numbers are easily recognized by inspection. (In this section, numerals are understood to be base-ten numerals.) It is a familiar fact that it is the last digit in the numeral that tells us whether or not the number is divisible by 2. *A number is divisible by 2 if the last digit in its numeral is 0, 2, 4, 6, or 8; otherwise, the number*

---

* Note the requirement that a be divisible by c. If neither a nor b is divisible by c, we can draw no conclusion about the divisibility of the sum $a + b$ by c. For example, $5 + 23$ is divisible by 4, although neither 5 nor 23 is divisible by 4.

is not divisible by 2. Even though this is a very easy test, it is worth-while to examine the basis on which it rests.

Since $10 = 2 \times 5$, 10 is divisible by 2. Similarly, 10×10, or 10^2, is also divisible by 2, because

$$10 \times 10 = (2 \times 5) \times 10$$
$$= 2 \times (5 \times 10)$$
$$= 2 \times 50.$$

In the same way it can be shown that 1000 (or 10^3) is divisible by 2, since $1000 = 2 \times (5 \times 10^2)$. Also 10,000 (or 10^4) equals $2 \times (5 \times 10^3)$ and, hence, is divisible by 2. Any power of 10 is divisible by 2. So is any multiple of a power of 10. For example, since

$$10,000 \ (\text{or } 10^4) = 2 \times (5 \times 10^3),$$

it follows that

$$70,000 = 10,000 \times 7$$
$$= 2 \times (5 \times 10^3) \times 7$$
$$= 2 \times (35 \times 10^3)$$

is divisible by 2.

Now consider the number 7918, which can be expressed as

$$(7000 + 900 + 10) + 8,$$

that is, as the sum of two addends. The first addend, $7000 + 900 + 10$, is divisible by 2 since 7000, 900, and 10 are each divisible by 2. It follows from the property of the divisibility of a sum that 7918 is divisible by 2, because the number named by the last digit, 8, is also divisible by 2.

Divisibility tests for 10 and 5 are justified in a similar way. The statements of these tests follow:

A number is divisible by 10 if, and only if, the last digit in its numeral is 0.

A number is divisible by 5 if, and only if, the last digit in its numeral is 0 or 5.

Divisibility by 3, 9

To test a number for divisibility by 2, 10, or 5, we need only to look at the last digit in its numeral. In the case of the number 3, things are not so easy. Check the following columns of numerals:

10	30
31	21
52	42
13	63

334	24
25	45
106	66
17	117
28	78
149	459

None of the numbers represented in the first column is divisible by 3, in spite of the fact that every possible digit appears as a last digit in a numeral. In the second column each number is divisible by 3, and again every possible digit appears as a last digit in a numeral. The last digit of a numeral, therefore, gives no clue (when considered by itself) as to the divisibility of the number by 3.

The two columns of numbers in the preceding paragraph appear again in Table III; and for each numeral the sum of its digits is shown in a separate column.

Note. When speaking of the sum of the digits of a numeral, we regard the digits as numbers, not symbols. Thus, the sum of the digits in the numeral 256 is $(2+5+6)$, or 13.

TABLE III

Numeral	Sum of Digits	Numeral	Sum of Digits
10	$1+0=1$	30	$3+0=3$
31	$3+1=4$	21	$2+1=3$
52	$5+2=7$	42	$4+2=6$
13	$1+3=4$	63	$6+3=9$
334	$3+3+4=10$	24	$2+4=6$
25	$2+5=7$	45	$4+5=9$
106	$1+0+6=7$	66	$\cdot 6+6=12$
17	$1+7=8$	117	$1+1+7=9$
28	$2+8=10$	78	$7+8=15$
149	$1+4+9=14$	459	$4+5+9=18$

Each numeral in the first column represents a number that is not divisible by 3, and the sum of the digits in the numeral is not divisible by 3. Each numeral in the third column represents a number that is divisible by 3, and the sum of the digits in the numeral is divisible by 3.

The truth of the following statement now seems plausible:

A number is divisible by 3 if the sum of the digits in its base-ten numeral is divisible by 3; otherwise, it is not divisible by 3.

According to this test, the number 7284 is divisible by 3 since $7+2+8+4$, or 21, is divisible by 3; but 18,514 is not divisible by 3 since $1+8+5+1+4$ is 19, which is not divisible by 3.

Let us see why this test works, using 528 as an example.

$$528 = (5 \times 100) + (2 \times 10) + 8$$
$$= [5 \times (99+1)] + [2 \times (9+1)] + 8 \quad (100 = 99+1; 10 = 9+1)$$
$$= [(5 \times 99) + (5 \times 1)] + [(2 \times 9) + (2 \times 1)] + 8 \quad \text{(Distributive property)}$$
$$= [(5 \times 99) + (2 \times 9)] + (5+2+8) \quad \text{(Associative and commutative properties of addition)}$$

Each of the numbers, 2×9 and 5×99, is divisible by 3 because:

$$2 \times 9 = 2 \times (3 \times 3) = (2 \times 3) \times 3$$
$$5 \times 99 = 5 \times (33 \times 3) = (5 \times 33) \times 3.$$

Therefore, the number $(5 \times 99) + (2 \times 9)$, is divisible by 3, by the property of the divisibility of a sum. Now, 528 is the sum of $(5 \times 99) + (2 \times 9)$ and $5+2+8$, the latter being precisely the sum of the digits in the numeral 528. By applying the property of the divisibility of a sum again, we see that the number 528 is divisible by 3 because $5+2+8$, or 15, is divisible by 3.

As a second example, consider the number 2173.

$$2173 = [2 \times (999+1)] + [1 \times (99+1)] + [7 \times (9+1)] + 3.$$

Proceeding as in the first example, you can show that

$$2173 = [(2 \times 999) + (1 \times 99) + (7 \times 9)] + (2+1+7+3).$$

The number $[(2 \times 999) + (1 \times 99) + (7 \times 9)]$ is divisible by 3; but the sum of the digits, $2+1+7+3$, or 13, is not divisible by 3, and hence neither is 2173.

The test for divisibility by 9 is very similar to the one for divisibility by 3. In the first example above, 528 was renamed:

$$528 = [(5 \times 99) + (2 \times 9)] + (5+2+8).$$

Now,

(5×99) is divisible by 9, since $5 \times 99 = 5 \times (11 \times 9)$
$$= (5 \times 11) \times 9;$$

and

(2×9) is also divisible by 9.

Hence,

$[(5 \times 99) + (2 \times 9)]$ is divisible by 9. (Property of the divisibility of a sum)

So,

$[(5 \times 99) + (2 \times 9)] + (5+2+8)$ is divisible by 9 if, and only if, $(5+2+8)$ is divisible by 9.

Of course,

$5+2+8=15$, which is not divisible by 9, and thus 528, also, is not divisible by 9.

A number is divisible by 9 if, and only if, the sum of the digits in its base-ten numeral is divisible by 9.

(It is interesting to note that in the numerals of the first ten multiples of 9:

9,   18,   27,   36,   45,   54,   63,   72,   81,   90,

the sum of the digits is, in each case, 9.) Is the number 218,462 divisible by 9? The sum of the digits, $2+1+8+4+6+2$, is 23. Since $2+3=5$, 23 is not divisible by 9, and hence, neither is 218,462.

It is worth noting that if a counting number, n, is divisible by a counting number, d, then it is divisible by any factor of d. For example, if n is divisible by 6, then it is also divisible by 2, and likewise by 3.

In order to help convince ourselves that this last statement is true, let us take n to be 516. The product expression, 6×86, is a name for 516. The product expression, 6×86, can be rewritten as $2 \times 3 \times 86$, and also as

$2 \times (3 \times 86)$, and as $3 \times (2 \times 86)$.

These last two expressions show that 516 is divisible by 2, and also by 3. Similarly, if a number is divisible by 15, it is also divisible by 3 and by 5. Since 2400 is divisible by 24, it is divisible by each of the following factors of 24:

2, 3, 4, 6, 12.

Exercise Set 4

1. Which of the numbers 415; 283; 2544; 1,000,011; 246,312 are divisible by the following?

   (a) 2   (b) 3   (c) 5   (d) 9

2. Which of the following numbers are divisible by 7?

   (a) $(7 \times 9167) + 12$ (c) $(7 \times 6 \times 5) + 1$
   (b) $(7 \times 48) + (7 \times 13)$ (d) $(7 \times 1000) + (7 \times 200) + 14$

3. What is the remainder when the number $(2 \times 3 \times 5) + 1$, or 31, is divided by each of the following?

(a) 2   (b) 3   (c) 5

4. Find the smallest number that yields the remainder 1 when it is divided by any one of the numbers 3, 5, and 7.

Divisibility Tests for Other Systems of Numeration

The divisibility tests developed in the preceding section depend directly on the numeration system used, namely, the base-ten place-value system. Note that in the statement of each test the words "digits" and "numeral" play an essential role. The dependence of divisibility tests on the numeration system used is made even more conspicuous by considering numerals in place-value systems with bases other than ten.

Place-value systems with bases five, six, and twelve will be used. Table IV (read from right-to-left) recalls for you the place values assigned to the first four positions in the numeral, in the base-five, base-six, and base-twelve systems. (See Booklet No. 3: *Systems of Numeration for the Whole Numbers.*)

TABLE IV

Place Value				Base
five^3	five^2	five^1	five^0 or one	five
six^3	six^2	six^1	six^0 or one	six
twelve^3	twelve^2	twelve^1	twelve^0 or one	twelve

The numerals for the counting numbers from one through twenty, in the base-ten, base-five, base-six, and base-twelve systems are shown in Table V.

Examination of Table V leads one to make the following observations:

1. A base-six numeral names an even number (a number that is divisible by two) if, and only if, the last digit in the numeral represents an even number. The same thing can be said about base-twelve numerals and about base-ten numerals. Divisibility by two in the base-six and base-twelve systems is tested in the same way as in the base-ten system; that is, by seeing whether the last digit in the numeral represents an even number.

TABLE V

Number	Base-Ten Numeral	Base-Five Numeral	Base-Six Numeral	Base-Twelve Numeral
one	1	1	1	1
two	2	2	2	2
three	3	3	3	3
four	4	4	4	4
five	5	10	5	5
six	6	11	10	6
seven	7	12	11	7
eight	8	13	12	8
nine	9	14	13	9
ten	10	20	14	T
eleven	11	21	15	E
twelve	12	22	20	10
thirteen	13	23	21	11
fourteen	14	24	22	12
fifteen	15	30	23	13
sixteen	16	31	24	14
seventeen	17	32	25	15
eighteen	18	33	30	16
nineteen	19	34	31	17
twenty	20	40	32	18

2. In the base-five system there is no similar test for divisibility by two. The numerals 13_{five} and 22_{five} both name even numbers, namely, eight and twelve; the last digit in one numeral represents an odd number, and in the other an even number. In Exercise Set 5, a test for divisibility by two for the base-five system is suggested.

You will find it is quite different from the one that is used in our base-ten system.

3. The test for divisibility by three in the base-ten system, which involved the sum of the digits in the numeral, cannot be used to test for divisibility by three in the base-five, base-six, and base-twelve systems. The numerals for the number twelve, for example, are

$$22_{\text{five}}, \quad 20_{\text{six}}, \quad \text{and} \quad 10_{\text{twelve}}.$$

Twelve is divisible by three, but in none of these three numerals for twelve is the sum of the digits divisible by three.

A systematic development of divisibility tests for these various place-value systems is not intended here. It is profitable, however, to discuss a few of the easier tests.

In the base-twelve system, divisibility of a number by 2, 3, 4, or 6 is tested by looking at the last digit in the numeral. If the number represented by this digit is divisible by 2, then the original number is divisible by 2, otherwise not. If the number represented by this digit is divisible by 3, then the original number is divisible by 3, otherwise not. The same kind of statement holds true for divisibility by 4 and by 6. The basis for these tests is the fact that 2, 3, 4, and 6 are factors of twelve.

Is the number 698_{twelve} divisible by 4?

$$698_{\text{twelve}} = (6 \times \text{twelve}^2) + (9 \times \text{twelve}) + 8$$

The number $(9 \times \text{twelve})$ is divisible by 4 and so is $(6 \times \text{twelve}^2)$. Therefore, $[(6 \times \text{twelve}^2) + (9 \times \text{twelve})]$ is divisible by 4 and, since 8 is also divisible by 4, the number 698_{twelve} is divisible by 4.

Is the number, $T7_{\text{twelve}}$, divisible by 3?

$$T7_{\text{twelve}} = (\text{ten} \times \text{twelve}) + 7$$

Here, $(\text{ten} \times \text{twelve})$ is divisible by 3, but 7 is not divisible by 3; so $T7_{\text{twelve}}$ is not divisible by 3 because 7 is not.

In the base-six system, there is a test for divisibility by 5 that is entirely similar to the test for divisibility by 9 in our base-ten system. Table VI shows the base-six numerals for seven numbers, each of which is divisible by 5. What do you notice about the sum of the digits * in each numeral? In each case the sum is divisible by 5. It can be shown that a number is divisible by 5 if, and only if, the sum of the digits in its base-six numeral is divisible by 5.

---

*Here the word "digits" is used instead of the phrase, "numbers named by the digits."

TABLE VI

Number	Base-Six Numeral
fifteen	23
twenty	32
thirty-five	55
forty	104
sixty-five	145
one hundred	244
one hundred fifty-five	415

Exercise Set 5

1. Examine the base-five numerals for the even numbers from two through twenty (see Table V, page 18). Find the sum of the digits for each numeral. Now do the same for the numerals which name the odd numbers from one through nineteen. Can you find a test for divisibility by two for a base-five system?

2. We have seen that a number is divisible by nine if the sum of the digits in its base-ten numeral is divisible by nine, and that a number is divisible by five if the sum of the digits in its base-six numeral is divisible by five. Give a similar test for divisibility by four in a base-five system. See if your test works by trying it out on the base-five numerals for the following numbers:

   four; eight; twelve; sixteen; twenty; fifty-two (202_{five}) ; twenty-four (44_{five}) ; one hundred eighty-four (1214_{five}) ; nine; eleven; seventeen.

3. There is a divisibility test in the base-twelve system of numeration that is like the tests in Exercise 2 above. This is a test for divisibility by what number? Try this test on the following numerals.

   29_{twelve} (names thirty-three)
   38_{twelve} (names forty-four)
   40_{twelve} (names forty-eight)
   146_{twelve} (names one hundred ninety-eight)

WRITING A NUMBER AS A PRODUCT OF PRIME NUMBERS

Recall that a counting number greater than 1 is either a prime number. or a composite number. A prime can be expressed as a product of counting numbers in only one way, namely, as the product of itself and one. (It is assumed here that the number 1 is written as a factor only once.) A composite number, on the other hand, has more than one product expression. For example, the number 15 can be written as (3×5) and as (1×15).

The numbers 3 and 5, as you know, are called factors of 15; and the product expression 3×5 is called a *factored form* of 15. From now on we shall not ordinarily be interested in factored forms, such as 1×15, that involve 1 as a factor. In other words, when we talk about writing a number in factored form we mean writing it as a product of counting numbers that are greater than one. The following are factored forms of the number 12: $2 \times 6, 3 \times 4, 2 \times 2 \times 3$. Sometimes we talk about *factoring* a number. By this, we mean the same thing as expressing the number as a product of counting numbers greater than one.

From the several different product expressions, or factored forms, for the number 12, we single out for special attention the expression,

$$2 \times 2 \times 3.$$

It expresses 12 as the product of primes, and is often called the *prime factorization* of 12.

Which of the following product expressions for 18 indicates a product of primes?

$$3 \times 6 \qquad 2 \times 9 \qquad 2 \times 3 \times 3$$

Do you agree that it is $2 \times 2 \times 3$? In the expression 3×6, the number 6 is not a prime; in the expression 2×9, the number 9 is not a prime.

The sentence, "Factor a number into its prime factors," means: "Express a number as a product of primes." Thus when we write 3×5 for 15, we have factored 15 into its prime factors. Factoring 12 into its prime factors means expressing it as $2 \times 2 \times 3$.

Can every composite number be factored into prime factors? That is, can it be written as a product of primes? The following argument makes it clear that the answer is yes.

> Every composite number can be factored; that is, it can be written as a product of factors* each of which is smaller than the original number. If one (or more) of these factors is composite, it can be written as the product of still smaller factors. This process cannot go on indefinitely since the factors are getting smaller. Eventually, we must come to a product expression that permits no

---

* By "factors," as we said earlier (page 6), we mean factors that are counting numbers greater than one.

further factoring. In this product expression, every factor
is prime. For example,

$$120 = 8 \times 15 \quad \text{(8 and 15 are both composite.)}$$
$$= 8 \times 3 \times 5 \quad \text{(8 is composite.)}$$
$$= 2 \times 4 \times 3 \times 5 \quad \text{(4 is composite.)}$$
$$= 2 \times 2 \times 2 \times 3 \times 5 \quad \text{(All factors are primes.)}$$

The above example illustrates the process of repeated factoring, which
comes to an end when all factors are prime.

Now that we know that every composite number can be factored into
primes, let us investigate some ways in which this is done in practice.

Using the number 84 for purposes of illustration, we might start by
writing a product expression for 84 that we know to be correct:

$$84 = 6 \times 14 \text{ (We might have started with } 4 \times 21.)$$

We know that $6 = 2 \times 3$ and that $14 = 2 \times 7$. Thus, 6×14 can be rewritten
as $2 \times 3 \times 2 \times 7$, which is a product expression involving only prime factors.
The above process can be shown very conveniently by the following
scheme:

The scheme shown at the left is
sometimes called a *factor tree*.

$$84 = 2 \times 3 \times 2 \times 7$$

If we start with 4×21 instead of 6×14, a different factor tree results:

$$\begin{array}{c} 84 \\ \diagup\diagdown \\ 4 \times 21 \\ \diagup\diagdown \ \ | \diagdown \\ 2 \times 2 \times 3 \times 7 \end{array}$$

$$84 = 2 \times 2 \times 3 \times 7.$$

We could also have started with 7×12:

$$\begin{array}{c} 84 \\ \diagup\diagdown \\ 7 \times 12 \\ \diagup \ \ \diagup\diagdown \\ 7 \times 3 \times 4 \\ \diagup \ \diagup \ \diagup\diagdown \\ 7 \times 3 \times 2 \times 2 \end{array}$$

$$84 = 7 \times 3 \times 2 \times 2.$$

Notice that the three product expressions $2\times3\times2\times7$, $2\times2\times3\times7$, and $7\times3\times2\times2$, resulting from using three different factor trees, are the same except for the order in which the factors are written.

The factor-tree method is further illustrated in Figure 2.

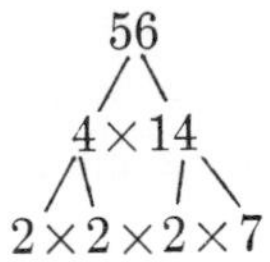

$$56=2\times2\times2\times7 \qquad\qquad 98=2\times7\times7$$

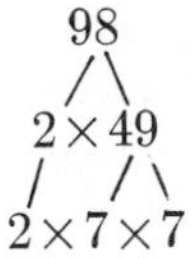

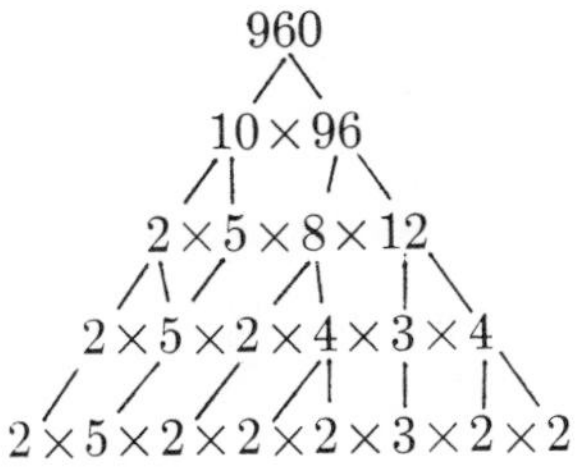

$$960=2\times5\times2\times2\times2\times3\times2\times2$$

$$=2\times2\times2\times2\times2\times2\times3\times5$$

Figure 2

Exponents can be used to write product expressions more compactly. Instead of writing $2\times7\times7\times7$ we may write 2×7^3, since 7^3 means $7\times7\times7$. The exponent 3 indicates that 7 is used as a factor three times. The prime factorizations in the preceding illustrations can be written as follows:

$$56=2^3\times7,$$
$$98=2\times7^2,$$
$$960=2^6\times3\times5.$$

The examples in this section point up a very important fact about composite numbers. It can be stated as follows:

Every composite number can be expressed as a product of one and only one set of primes. (Note, however, that although every composite number is expressed uniquely, the order in which the prime factors are named can be varied.)

This is called the *Fundamental Theorem of Arithmetic,* or the *Unique Factorization Theorem.*

We do not present the proof of this theorem in this booklet. You will find, however, as you work more and more with the prime factorization of numbers, that the truth of the theorem becomes more and more evident. We have seen that in beginning the factoring process on the number 84 in three different ways the resulting product expressions were $2 \times 3 \times 2 \times 7$, $2 \times 2 \times 3 \times 7$, $7 \times 2 \times 3 \times 2$. These expressions are all the same except for the order in which the prime factors are written.

The number 1, as you recall, is by definition not a prime. If it were included among the primes, the Fundamental Theorem of Arithmetic would not be true. The number 15, for example, would then have indefinitely many different prime factorizations such as 3×5, $1 \times 3 \times 5$, $1 \times 1 \times 3 \times 5$, $1 \times 1 \times 1 \times 3 \times 5$, and so on.

Exercise Set 6

1. Write each of the following numbers as a product of two smaller factors.

    (a) 28   (b) 36   (c) 54   (d) 75

2. Express each of the numbers in Exercise 1 as a product of primes by using a factor tree. Start with the product of the two smaller factors which you wrote for Exercise 1.

3. Use the factor tree method again for each of the numbers in Exercise 1. This time start with a different pair of factors.

4. Write the prime factorization of each of the following.

    (a) 4   (b) 8   (c) 16   (d) 27

5. Write 972 as a product of primes. (Hint: $972 = 27 \times 36$.)

6. Rewrite each of the following product expressions using exponents.

    (a) $2 \times 2 \times 11 \times 11$
    (b) $3 \times 31 \times 31 \times 31 \times 31$
    (c) $3 \times 3 \times 3 \times 7 \times 7 \times 19$

The Consecutive-Primes Method

Let us consider again the procedure followed to express a composite number as a product of primes. So far we have really shown only one method: We started with a pair of easily identified factors, factored these numbers if possible, and so on, until only prime numbers occurred in the product expression. This method is certainly a very practical one in many cases. Sometimes, however, it is not easy to choose an initial product of smaller factors with which to start the process, especially when the number to be factored is large.

There is a more systematic way of factoring a composite number into prime factors. Let us illustrate it, using the number 84 again. We begin with the smallest prime, 2, and see whether or not it is a factor of 84. We find by division (or by inspection) that

$$84 = 2 \times 42.$$

Now 2 is a factor also of 42 and $42 = 2 \times 21$. This means that

$$84 = 2 \times 2 \times 21.$$

But 2 is not a factor of 21. We go on to the next prime, 3. Is 3 a factor of 21? Yes, $21 = 3 \times 7$. Hence,

$$84 = 2 \times 2 \times 3 \times 7$$
$$= 2^2 \times 3 \times 7.$$

The factors in this expression are all prime, which means that the job is done.

As a second example, let us express the number 1144 as a product of primes. Again we try consecutive primes 2, 3, 5, 7, and so on as possible factors:

$1144 = 2 \times 572$ (2 is a factor, and $1144 \div 2 = 572$.)
$1144 = 2 \times 2 \times 286$ (2 is a factor of 572, and $572 \div 2 = 286$.)
$1144 = 2 \times 2 \times 2 \times 143$ (2 is a factor of 286, and $286 \div 2 = 143$.)

Now 2 is not a factor of 143, nor is the next prime, 3. We can check this either by division or by applying the divisibility test for 3 $(1+4+3=8,$ which is not divisible by 3). The next primes are 5 and 7, neither of which is a factor of 143; the next prime is 11, and $143 \div 11 = 13$. Hence, $143 = 11 \times 13$, and we can now write

$$1144 = 2 \times 2 \times 2 \times 11 \times 13.$$

Since 13 is a prime, this last expression is the desired product of primes.

For convenience, we shall refer to the method used in the last two examples as the *consecutive primes method* of obtaining the prime factorization of a number.

The essential results of our work in the last example can be shown in abbreviated form as follows:

$$
\begin{array}{r|l}
2 & 1144 \\ \hline
2 & 572 \\ \hline
2 & 286 \\ \hline
11 & 143 \\ \hline
& 13
\end{array}
\qquad 1144 = 2 \times 2 \times 2 \times 11 \times 13.
$$

This form does not show all of the work that was done. It does not show, for example, that 5 and 7 were tried as factors. Nevertheless, the form becomes very useful after one has become better acquainted with this systematic method.

The short form is used in the next example to show the factorization of 1500 into primes:

$$
\begin{array}{r|l}
2 & 1500 \\
\hline
2 & 750 \quad (2 \times 750 = 1500) \\
\hline
3 & 375 \quad (2 \times 375 = 750) \\
\hline
5 & 125 \quad (3 \times 125 = 375) \\
\hline
5 & 25 \quad (5 \times 25 = 125) \\
\hline
 & 5 \quad (5 \times 5 = 25) \qquad 1500 = 2^2 \times 3 \times 5^3.
\end{array}
$$

By applying the commutative and associative properties of multiplication, all two-factor product expressions of a number can be obtained from the prime factorization of the number. Consider, for example, the number 110, whose prime factorization is

$$2 \times 5 \times 11.$$

The product expression can be rewritten in each of the following ways:

$$(2 \times 5) \times 11 = 10 \times 11,$$
$$(2 \times 11) \times 5 = 22 \times 5,$$
$$(5 \times 11) \times 2 = 55 \times 2.$$

This shows that 110 is a multiple of each of the following numbers: 2, 5, 10, 11, 22, 55. These six numbers together with 1 and 110 constitute the set of all factors of 110.

Prime factorization of numbers is used later in this booklet to find the greatest common factor and also the least common multiple of two or more numbers. The first of these applications is useful in finding the simplest name, or expression, for a rational number, for example $\frac{24}{36} = \frac{2}{3}$; and the second is useful in the addition of rational numbers, for example $\frac{2}{3} + \frac{3}{4} = \frac{8}{12} + \frac{9}{12} = \frac{17}{12}$.

Exercise Set 7

1. In each of the following products, the prime factorization of a number is given. Write the base-ten numeral for each number.

Example: $2^2 \times 3 \times 5^3 = 4 \times 3 \times 125$
$$= 4 \times 375$$
$$= 1500 \qquad \text{(base-ten numeral)}$$

(a) $2\times2\times2$

(b) 3×5

(c) $3\times3\times7$

(d) $2^4\times5$ $(2^4=2\times2\times2\times2)$

(e) 7^2

(f) $2\times5\times7\times11$

2. Use the consecutive primes method to express each of the following numbers as a product of primes.

(a) 54

(b) 100

(c) 121

(d) 245

(e) 442

(f) 1001

Determining Primes

Suppose that you were asked to test whether the number 67 is a prime or a composite number. You could use the Sieve of Eratosthenes, but this is not a very practical device. A better way is to try out, as possible factors, the consecutive primes 2, 3, 5, 7, 11, and so on. You might think that you would have to test all of the primes less than 67 before you could declare 67 to be a prime (if indeed it is). You can easily check that none of the first four primes, 2, 3, 5, and 7, is a factor of 67. Do we need to check the next prime, 11, or any prime greater than 11? No, for if 67 is not prime, then it must be a product of at least two primes from the set of primes which are greater than 7, {11, 13, 17, 19, . . .}. This is impossible because 67 is less than any such product for it is less than (11×11). Hence, 67 is prime.

In general, in determining whether or not a number is a prime by testing as possible factors the primes 2, 3, 5, and so on, in sequence, it is unnecessary to test any prime whose second power is greater than the original number. No composite number can have as a factor a prime whose square is greater than the number. If we were to check 677 as to whether or not it is prime, we would not need to try any prime greater than 23, because the second power of the next greater prime, 29, is greater than 677; thus, $29^2=29\times29=841$, $841>677$.

Now let us consider one more example in which we shall show the use of the divisibility tests developed earlier in this booklet. Is the number 299 prime or composite? Since 19^2 is greater than 299, we need not test any prime greater than 17 as a possible factor. We may have to try out each of the following:

$$2, 3, 5, 11, 13, 17.$$

Prime   *Is This Prime a Factor of 299? Why, or Why Not?*

2   No; the last digit in "299" is 9, which is not an even number.

3   No; $2+9+9=20$, and 20 is not divisbile by 3.

5   No; the last digit in 299 is neither 0 nor 5.
7   No; since $299 = (7 \times 42) + 5$, the remainder when 299 is divided
       by 7 is 5, not 0.
11   No; $299 = (11 \times 27) + 2$.
13   Yes; $299 = 13 \times 23$.

We see that the number 299 is composite; it is the product of two primes, 13 and 23.

The Set of Whole Numbers as the Union of Disjoint Sets

We said earlier that the set of whole numbers is the union of the following four disjoint sets:

1. The set having 0 as its only member,
2. The set having 1 as its only member,
3. The set of prime numbers,
4. The set of composite numbers.

The prime numbers are the *basic building blocks*, as far as composite numbers are concerned. Any composite number can be obtained by forming a product of members of the set of primes, where any prime can be used as a factor as many times as desired. The numbers 0 and 1 are neither prime nor composite, by definition. You can see that as a building block in a product, the number 1 serves no purpose, since

$$1 \times 3 \times 5 \text{ is the same number as } 3 \times 5,$$
$$1 \times 1 \times 1 \times 2^2 \times 7 \text{ is the same number as } 2^2 \times 7.$$

The case with the number zero is even worse. It cannot be used as a factor of any number other than zero. Any product involving zero as a factor names the number zero.

Exercise Set 8

1. Which of the following numbers are primes and which are composite numbers?

   (a) 69   (d) 101
   (b) 67   (e) 1001
   (c) 89   (f) 97,248,654

2. There is only one pair of primes whose difference is 1. Name the pair.

3. Two odd primes whose difference is 2 are called twin primes. For example, 3 and 5 are twin primes. Give three other examples of twin primes.

GREATEST COMMON FACTOR

Suppose that you wish to find the simplest name for the number named by the fraction, $\frac{36}{48}$.* Accomplishing this renaming efficiently involves finding the greatest number that is a factor of 36 and also a factor of 48. This greatest number is called the *greatest common factor* of the numbers 36 and 48.

To find this greatest common factor, let us begin by writing the set of all factors of 36 and the set of all factors of 48, calling these sets A and B, respectively. Then,

$$A = \{1, 2, 3, 4, 6, 9, 12, 18, 36\},$$
$$B = \{1, 2, 3, 4, 6, 8, 12, 16, 24, 48\}.$$

These two sets have the following members in common: 1, 2, 3, 4, 6, and 12. Each of these factors is a factor of both 36 and 48; for this reason, each of them is called a common factor of these two numbers. The number 12 is the greatest of these common factors, and hence, it is called the *greatest common factor* of 36 and 48.

Recall that the intersection of two sets (see Booklet No. 1: *Sets*) is the set that contains all of the members common to the two original sets, and has no other members. For example, if

$$P = \{1, 2, 3, 4, 5\},$$
$$Q = \{0, 2, 4, 6, 8\},$$

then the intersection of sets P and Q is given by

$$P \cap Q = \{2, 4\}.$$

Thus the set $\{1, 2, 3, 4, 6, 12\}$ is the intersection of the sets A and B of the preceding paragraph, and we write,

$$A \cap B = \{1, 2, 3, 4, 6, 12\}.$$

The greatest number in this set, namely 12, is the greatest common factor of 36 and 48. Notice that all the other common factors of 36 and 48 are factors of 12.

Set language is useful in describing what is meant by common factors and the greatest common factor of two given numbers. The following general statement can be made:

If A *and* B *denote the sets of factors of two counting numbers, then the greatest common factor of these numbers is the greatest number that is a member of the intersection of sets* A *and* B.

---

* Such a number is called a rational number. See Booklet No. 6: *The Rational Numbers*.

Although listing all the factors of two given numbers is a good way to introduce the concept of greatest common factor, it does not provide, in all cases, the easiest way of finding the greatest common factor. Often the most efficient way to find the greatest common factor is to express each of the given numbers as a product of primes.

Factoring 36 and 48 into primes, we have

$$36 = 2 \times 2 \times 3 \times 3,$$
$$48 = 2 \times 2 \times 2 \times 2 \times 3.$$

We are looking for the greatest number that is a factor of both 36 and 48. By looking at the factored forms, we see that

2 is a common factor of 36 and 48,
(2×2) is a common factor of 36 and 48,
but $(2 \times 2 \times 2)$ is not a common factor of 36 and 48.

Similarly,

3 is a common factor of 36 and 48,
but 3×3 is not a common factor of 36 and 48.

Using the commutative and associative properties of multiplication, and associating the common factors, we have

$$36 = (2 \times 2 \times 3) \times 3,$$
$$48 = (2 \times 2 \times 3) \times 2 \times 2.$$

Thus $(2 \times 2 \times 3)$, or 12, is the greatest common factor of 36 and 48.

We may use the exponent form for the product of primes:

$$36 = 2^2 \times 3^2,$$
$$48 = 2^4 \times 3^1.$$

The greatest common factor, or g.c.f., of 36 and 48 can have no prime factor other than 2 and 3. It can have 2^2 as a factor, but not 2^3; and it can have 3^1 as a factor, but not 3^2. Thus 2^2 is the highest power of 2 that is a factor of both $2^2 \times 3^2$ and $2^4 \times 3^1$; and 3^1 is the highest power of 3 that is a factor of both $2^2 \times 3^2$ and $2^4 \times 3^1$. Hence, $2^2 \times 3^1$, or 12, is the g.c.f. of 36 and 48.

Now let us use the method of prime factorization to find the g.c.f. of 135 and 126. First we write 135 and 126 as products of primes:

$$
\begin{array}{r|r}
3 & 135 \\ \hline
3 & 45 \\ \hline
3 & 15 \\ \hline
& 5
\end{array}
\qquad 135 = 3^3 \times 5
$$

$$\begin{array}{r|l}
2 & 126 \\
\hline
3 & 63 \\
\hline
3 & 21 \\
\hline
 & 7
\end{array}$$
$$126 = 2 \times 3^2 \times 7.$$

The factored forms, $3^3 \times 5$ and $2 \times 3^2 \times 7$, make it clear that the g.c.f. can involve no prime factor other than 3, because 2, 5, and 7 are not common factors; $3^3 \times 5$ has 5 as a factor, but not 2 and 7; whereas $2 \times 3^2 \times 7$ has 2 and 7 as factors, but not 5. What is the highest power of 3 that is a common factor or $3^3 \times 5$ and $2 \times 3^2 \times 7$? It is obviously 3^2. Thus 9 is the greatest common factor of 135 and 126.

As our final example, suppose that we are given two numbers, call them a and b, whose prime factorizations are as follows:

$$a = 2^2 \times 3^1 \times 5^2 \times 11^3 \times 13,$$
$$b = 3^3 \times 5^1 \times 11^4 \times 17.$$

(We are not interested here in performing the multiplication necessary to find the simplest numerals for a and b.) The g.c.f. of a and b will have as prime factors 3, 5, and 11, since these are the only primes appearing in both product expressions. What are the highest powers of 3, 5, and 11 that are common factors of a and b? Do you see that they are 3^1, 5^1, and 11^3? The g.c.f of a and b is $(3 \times 5 \times 11^3)$.

The greatest common factor of three counting numbers, a, b, and c, is the greatest counting number that is a factor of each of the three numbers. The procedures used to find the g.c.f. of three numbers is similar to the procedure used for two numbers. Let us illustrate by letting

$$a = 2^2 \times 5^3 \times 11^1,$$
$$b = 2^1 \times 5^2 \times 7^1,$$
$$c = 2^3 \times 3^1 \times 5^4 \times 11^2.$$

The g.c.f. will have the prime factors 2 and 5 and no others. The highest powers of 2 and 5 that are factors of a, b, and c are 2^1 and 5^2, respectively. The product of these powers, $2^1 \times 5^2$, or 50, is the g.c.f. of a, b, and c.

If one member of the set of counting numbers is a prime number, then the g.c.f. of these numbers is either that prime number or 1. For example,

the g.c.f. of 7, 12, and 49 is 1, because 7 is a prime that is not a common factor of 12 and 49;

the g.c.f. of 13, 52, 130, and 650 is 13, because 13 is a prime that is a factor of each of the other three numbers.

Exercise Set 9

1. For each of the following number pairs, write the set of factors of each number. Denote the two sets by A and B. Then find the intersection

set $A \cap B$. Finally write the greatest common factor of the original pair of numbers.

(a) 45,   75   (c) 24,   48
(b) 21,   77   (d) 27,   80

2. Use the method of prime factorization to find the g.c.f. of each of the following pairs of numbers.

(a) 35,   275   (c) 36,   108
(b) 700,   90   (d) 72,   175

3. If the prime factorizations of three numbers, a, b, and c, are as indicated below, find the g.c.f. of a, b, and c expressed as a product of primes.

$$a = 2^3 \times 11 \times 17^2,$$
$$b = 2 \times 17^2 \times 67,$$
$$c = 2 \times 3^3 \times 17^6 \times 67^2.$$

4. Answer each of the following.

(a) Is $2^2 \times 3 \times 5$ a factor of $2^2 \times 3^2 \times 5$?
(b) Is 5×7^2 a factor of $5^2 \times 7$?
(c) Is 5×7^2 a factor of $5^2 \times 7^2$?
(d) Is $3^2 \times 11^3$ a multiple of $3^2 \times 11^2$?

LEAST COMMON MULTIPLE

We are often concerned with finding a simple name for the sum of two numbers named by fractions (see Booklet No. 6: *The Rational Numbers*), for example, $\frac{3}{8} + \frac{7}{12}$. We wish to denote $\frac{3}{8} + \frac{7}{12}$ by a single fraction. To do this, it is first necessary to rename $\frac{3}{8}$ and $\frac{7}{12}$ as fractions having a common denominator. Thus the first step is to find a number to use as a common denominator. It must be a multiple of 8 and also a multiple of 12; that is, it must have 8 and 12 as factors. One such number is 48, since $48 = 6 \times 8$ and $48 = 4 \times 12$. This common multiple can be used to rename $\frac{3}{8}$ as $\frac{18}{48}$, and $\frac{7}{12}$ as $\frac{28}{48}$. Then,

$$\frac{3}{8} + \frac{7}{12} = \frac{18}{48} + \frac{28}{48}$$
$$= \frac{18 + 28}{48}$$
$$= \frac{46}{48}.$$

The words "factor" and "multiple" are often confused. The relation between these words is analogous to that between "father" and "son" in the sentence: Tom is the son of Mr. Jones, and Mr. Jones is the father of Tom. Analogously, 5 is a factor of 35, and 35 is a multiple of 5. The number 2×3^2 is a factor of the number $2^3 \times 3^2$, and $2^3 \times 3^2$ is a multiple of 2×3^2.

The set of multiples of 8 has indefinitely many members, and so does the set of multiples of 12. If we denote these sets by P and Q, we can write:

$$P = \{8, 16, 24, 32, 40, 48, 56, 64, 72, \ldots\},$$
$$Q = \{12, 24, 36, 48, 60, 72, \ldots\},$$

where the three dots indicate that the sequence can be continued indefinitely. There is neither a greatest multiple of 8 nor a greatest multiple of 12.

Do the sets P and Q have any members in common? Yes: 24, 48, and 72 are seen to be common members; and we call them *common multiples* of 8 and 12.

Actually, there are many more members common to P and Q; in fact, they have indefinitely many members in common. Another way of saying this is to say that $P \cap Q$ has indefinitely many members. We can write

$$P \cap Q = \{24, 48, 72, \ldots\},$$

the three dots indicating, again, that the sequence of numbers could be continued indefinitely. What would be the next two?

Perhaps the fact that $P \cap Q$ has indefinitely many members is worrisome to you. It need not be, since the question which really interests us is this: What is the smallest member of $P \cap Q$? We can see that it is 24. This number is called the *least common multiple* of 8 and 12 for there is no counting number less than 24 that is a multiple of both 8 and 12. Alternatively, we could say that there is no number less than 24 which has both 8 and 12 as factors.

In general, if A is the set of multiples of a counting number, and B is the set of multiples of a second counting number, then the smallest number in the set $A \cap B$ is called the least common multiple of the two counting numbers.

Let us find the least common multiple of the numbers 10, 12, and 15. The sets of multiples of these numbers are

$$\{10, 20, 30, 40, 50, 60 \ldots\},$$
$$\{12, 24, 36, 48, 60, 72 \ldots\},$$
$$\{15, 30, 45, 60, 75, 90, 105, \ldots\},$$

respectively. The number 60 is seen to be a common member of the three sets; hence, 60 is a common multiple of 10, 12, and 15. The numbers 120,

180, 240, and many other numbers (in fact, indefinitely many) are also common multiples of 10, 12, and 15. The smallest number in this set of common multiples,

$$\{60, 120, 180, 240, \ldots\},$$

is 60. It is the least common multiple of 10, 12 and 15. There is no number less than 60 that has 10, 12, and 15 as factors. Notice that 120, 180, 240, and so on, are all multiples of the least common multiple, 60.

Another method of finding the least common multiple (or l.c.m., as it is commonly abbreviated) of two or more numbers employs the prime factorization of these numbers. We shall illustrate this method by using the numbers of the preceding example: 10, 12, and 15. We begin by expressing each of these as a product of primes, writing the factorization in such a way that if a prime occurs in more than one factorization, this fact is clearly in evidence:

$$10 = 2 \times 5,$$
$$12 = 2^2 \quad \times 3,$$
$$15 = \quad\quad 5 \times 3.$$

Remember that we are not looking for a common factor of 10, 12, and 15, but for a common multiple, in particular, the least common multiple. The l.c.m. must be a multiple of 2×5, a multiple of $2^2 \times 3$, and also a multiple of 3×5. This means, first of all, that the prime factorization of the l.c.m. must involve each of the primes 2, 3, and 5; that is, the l.c.m. is equal to *a power of 2* times *a power of 3* times *a power of 5*. What power of each of these is required? The answer is 2^2, 3^1, and 5^1. The l.c.m. of 10, 12 and 15 is $2^2 \times 3^1 \times 5^1$, or 60 (this agrees with our previous result). If we were to increase any of the exponents in $2^2 \times 3^1 \times 5^1$, the resulting number would be a common multiple of 10, 12, and 15, but it would not be the least common multiple.

Let us use the method of prime factorization to find the l.c.m. of the three numbers 40, 48, and 75. We have the following prime factorizations:

$$40 = 2^3 \times 5,$$
$$48 = 2^4 \quad \times 3,$$
$$75 = \quad\quad 5^2 \times 3.$$

The l.c.m. must have 2, 3, and 5 as factors. The powers of these that are needed are 2^4, 3^1, and 5^2. Hence the l.c.m. of 40, 48, and 75 is

$$2^4 \times 3 \times 5^2 \text{ or } 1200.$$

Exercise Set 10

1. Write the first ten multiples of each of the following numbers.

$$6, \quad 9, \quad 8, \quad 15.$$

2. From the lists of multiples that you wrote for Exercise 1, write two common multiples of each of the following pairs of numbers.

(a) 6 and 9,   (b) 9 and 15,   (c) 6 and 8.

3. What is the least common multiple of each of the following pairs of numbers?

(a) 6 and 9,   (b) 9 and 15,   (c) 6 and 8.

4. Find the g.c.f. and l.c.m. of the three numbers 2, 5, and 7.

5. Use the method of prime factorization of find the l.c.m. of each set of numbers.

(a) 12 and 18   (d) 13 and 26
(b) 24 and 32   (e) 8, 14, and 21
(c) 25 and 60   (f) 15, 25, and 45.

6. There is an interesting fact that relates the g.c.f. and the l.c.m. of any two counting numbers. It is this: If a and b are any two counting numbers, then

$$\text{(the g.c.f. of } a \text{ and } b) \times \text{(the l.c.m. of } a \text{ and } b) = a \times b.$$

EXAMPLE: the g.c.f. of 12 and 20 is *4;* the l.c.m. of 12 and 20 is *60.* The product 4×60 is equal to the product 12×20. This illustrates the statement made above.

Illustrate the statement for each of the following pairs of numbers.

(a) 12 and 10   (c) 2 and 10
(b) 24 and 18   (d) 8 and 14.

SOME QUESTIONS ABOUT NUMBERS

In this section, several questions about numbers are discussed. Some of the questions are answered quite easily, but they may serve the purpose of providing you with material for classroom use. Other questions are more difficult, but their answers have been worked out by great mathematicians. Still other questions are unanswered in spite of years of effort on the part of mathematicians to resolve them.

Some Things That Are Known About Primes

Mathematicians are very much interested in the distribution of primes, that is, in the way in which they are spread out among the counting numbers. A great deal of study and research is still going on in this area of mathematics.

1. Is there a greatest prime number? Another way of stating this question is: Is the number of primes finite?

Perhaps this question seems difficult, but the answer is known. Euclid, the great geometer, proved that there is no greatest prime. This means that no matter how large a prime you may find, there are greater ones.

2. In 1845 the French mathematician Bertrand made the following educated guess: Between any counting number, other than 1, and its double there is at least one prime. This was known for a long time as the *Postulate of Bertrand*.

Did Bertrand make a good guess? See if you can find a prime between 2 and 4, between 3 and 6, between 4 and 8, and between 5 and 10. Perhaps you are convinced that the guess was a good one. Remember, however, that the verification of an assertion, such as the assertion made by Bertrand, through the use of examples does not constitute a proof of its truth, no matter how many examples are found.

In 1911, sixty-six years after the statement had been made by Bertrand, a Russian mathematician, Tchebyshev, proved that it is true.

Some Unanswered Questions About Primes

1. Is there a formula that can be used to generate all the primes? No such formula has been obtained. It is interesting, however, that there are formulas that yield quite a large number of primes. One such formula is $n^2 - n + 41$. If you choose the number 1 for n, you get $1^2 - 1 + 41 = 41$, which is a prime. Substituting 2 for n, you get $2^2 - 2 + 41 = 43$, which is a prime. You will find that you keep getting primes if you substitute for n the numbers 3, 4, 5, 6, and so on, through 40. By this time you might be ready to make the following (uneducated) guess: The formula $n^2 - n + 41$ yields a prime number no matter what counting number is substituted for n. Alas, substitution of one more number, namely 41, proves the guess to be a poor one, since $(41)^2 - 41 + 41 = (41)^2 = 41 \times 41$, which is not a prime.

2. In Exercise 3 of Exercise Set 8, twin primes were mentioned as a pair of odd primes whose difference is 2. The pair $(3, 5)$ was given as an example, and you were asked to produce a few more examples. Here are some: $(5, 7)$, $(11, 13)$, $(17, 19)$, and $(29, 31)$. It is known that twin primes occur less often as numbers increase in size. There are none between 700 and 800 and none between 900 and 1000. *Is there a last pair of twin primes?* This is as yet an unanswered question.

3. The mathematician Goldbach once made a very famous conjecture, which is known as Goldbach's Conjecture. This conjecture is that *every even number greater than 2 is the sum of two primes.*

Do you think that Goldbach's Conjecture is true? Working with examples might convince you that it is. We have

$$4 = 2 + 2, \qquad 10 = 7 + 3,$$
$$40 = 11 + 29, \qquad 122 = 61 + 61.$$

If you could find just one even number greater than 2 that is not the sum of two primes, you would show the conjecture to be false. No one has ever been able to find such an even number. This, however, is no proof that the conjecture is true.

Mathematicians have worked long and hard to find a way of proving Goldbach's Conjecture, but to this day they have not succeeded.

Some Interesting Questions About Sums

Examine the following true sentences about the first odd number, the sum of the first two odd numbers, the sum of the first three odd numbers, the sum of the first four odd numbers, and the sum of the first five odd numbers:

$$1 = 1$$
$$1 + 3 = 4$$
$$1 + 3 + 5 = 9$$
$$1 + 3 + 5 + 7 = 16$$
$$1 + 3 + 5 + 7 + 9 = 25.$$

You notice that the first odd number is 1, which is 1^2; the sum of the first two odd numbers is 4, which is 2^2; the sum of the first three odd numbers is 9, which is 3^2; and so on. This suggests the following question: Is the sum of the first n odd numbers equal to $(n \times n)$, or n^2, no matter what counting number n represents?

This question, when raised in the classroom (less formally and in numerical terms), can lead to useful experimentation on the part of the pupil. In fact, experimentation should probably precede the raising of the question, so that the pupil might perhaps ask the question himself. He might ask: Is the sum of the first ten odd numbers 10^2; is the sum of the first 1000 odd numbers 1000^2?

That the sum of the first n odd numbers is in every case n^2 can be proved with the use of algebra. Rather than present the proof, let us look at these sums in another way.

Let the unit square ☐ represent 1. How many unit squares must be added to the one-unit square to make a 2 by 2 square? (See Fig. 3.)

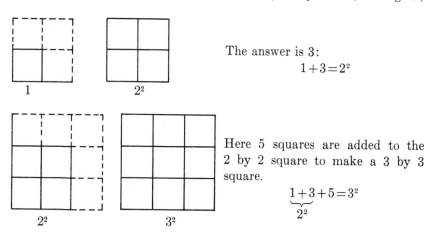

The answer is 3:
$$1+3=2^2$$

Here 5 squares are added to the 2 by 2 square to make a 3 by 3 square.

$$\underbrace{1+3+5}_{2^2}=3^2$$

FIGURE 3

3 squares added here

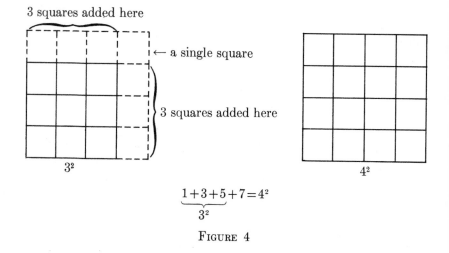

← a single square

} 3 squares added here

$$\underbrace{1+3+5+7}_{3^2}=4^2$$

FIGURE 4

How many unit squares are added to the 3 by 3 square to make the 4 by 4 square? We add, as shown in Figure 4, two blocks of 3-unit squares and an extra unit square:

$$\underbrace{1+3+5}_{3^2}+\underbrace{(2\times3)+1}_{7}=4^2.$$

Recall that $(2 \times n) + 1$ is the general form for an odd number. Thus, $(2 \times 3) + 1$ is the fourth number in the set of odd numbers,

$$\{1, 3, 5, 7, 9, \ldots\}.$$

To make a 5 by 5 square from the 4 by 4 square, two blocks of 4-unit squares and an extra unit square are added. Thus we have

$$\underbrace{1+3+5+7}_{4^2} + \underbrace{(2 \times 4) + 1}_{\substack{\text{The 5th odd} \\ \text{number, 9}}} = 5^2.$$

In this way, our statement about the sum of the first n odd numbers can be made to seem geometrically reasonable.

Another interesting result pertaining to sums of certain groups of odd numbers can be obtained from the following triangular arrangement of the odd numbers:

(1)	1			
(2)	3	5		
(3)	7	9	11	
(4)	13	15	17	19
(5)	21	23	25	27	29

The triangular array can of course be extended indefinitely.

Now find the sum of the numbers in each row. For the first row, the sum is 1; for the second, it is 8; for the third, it is 27; for the fourth, it is 64; and for the fifth, it is 125. Do you see that these sums have a certain relationship to the number of the row? Table VII shows the relationship.

TABLE VII

Row	Sum for That Row
(1)	$1 = 1 \times 1 \times 1 = 1^3$
(2)	$8 = 2 \times 2 \times 2 = 2^3$
(3)	$27 = 3^3$
(4)	$64 = 4^3$
(5)	$125 = 5^3$

If the table were extended, we would find that the sum of the numbers in the sixth row would be 6^3, or 216; and the sum of the numbers in the seventh row would be 7^3, or 343. (Verification of these facts by pupils might provide them with an incentive for practice in addition and finding powers of numbers.)

The Greeks discovered that there are numbers with a very striking property. They called them *perfect numbers:* 6 and 28 are two such numbers. Each of these numbers is equal to the sum of all of its factors, including 1 but excluding itself. Thus,

$6 = 1 + 2 + 3$ (1, 2, 3, 6 is the set of all factors of 6);

$28 = 1 + 2 + 4 + 7 + 14$ (1, 2, 4, 7, 14, 28 is the set of all factors of 28).

Actually, the first five perfect numbers were known to the Greeks. They are

6,   28,   496,   8128,   and   33,550,336.

Mathematicians have been able to answer many interesting questions about perfect numbers, but there are still unanswered questions. By 1953, seventeen perfect numbers were known, the base-ten numeral for the seventeenth one having 1937 digits.

The following are unanswered questions:

1. How many perfect numbers are there?
2. Are there any odd perfect numbers? (None have been found so far).

It may be surprising to you that it is known that the numeral for every even perfect number (remember, we do not know how many there are) ends in 28 or in 6.

ANSWERS TO EXERCISE SETS

Exercise Set 1

1. (a) {12, 14, 16, 18, 20, 22, 24, 26, 28}
   (b) {83, 85}

2. (a) 402
   (b) 11,   29,   1001

3. (a) $36 = 2 \times 18$ (c) $328 = 2 \times 164$
   (b) $142 = 2 \times 71$ (d) $1000 = 2 \times 500$

4. (a) $17 = (2 \times 8) + 1$ (c) $121 = (2 \times 60) + 1$
   (b) $39 = (2 \times 19) + 1$ (d) $1363 = (2 \times 681) + 1$

5. 8, 12, and 30 are divisible by 2.
   12 and 30 are divisible by 3.
   25 and 30 are divisible by 5.

6. (a) $B = \{1, 4, 7, 10 \ldots\}$
   (b) $C = \{2, 5, 8, 11 \ldots\}$

(c) Yes.

(d) Yes.

(e) $A = \{0, 3, 6, 9 \ldots\}$

$B = \{1, 4, 7, 10 \ldots\}$

$C = \{2, 5, 8, 11 \ldots\}$

1 is a member of Set B

2 is a member of Set C

$(1+2)$ is a member of Set A

4 is a member of Set B

5 is a member of Set C

$(4+5)$ is a member of Set A

7. $(2 \times n) + [(2 \times k) + 1] = [(2 \times n) + (2 \times k)] + 1$ Associative property
of addition

$\qquad\qquad\qquad = [2 \times (n+k)] + 1$ Distributive property

$[2 \times (n+k)] + 1$ is an odd number.

8. Let the numbers be $[(2 \times n) + 1]$ and $[(2 \times k) + 1]$.

$[(2 \times n) + 1] + [(2 \times k) + 1] = [1 + (2 \times n)] + [(2 \times k) + 1]$

$\qquad\qquad$ Commutative property of addition

$\qquad\qquad = \{[1 + (2 \times n)] + (2 \times k)\} + 1$

$\qquad\qquad$ Associative property of addition

$\qquad\qquad = \{1 + [(2 \times n) + (2 \times k)]\} + 1$

$\qquad\qquad$ Associative property of addition

$\qquad\qquad = \{1 + [2 \times (n+k)]\} + 1$

$\qquad\qquad$ Distributive property

$\qquad\qquad = \{[2 \times (n+k)] + 1\} + 1$

$\qquad\qquad$ Commutative property of addition

$\qquad\qquad = [2 \times (n+k)] + (1+1)$

$\qquad\qquad$ Associative property of addition

$\qquad\qquad = [2 \times (n+k)] + (2 \times 1)$

$\qquad\qquad = 2 \times (n+k+1)$ Distributive property

$2 \times (n+k+1)$ is an even number.

9. Let the even number be $(2 \times n)$ and the odd number $[(2 \times k) + 1]$.

$(2 \times n) \times [(2 \times k) + 1] = [(2 \times n) \times (2 \times k)] + [(2 \times n) \times 1]$

$\qquad\qquad$ Distributive property

$\qquad\qquad = \{2 \times [n \times (2 \times k)]\} + (2 \times n)$

$\qquad\qquad$ Associative property of multiplication

$\qquad\qquad = 2 \times \{[n \times (2 \times k)] + n\}$

$\qquad\qquad$ Distributive property

$2 \times \{[n \times (2 \times k)] + n\}$ is an even number.

Exercise Set 2

1. (a) 1, 2, 7, 14
   (b) 1, 19
   (c) 1, 2, 3, 6, 7, 14, 21, 42
   (d) 1, 2, 3, 4, 6, 9, 12, 18, 36
   (e) 1, 2, 4, 8, 16

2. For each of these there are still other product expressions.

   (a) $18 = 2 \times 9$
   $18 = 3 \times 6$
   $18 = 1 \times 18$

   (b) $24 = 6 \times 4$
   $24 = 2 \times 12$
   $24 = 3 \times 8$

   (c) $50 = 1 \times 50$
   $50 = 2 \times 25$
   $50 = 5 \times 10$

   (d) $27 = 1 \times 27$
   $27 = 3 \times 9$
   $27 = 3 \times 3 \times 3$

3. (a) $8 = 1 \times 8$
   $8 = 2 \times 4$

   (b) $18 = 1 \times 18$
   $18 = 2 \times 9$
   $18 = 3 \times 6$

   (c) $100 = 1 \times 100$
   $100 = 2 \times 50$
   $100 = 4 \times 25$
   $100 = 5 \times 20$
   $100 = 10 \times 10$

Exercise Set 3

1.

X̶	2	3	4̶	5	6̶	7	8̶	9̶	1̶0̶
11	1̶2̶	13	1̶4̶	1̶5̶	1̶6̶	17	1̶8̶	19	2̶0̶
2̶1̶	2̶2̶	23	2̶4̶	2̶5̶	2̶6̶	2̶7̶	2̶8̶	29	3̶0̶
31	3̶2̶	3̶3̶	3̶4̶	3̶5̶	36	37	3̶8̶	3̶9̶	4̶0̶
41	4̶2̶	43	4̶4̶	4̶5̶	4̶6̶	47	4̶8̶	4̶9̶	5̶0̶
5̶1̶	5̶2̶	53	5̶4̶	5̶5̶	5̶6̶	5̶7̶	58	59	6̶0̶
61	6̶2̶	6̶3̶	6̶4̶	6̶5̶	6̶6̶	67	6̶8̶	6̶9̶	7̶0̶
71	7̶2̶	73	7̶4̶	7̶5̶	7̶6̶	7̶7̶	7̶8̶	79	8̶0̶
8̶1̶	8̶2̶	83	8̶4̶	8̶5̶	8̶6̶	87	8̶8̶	89	9̶0̶
9̶1̶	9̶2̶	9̶3̶	9̶4̶	9̶5̶	9̶6̶	97	9̶8̶	9̶9̶	1̶0̶0̶

2. All even numbers have 2 as one of their factors. This means that each even number (except 2) has at least three factors—1, 2, and the number itself; hence, such a number cannot be prime, because prime numbers have only two factors—1 and the number itself.

3. 5, 7, and 11, because $5 \times 7 \times 11 = 385$.

4. In Exercise 8 of Exercise Set 1, you showed that the sum of two odd numbers is an even number. It follows that the sum of two odd primes

is an even number greater than 2 (the smallest odd prime is 3). An even number greater than 2 cannot be a prime.

Exercise Set 4

1. (a) 2544 and 246,312 are divisible by 2.
   (b) 2544; 1,000,011; and 246,312 are divisible by 3.
   (c) 415 is divisible by 5.
   (d) 246,312 is divisible by 9.

2. $(7 \times 48) + (7 \times 13)$ and $(7 \times 1000) + (7 \times 200) + 14$ are divisible by 7.

3. In each case the remainder is 1.

4. The number is $(3 \times 5 \times 7) + 1$, which is 106.

Exercise Set 5

1.

Number	Base-Five Numeral	Sum of Digits
two	2	2
four	4	4
six	11	2
eight	13	4
ten	20	2
twelve	22	4
fourteen	24	6
sixteen	31	4
eighteen	33	6
twenty	40	4

Number	Base-Five Numeral	Sum of Digits
one	1	1
three	3	3
five	10	1
seven	12	3
nine	14	5
eleven	21	3
thirteen	23	5
fifteen	30	3
seventeen	32	5
nineteen	34	7

A number is divisible by two provided that the sum of the digits in its base-five numeral in divisible by two.

2.

Number	Base-Five Numeral	Sum of Digits	Divisible by Four?
four	4	4	yes
eight	13	4	yes
twelve	22	4	yes
sixteen	31	4	yes
twenty	40	4	yes
fifty-two	202	4	yes
twenty-four	44	8	yes
one-hundred eighty-four	1214	8	yes
nine	14	5	no
eleven	21	3	no
seventeen	32	5	no

If the sum of the digits in a base-five numeral is divisible by four, the number named by the numeral is divisible by four.

3. It would be a test for divisibility by eleven.

Number	Base-Twelve Numeral	Sum of Digits	Divisible by Eleven?
thirty-three	29	11	yes
forty-four	38	11	yes
forty-eight	40	4	no
one-hundred ninety-eight	146	11	yes

If the sum of the digits in a base-twelve numeral is divisible by eleven, the number named by the numeral is divisible by eleven.

Exercise Set 6

1. (a) $28 = 4 \times 7$ (c) $54 = 6 \times 9$
  (b) $36 = 2 \times 18$ (d) $75 = 3 \times 25$
    In each case, there are other correct answers.

2. (a)

$$28$$
$$4 \times 7$$
$$2 \times 2 \times 7$$
$$28 = 2 \times 2 \times 7$$

(b)

$$36$$
$$2 \times 18$$
$$2 \times 2 \times 9$$
$$2 \times 2 \times 3 \times 3$$
$$36 = 2 \times 2 \times 3 \times 3$$

(c)

$$54$$
$$6 \times 9$$
$$2 \times 3 \times 3 \times 3$$
$$54 = 2 \times 3 \times 3 \times 3$$

(d)
$$
\begin{array}{c}
75 \\
/\ \backslash \\
3 \times 25 \\
/\ \ /\ \backslash \\
3 \times 5 \times 5
\end{array}
$$

$75 = 3 \times 5 \times 5$

3. (a)

$28 = 2 \times 2 \times 7$

$54 = 3 \times 2 \times 3 \times 3$

(c)
$$
\begin{array}{c}
54 \\
/\ \backslash \\
3 \times 18 \\
/\ \ /\ \backslash \\
3 \times 2 \times 9 \\
/\ \ /\ \ /\ \backslash \\
3 \times 2 \times 3 \times 3
\end{array}
$$

(b)

$36 = 2 \times 2 \times 3 \times 3$

(d)
$$
\begin{array}{c}
75 \\
/\ \backslash \\
5 \times 15 \\
/\ \ /\ \backslash \\
5 \times 5 \times 3
\end{array}
$$

$75 = 5 \times 5 \times 3$

4. (a) $4 = 2 \times 2$ (c) $16 = 2 \times 2 \times 2 \times 2$

(b) $8 = 2 \times 2 \times 2$ (d) $27 = 3 \times 3 \times 3$

5. $972 = 27 \times 36$
$972 = (3 \times 3 \times 3) \times (2 \times 2 \times 3 \times 3)$

The order of the factors can be changed:

$$972 = 2 \times 2 \times 3 \times 3 \times 3 \times 3 \times 3.$$

6. (a) $2^2 \times 11^2$ (b) 3×31^4 (c) $3^3 \times 7^2 \times 19$

Exercise Set 7

1. (a) $2 \times 2 \times 2 = 8$

(b) $3 \times 5 = 15$

(c) $3 \times 3 \times 7 = 3 \times 21$
$$= 63$$

(d) $2^4 \times 5 = 2 \times 2 \times 2 \times 2 \times 5$
$$= 16 \times 5$$
$$= 80$$

(e) $7^2 = 7 \times 7$
$$= 49$$

(f) $2 \times 5 \times 7 \times 11 = 10 \times 7 \times 11$
$$= 10 \times 77$$
$$= 770$$

2. (a) $\underline{2\ |}$ 54   (c) $\underline{11\ |}$ 121   (e) $\underline{2\ |}$ 442
          $\underline{3\ |}$ 27   11 $\underline{13\ |}$ 221
          $\underline{3\ |}$ 9 $121 = 11 \times 11$ 17
             3 $442 = 2 \times 13 \times 17$
    $54 = 2 \times 3 \times 3 \times 3$

(b) $\underline{2\ |}$ 100   (d) $\underline{5\ |}$ 245   (f) $\underline{7\ |}$ 1001
     $\underline{2\ |}$ 50 $\underline{7\ |}$ 49 $\underline{11\ |}$ 143
     $\underline{5\ |}$ 25   7   13
          5                          $245 = 5 \times 7 \times 7$ $1001 = 7 \times 11 \times 13$
$100 = 2 \times 2 \times 5 \times 5$

Exercise Set 8

1. (a) 69 is composite; $69 = 3 \times 23$.
   (b) 67 is prime.
   (c) 89 is prime.
   (d) 101 is prime.
   (e) 1001 is composite; $1001 = 7 \times 143$.
   (f) 97,248,654 is composite; it is divisible by 2.

2. The pair is 2 and 3.

3. Other examples of twin primes are

   (a) 5 and 7   (b) 11 and 13   (c) 17 and 19.

Exercise Set 9

1. (a) $A = \{1,\ 3,\ 5,\ 9,\ 15,\ 45\}$
              $B = \{1,\ 3,\ 5,\ 15,\ 25,\ 75\}$
         $A \cap B = \{1,\ 3,\ 5,\ 15\}$
   The g.c.f. of 45 and 75 is 15.

   (b) $A = \{1,\ 3,\ 7,\ 21\}$
              $B = \{1,\ 7,\ 11,\ 77\}$
         $A \cap B = \{1,\ 7\}$
   The g.c.f. of 21 and 77 is 7.

   (c) $A = \{1,\ 2,\ 3,\ 4,\ 6,\ 8,\ 12,\ 24\}$
              $B = \{1,\ 2,\ 3,\ 4,\ 6,\ 8,\ 12,\ 16,\ 24,\ 48\}$
         $A \cap B = \{1,\ 2,\ 3,\ 4,\ 6,\ 8,\ 12,\ 24\}$
   The g.c.f. of 24 and 48 is 24.

   (d) $A = \{1,\ 3,\ 9,\ 27\}$
              $B = \{1,\ 2,\ 4,\ 5,\ 8,\ 10,\ 16,\ 20,\ 40,\ 80\}$
         $A \cap B = \{1\}$
   The g.c.f. of 27 and 80 is 1.

2. (a) $35 = 5 \times 7$
$275 = 5^2 \times 11$
g.c.f. $= 5$

(c) $36 = 2^2 \times 3^2$
$108 = 2^2 \times 3^3$
g.c.f. $= 2^2 \times 3^2$
$= 36$

(b) $700 = 2^2 \times 5^2 \times 7$
$90 = 2 \times 5 \times 3^2$
g.c.f. $= 2 \times 5$
$= 10$

(d) $72 = 2^3 \times 3^2$
$175 = 5^2 \times 7$
g.c.f. $= 1$

3. The g.c.f. of a, b, and c is 2×17^2.

4. (a) Yes.　　(b) No.　　(c) Yes.　　(d) Yes.

Exercise Set 10

1. The first ten multiples of 6 are
6, 12, 18, 24, 30, 36, 42, 48, 54, 60.
The first ten multiples of 9 are
9, 18, 27, 36, 45, 54, 63, 72, 81, 90.
The first ten multiples of 8 are
8, 16, 24, 32, 40, 48, 56, 64, 72, 80.
The first ten multiples of 15 are
15, 30, 45, 60, 75, 90, 105, 120, 135, 150.

2. (a) 18 and 36　　(b) 45 and 90　　(c) 24 and 48

3. (a) 18　　(b) 45　　(c) 24

4. The g.c.f. is 1.　　The l.c.m. is $2 \times 5 \times 7$ or 70.

5. (a) $12 = 2^2 \times 3$
$18 = 2 \times 3^2$
l.c.m. $= 2^2 \times 3^2$
$= 36$

(d) $13 = 13$
$26 = 2 \times 13$
l.c.m. $= 2 \times 13$
$= 26$

(b) $24 = 2^3 \times 3$
$32 = 2^5$
l.c.m. $= 2^5 \times 3$
$= 96$

(e) $8 = 2^3$
$14 = 2 \times 7$
$21 = 3 \times 7$
l.c.m. $= 2^3 \times 3 \times 7$
$= 168$

(c) $25 = 5^2$
$60 = 2^2 \times 3 \times 5$
l.c.m. $= 2^2 \times 3 \times 5^2$
$= 300$

(f) $15 = 3 \times 5$
$25 = 5^2$
$45 = 5 \times 3^2$
l.c.m. $= 3^2 \times 5^2$
$= 225$

6. (a) $10 = 2 \times 5$
$\quad\quad 12 = 2^2 \times 3$
$\quad\quad$ g.c.f. $= 2$
$\quad\quad$ l.c.m. $= 2^2 \times 3 \times 5 = 60$
$\quad 10 \times 12 = 2 \times 60$

(b) $24 = 2^3 \times 3$
$\quad\quad 18 = 2 \times 3^2$
$\quad\quad$ g.c.f. $= 2 \times 3 = 6$
$\quad\quad$ l.c.m. $= 2^3 \times 3^2 = 72$
$\quad 24 \times 18 = 6 \times 72$

(c) $\quad 2 = 2$
$\quad\quad 10 = 2 \times 5$
$\quad\quad$ g.c.f. $= 2$
$\quad\quad$ l.c.m. $= 2 \times 5 = 10$
$\quad 2 \times 10 = 2 \times 10$

(d) $\quad 8 = 2^3$
$\quad\quad 14 = 2 \times 7$
$\quad\quad$ g.c.f. $= 2$
$\quad\quad$ l.c.m. $= 2^3 \times 7 = 56$
$\quad 8 \times 14 = 2 \times 56$

THE RATIONAL NUMBERS

INTRODUCTION

The first section of the *Rhind Papyrus,* an Egyptian writing on mathematics, circa 1700 B.C., contains a table of quotients resulting when 2 is divided by an odd number greater than 1 and less than 103. Today, we would express these quotients by means of fractions, namely $\frac{2}{3}, \frac{2}{5}, \frac{2}{7}, \frac{9}{2}, \ldots$; but the Egyptians apparently had symbols only for unit fractions such as $\frac{1}{2}, \frac{1}{3}, \frac{1}{4}$ $\left(\text{the single exception was } \frac{2}{3}\right)$. Nevertheless, they were quite familiar with the concept of a numeral denoting a part of a whole and could use their complicated symbolism to solve some relatively sophisticated problems. Picture to yourself the necessity of having to represent $\frac{47}{60}$ by

or by

In each case, this is equivalent to our $\frac{1}{3} + \frac{1}{4} + \frac{1}{5}$ —all this *before beginning calculations* involving forty-seven parts from a total of sixty.

In the succeeding 3600 or so years, man has developed different and more efficient means for expressing numbers used to denote parts of a whole; he has been able, moreover, to fit these numbers into larger and more versatile systems, and to view them simply as special cases of numbers behaving according to a few powerful laws.

Numbers denoted by fractions such as $\frac{1}{3}$, $\frac{1}{4}$, or $\frac{47}{60}$ are called *rational numbers*. It is our purpose in this booklet to develop an intuitive notion of what these numbers are, to determine alternative ways of representing them, and to see what we can do with them. Although there are negative rational numbers, just as there are negative integers, we shall here consider only positive numbers.

CONGRUENT REGIONS

One way of approaching the notion of a rational number is through the consideration of congruent regions in the plane. These are regions such that a tracing of the boundary of any one of them can be made to fit the boundary of any other one perfectly. They might, for example, be subregions of a given region, as illustrated in Figure 1.

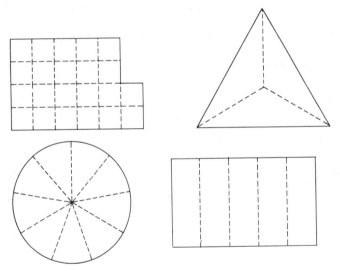

FIGURE 1

Alternatively, they might be discrete regions such as the circular ones or the square ones shown in Figure 2.

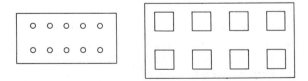

FIGURE 2

Now, let us count the congruent regions in each of the six illustrations of sets of congruent regions shown in Figures 1 and 2. For each successive set, the number of congruent regions is given by the respective entry in Table I.

TABLE I

Figure	1(a)	1(b)	1(c)	1(d)	2(a)	2(b)
Total Number of Congruent Regions	22	3	9	5	10	8

Next, let us choose certain of these congruent regions in each set, and let us indicate the regions chosen by shading them as indicated in Figure 3.

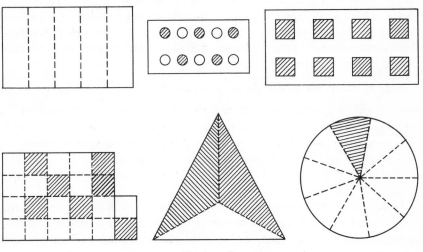

FIGURE 3

In Table I we recorded the number of congruent regions in the successive illustrations. Let us now record also the corresponding number of chosen (shaded) regions, as shown in Table II.

If we associate the number of chosen regions with the corresponding total number of congruent regions, writing the result in this form:

$(7, 22)$, $(2, 3)$, $(1, 9)$, $(0, 5)$, $(5, 10)$, $(8, 8)$,

TABLE II

Figure 3	a	b	c	d	e	f
Number of Congruent Regions Shaded	7	2	1	0	5	8
Total Number of Congruent Regions	22	3	9	5	10	8

or in this form:

$$\frac{7}{22}, \quad \frac{2}{3}, \quad \frac{1}{9}, \quad \frac{0}{5}, \quad \frac{5}{10}, \quad \frac{8}{8},$$

then we have taken a first step toward an understanding of what a rational number is.

Note that in the first form (the ordered-pair form) the number of chosen regions is written *first,* and the total number of regions is written *second.* In the second form (the fractional form) the chosen number of regions is written *above* the bar, and the total number is written *below* the bar. Both forms serve the same purpose: to indicate which is the chosen number and which is the total number.

Note also that one of the above examples is $(0, 5)$, or $\frac{0}{5}$; we have chosen *none* of the five congruent regions. Physically, this sort of situation is quite meaningful and significant. On the other hand, 0 never appears as second entry; we never consider the given set of congruent regions to consist of *no* congruent region. The only possible number of congruent regions that could then be chosen would be 0, hardly an interesting situation.

To review the foregoing material, you might record in ordered-pair form and also in fractional form the result of considering the unshaded regions, instead of the shaded regions, as being the chosen regions in Figure 3; and you might also construct other sets of congruent regions of still different shapes.

UNIT FIGURES

It might be noted regarding the number pairs formed from Table II:

$$(7, 22), \quad (2, 3), \quad (1, 8), \quad (0, 5), \quad (5, 10), \quad (8, 8),$$

that the first number is never greater than the second. How could we possibly choose more than all of the congruent regions in a set?

Let us, however, extend our notions a bit by considering several replications—or an indefinite number of replications—of any of our sets of congruent regions, as shown in Figure 4. Each replication is an exact copy of every other replication. When we consider such a set of replications, we call each replication a *unit figure*.

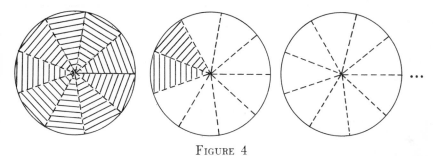

FIGURE 4

Our concern now is not with how many unit figures we have; we ordinarily shall consider, in fact, that we have an indefinite number of them. Rather, as before, we are concerned first with the *number of congruent regions that make up a unit figure*, and secondly with the *total number of congruent regions chosen from all the unit figures taken together*.

Thus in Figure 4 there are 9 congruent regions in each unit figure, and 11 congruent regions have been chosen (shaded); to describe this, we write (11, 9) or $\frac{11}{9}$.

We can interpret Figure 4, for example, in terms of a baseball team (consisting of nine regular players plus one extra pitcher and one utility player) by identifying the congruent regions with individual players, and identifying a unit figure with the set of players of the team permitted on the field at one time during the game.

LINEAR REPRESENTATION

For uniformity, let us now use only congruent squares as unit figures; and let us subdivide them by means of vertical dashed-line segments into congruent regions only. Thus in Figure 5 the successive congruent unit figures after the first are divided into two, three, and four congruent regions by means of one, two, and three dashed lines, respectively.

Further, starting with an original unit figure, let us string successive

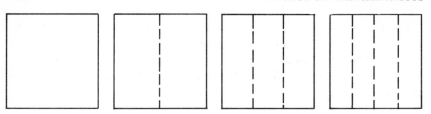

Figure 5

unit figures after it, proceeding to the right, as in Figure 6. Here, by way of illustration, each unit figure is divided into three congruent regions.

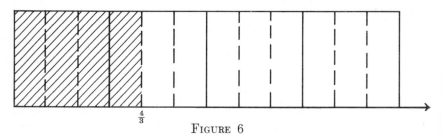

Figure 6

Also, in choosing (shading) congruent regions, let us agree, unless otherwise indicated, to take consecutive ones starting at the extreme left, and to record our choice in fraction form, beside the lower right-hand corner of the last chosen region.

It is not necessary, however, to wait until a choice has been made before recording how we would indicate various choices. This has been done for four unit figures consisting of three congruent regions each, as shown in Figure 7.

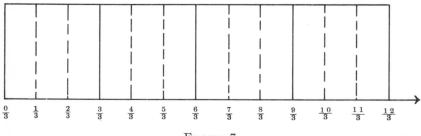

Figure 7

If you are acquainted with the number line, you are probably beginning to recognize an old friend! If you are not acquainted with the number line, or even if you are, you might at this time want to read the material on the number line in Booklet No. 1: *Sets*, and in Booklet No. 2: *The Whole Numbers.*

As one further item of preparedness for choices, let us consider each unit figure as being subdivided into different numbers of congruent regions. For example, in Figure 8 the unit figure is subdivided into two congruent

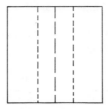

FIGURE 8

regions by the dashed line, and into three congruent regions by the dotted lines. This is further illustrated, for rectangular unit figures consisting of one, two, three, and four congruent regions, in Figure 9.

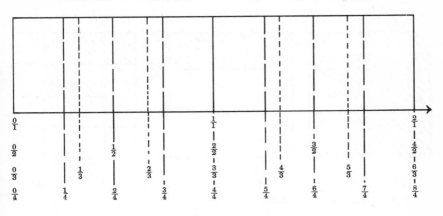

FIGURE 9

To simplify our discussion, let us now concentrate our attention on the common base line of the unit figures, considering congruent line segments in place of congruent regions, as shown in Figure 10.

$$\frac{0}{1} \quad\quad \frac{1}{4} \;\; \frac{1}{3} \quad\quad \frac{1}{2} \quad\quad \frac{2}{3} \;\; \frac{3}{4} \quad\quad \frac{1}{1} \quad\quad \frac{5}{4} \;\; \frac{4}{3} \quad\quad \frac{3}{2} \quad\quad \frac{5}{3} \;\; \frac{7}{4} \quad\quad \frac{2}{1}$$

$$\frac{0}{2} \quad\quad\quad\quad \frac{1}{2} \quad\quad\quad\quad \frac{2}{2} \quad\quad\quad\quad \frac{3}{2} \quad\quad\quad\quad \frac{4}{2}$$

$$\frac{0}{3} \quad\quad\quad \frac{1}{3} \quad\quad\quad \frac{2}{3} \quad\quad\quad \frac{3}{3} \quad\quad\quad \frac{4}{3} \quad\quad\quad \frac{5}{3} \quad\quad\quad \frac{6}{3}$$

$$\frac{0}{4} \quad\quad \frac{1}{4} \quad\quad \frac{2}{4} \quad\quad \frac{3}{4} \quad\quad \frac{4}{4} \quad\quad \frac{5}{4} \quad\quad \frac{6}{4} \quad\quad \frac{7}{4} \quad\quad \frac{8}{4}$$

FIGURE 10

Exercise Set 1

1. What ordered pair of numbers is associated with the shaded part in each of the following unit regions?

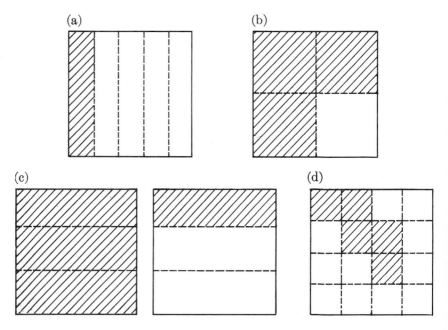

2. What ordered pair of numbers is associated with the unshaded region in each unit region in Exercise 1?

3. (a) What does the symbol $\frac{0}{7}$ mean when it corresponds to a point on a number line?

(b) What does the symbol $\frac{5}{9}$ mean in terms of congruent regions?

(c) Why is it impossible to speak of $\frac{8}{0}$ as a symbol related to sets of discrete objects?

4. Using , which contains six discrete objects, as a unit figure,

make drawings to show $\frac{15}{6}, \frac{8}{6}, \frac{4}{6}, \frac{5}{6}, \frac{13}{6}$.

5. Write fractions that correspond to all the indicated points on the number lines in Figure 11.

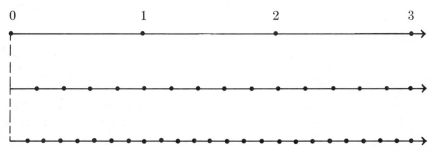

FIGURE 11

RATIONAL NUMBERS

Suppose a child is shown a set of blocks, as illustrated in Figure 12. If he is asked how many blocks there are in the set, he might answer: "Three." If so, he is beginning to become acquainted with the abstract notion of *counting number*.

FIGURE 12

In the same way, somewhat later in his mental development, he might be asked what *rational number* is represented by the configuration shown in Figure 13. To avoid the possibility of misunderstanding, however, it should be made entirely clear to him just what objects (corresponding to the congruent regions we have been discussing) are being considered, and how many of the objects are being taken to constitute a unit figure. Here

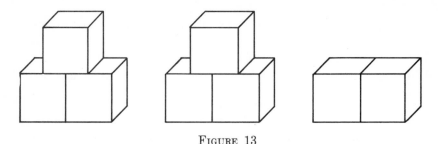

the objects are the blocks, and a unit figure consists of three blocks. Accepting the convention that a unit figure now consists of three blocks, he will answer: "Eight-thirds."

The rational numbers, then, are abstract mathematical ideas, just as are the counting numbers. They can be made to correspond to points on the number line, as illustrated in Figure 10. Further, we can denote rational numbers by means of fractions, which are *numerals* (names of numbers).

Thus if, on the number line, we divide each unit figure—in this case a unit interval—into the same number (say 10) of congruent regions (or congruent subintervals) and take a certain number (say 23) of these, starting at the extreme left, then we say that the right-hand endpoint of the last subinterval we have taken corresponds to a rational number, which we represent by a fraction $\left(\dfrac{23}{10}\text{ in our present example}\right)$.

In the example we have just given, the number 23 is called the *numerator* of the fraction because it expresses the number of chosen subintervals. The number 10 is called the *denominator* because it denotes the number of congruent subintervals into which the unit intervals are divided.

A twelve-inch ruler, for example, might be marked in preparation for approximate measurements with fractions having denominators 1, 2, 4, 8, and 16. We do not count these sets of marks each time, for we are familiar with them. The numerator, on the other hand, varies from measurement to measurement and is ordinarily determined in part by counting. In the metric system, of course, the denominators would be 1, 10, and 100.

One cannot recall too emphatically that, though it makes perfectly good sense for the numerator of a fraction to be 0, the denominator is never 0.

To become quite familiar with all these notions, one should construct several number lines to show different denominators, and on each of them locate and name several points corresponding to rational numbers.

DIFFERENT FRACTIONS FOR THE SAME RATIONAL NUMBER

On the number line of Figure 9, as well as of Figure 10, the point at the right-hand end of the first unit figure—or unit segment—has been denoted by several different numerals: $\frac{1}{1}, \frac{2}{2}, \frac{3}{3},$ and $\frac{4}{4}.$ We write

$$\frac{1}{1}=\frac{2}{2}=\frac{3}{3}=\frac{4}{4},$$

meaning that these fractions all name the same rational number. Similarly, we have

$$\frac{0}{1}=\frac{0}{2}=\frac{0}{3}=\frac{0}{4},$$

$$\frac{2}{1}=\frac{4}{2}=\frac{6}{3}=\frac{8}{4},$$

$$\frac{1}{2}=\frac{2}{4}, \ \frac{3}{2}=\frac{6}{4},$$

and so on.

It is easy to see a pattern emerging here, and almost as easy to understand it. We know that

$$\frac{1}{3}=\frac{2}{6}$$

because for the second expression, $\frac{2}{6},$ we have divided the unit interval into twice as many subintervals as for the first expression, $\frac{1}{3},$ but we have also taken twice as many of the smaller subintervals.

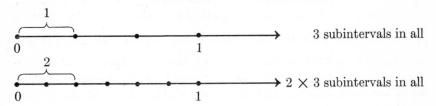

3 subintervals in all

2 × 3 subintervals in all

FIGURE 14

If the numerator and denominator of a given fraction are both multiplied by the same counting number (0 is excluded!), then the resulting fraction names the same rational number as does the given fraction.

A better understanding of the foregoing rule can be acquired by showing on the number line how it is that

$$\frac{1}{3}=\frac{3}{9}, \qquad \frac{6}{5}=\frac{12}{10}=\frac{18}{15}, \qquad \text{etc.}$$

The same rule works in reverse: We have

$$\frac{8}{12}=\frac{2}{3},$$

because in the second expression, $\frac{2}{3}$, we have divided the unit interval into only one-fourth as many subintervals as in the first expression, $\frac{8}{12}$; but we have also taken only one-fourth as many of the unit intervals. Thus, for the second expression we have combined four of the subintervals for the first expression into larger subintervals, but then we have taken only one-fourth as many of the larger subintervals as we have of the smaller ones.

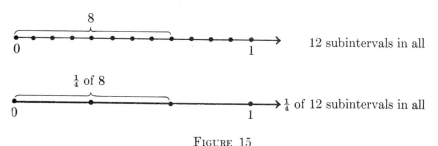

FIGURE 15

A word of caution regarding the reverse rule is required here. It will be recalled that we always divide our unit intervals into a counting number of subintervals, and then take only a whole number of these. The fraction $\frac{8}{12}$, for example, indicates that we have divided the unit interval into 12 congruent subintervals and taken 8 of these. To obtain an alternative fraction name for the same number, we would not, for instance, combine the 12 congruent subintervals into sets of 5 each, for then the unit interval would not be divided into congruent subintervals, since 5 is not a factor of 12; see Figure 16(a). As far as the denominator is concerned, we might combine the subintervals into sets of 3 each, since 3 is a factor of 12—but then we would not have taken a whole number of these, since 3 is not a factor of 8; see Figure 16(b). We might, however, combine the subintervals into sets of 4 each, since 4 is a factor both of 12 and of 8; see Figure 16(c).

It would be advantageous at this point to review the material on factors and multiples, common factors and common multiples, and greatest com-

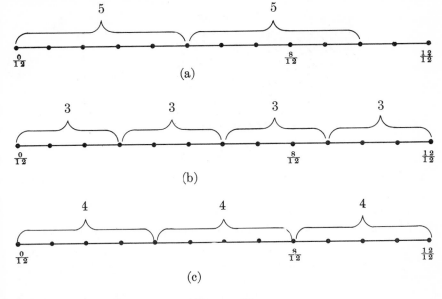

FIGURE 16

mon factor and least common multiple in Booklet No. 5: *Numbers and Their Factors.*

We have illustrated the following rule:

> *If the numerator and denominator of a given fraction are both divided by a common factor of the numerator and the denominator, then the resulting fraction names the same rational number as does the given fraction.*

In particular, if the numerator and denominator of a fraction naming a rational number are both divided by their greatest common divisor, then the rational number is given its *simplest fraction name.*

For example, to find the simplest fraction name of the rational number named by $\frac{36}{48}$, write 36 and 48 as products of prime factors,

$$36 = 2 \times 2 \times 3 \times 3,$$
$$48 = 2 \times 2 \times 2 \times 2 \times 3.$$

Observe that the greatest common factor is

$$2 \times 2 \times 3 = 12,$$

and divide both 36 and 48 by 12 to obtain

$$\frac{36}{48} = \frac{3}{4};$$

accordingly, the simplest fraction name for our rational number is $\frac{3}{4}$.

Exercise Set 2

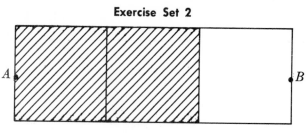

FIGURE 17

1. What fraction is associated with the shaded part of the rectangular unit region in Figure 17?

2. Draw a dotted line segment from point A to point B (Fig. 17). What fraction is now associated with the shaded part of the unit region?

3. (a) After the dotted line segment from point A to point B has been drawn, each subinterval of the unit region has been separated into how many congruent regions?

   (b) Is 2 a common factor of the numerator and denominator in the fraction $\frac{4}{6}$?

   (c) When the numerator and denominator of the fraction $\frac{4}{6}$ are both divided by 2, does the resulting fraction name the same rational number that $\frac{4}{6}$ names?

4. (a) Write 35 as a product of prime factors.

   (b) Write 49 as a product of prime factors.

   (c) What is the greatest common factor of 35 and 49?

   (d) Write the simplest fraction for the rational number named by $\frac{35}{49}$.

5. Show that $\frac{12}{52} = \frac{30}{130}$ by finding the simplest fraction names for each of these rational numbers.

EQUAL DENOMINATORS

In much of our work with the fractions that name rational numbers, it is convenient to have the numbers named by fractions with the same denominator. Is this always possible?

Consider, for example, the rational numbers named by $\frac{1}{4}$ and $\frac{2}{3}$. These are picture on the number line in Figure 18. Geometrically, the question is

FIGURE 18

this: Can we divide the unit interval into congruent subintervals in such a way that a point of division falls on the point corresponding to $\frac{1}{4}$ and so that a point of division *also* falls on the point corresponding to $\frac{2}{3}$?

One sure way to do this is to divide the interval into $4 \times 3 = 12$ congruent subintervals, as shown in Figure 19, because 4 is a factor of 4×3, and so is

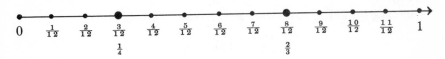

FIGURE 19

3 a factor of 4×3. We have

$$\frac{1}{4} = \frac{3}{12} \quad \text{and} \quad \frac{2}{3} = \frac{8}{12}.$$

Thus the two rational numbers $\frac{1}{4}$ and $\frac{2}{3}$ have been renamed by fractions with a common denominator 12. Note that this number, 12, is the same as the least common multiple * of 3 and 4.

If you want to name $\frac{1}{4}, \frac{2}{3},$ and $\frac{3}{5}$ by fractions which have the same denominator, you must find a common multiple (say the least common multiple) of 3, 4, and 5. We know that the least common multiple of 3 and 4 is 12; then we must find the least common multiple of 12 and 5. Since 5 is prime, the least common multiple is 12×5, or 60, and we write

$$\frac{1}{4} = \frac{1 \times 15}{4 \times 15} = \frac{15}{60},$$

$$\frac{2}{3} = \frac{2 \times 20}{3 \times 20} = \frac{40}{60},$$

$$\frac{3}{5} = \frac{3 \times 12}{5 \times 12} = \frac{36}{60}.$$

---

* Discussed in Booklet No. 5: *Numbers and Their Factors.*

EQUIVALENT FRACTIONS

We have seen that a rational number may have more than one fraction name. In fact, every rational number has indefinitely many fraction names. For example:

$$\frac{3}{4} = \frac{2 \times 3}{2 \times 4} = \frac{3 \times 3}{3 \times 4} = \frac{4 \times 3}{4 \times 4} = \frac{5 \times 3}{5 \times 4} = \cdots .$$

The question naturally arises: How can we tell whether or not two given fractions name the same rational number?

There is a point on the number line associated with each of two fractions. This point corresponds to a number. If one and the same point corresponds to both fractions, then the two fractions name the same number.

Suppose, for example, we want to determine whether or not

$$\frac{11}{52} \quad \text{and} \quad \frac{4}{17}$$

name the same rational number.

The rational numbers named by $\frac{11}{52}$ and $\frac{4}{17}$ can be expressed by fractions having the same denominator, and the numbers can then be compared by comparing the numerators. The least common multiple of 52 and 17, which is 52×17, can be used as the common denominator (it is, in fact, the least common denominator).

We write

$$\frac{11}{52} = \frac{17 \times 11}{17 \times 52} = \frac{187}{52 \times 17},$$

$$\frac{4}{17} = \frac{52 \times 4}{52 \times 17} = \frac{208}{52 \times 17}.$$

It is not necessary to carry out the multiplication indicated by 52×17, for both denominators indicate that we should divide the unit interval into the *same number* of congruent subintervals, whatever that number is. Looking at the two numerators, we see that we would take a larger number (208 as compared to 187) of the congruent subintervals in locating the point that corresponds to the second rational number than we would in locating the point that corresponds to the first. Thus the points would not coincide, and hence they would not correspond to the same rational number.

Again, to test whether or not

$$\frac{323}{133} \quad \text{and} \quad \frac{221}{91}$$

are names for the same number, we write

$$\frac{323}{133} = \frac{91 \times 323}{91 \times 133} = \frac{29{,}393}{91 \times 133},$$

$$\frac{221}{91} = \frac{133 \times 221}{133 \times 91} = \frac{29{,}393}{91 \times 133},$$

and conclude, since the numerators as well as the denominators are now equal, that these two fractions do name the same rational number; that is,

$$\frac{323}{133} = \frac{221}{91}.$$

Two fractions that name the same rational number, such as $\frac{323}{133}$ and $\frac{221}{91}$, are said to be *equivalent*.

If, in his own words, the reader can formulate and understand a rule for testing whether or not two fractions name the same rational number, that is, whether or not the two fractions are equivalent, then he probably has mastered the material of this section quite well.

ORDERING OF THE RATIONAL NUMBERS

In the preceding section we saw that the rational numbers named by $\frac{11}{52}$ and $\frac{4}{17}$ correspond to different points on the number line. We say that these numbers are *not equal*, or that they are *unequal*, and in symbols we express this fact by writing

$$\frac{11}{52} \neq \frac{4}{17}.$$

We saw more, however. Explicitly, when we note that

$$\frac{4}{17} = \frac{208}{52 \times 17},$$

and that

$$\frac{11}{52} = \frac{187}{52 \times 17},$$

it is evident that the point on the number line corresponding to the rational number named by $\frac{4}{17}$ lies to the right of the point corresponding to the rational number named by $\frac{11}{52}$. We say that the first of these numbers is *greater than* the second, or that the second is *less than* the first, expressing this in symbols by

$$\frac{4}{17} > \frac{11}{52} \quad \text{or} \quad \frac{11}{52} < \frac{4}{17}.$$

Note that the fraction naming the greater rational number appears on the open side of the inequality symbol, and the fraction naming the lesser rational number appears on the closed side of the symbol. In the same way, we have

$$\frac{1}{2} < \frac{2}{3}, \qquad \frac{7}{4} > \frac{3}{2}, \qquad \frac{1}{1} < \frac{2}{1}.$$

We have seen that each rational number can be made to correspond to a point on the number line. For any two given rational numbers, the point corresponding to the first number lies to the left of the point corresponding to the second number, coincides with it, or lies to the right of it. Thus, for any two given rational numbers, the first is either less than, equal to, or greater than the second. For this reason, we say that the set of rational numbers is *ordered*, or that there is an *order relation* between pairs of its members.

Suppose we wish to determine the order relation between the rational numbers named by $\frac{4}{17}$ and $\frac{10}{52}$, when we already know that $\frac{4}{17} > \frac{11}{52}$. Is the first rational number less than, equal to, or greater than the second?

Here is a short cut that we can readily understand by considering corresponding points on the number line: We have seen in a previous example that we have

$$\frac{4}{17} > \frac{11}{52},$$

and of course we have

$$\frac{11}{52} > \frac{10}{52},$$

since the denominators are equal and $11 > 10$. We therefore conclude that

$$\frac{4}{17} > \frac{10}{52}.$$

The reason for this conclusion is, of course, that since the first representative point is to the right of the second on the number line, and the second is to the right of the third on the number line, the first must be to the right of the third.

We describe this by saying that "$>$" is a *transitive relation;* that is, if a first rational number is greater than a second rational number, and the second is greater than a third, then the first is greater than the third. Similarly, "$<$" is a transitive relation.

For a quick review of the material in this section, you might use the notion of transitivity and the foregoing inequalities to determine the order relation between the rational numbers named by

$$\frac{5}{17} \quad \text{and} \quad \frac{9}{52}.$$

Exercise Set 3

Determine the order relation between each of the following pairs by multiplying the numerator and denominator of each fraction by the denominator of the other fraction. The first problem is completed for you.

1. $\frac{5}{17} \quad \text{and} \quad \frac{9}{52}$

$$\frac{5}{17} = \frac{5 \times 52}{17 \times 52} = \frac{260}{17 \times 52}$$

$$\frac{9}{52} = \frac{9 \times 17}{52 \times 17} = \frac{153}{52 \times 17}$$

Since $17 \times 52 = 52 \times 17$, it is not necessary to find what number this product represents. The order relation of the two fractions can be determined from the numerators of the fractions, $\frac{260}{17 \times 52}$ and $\frac{153}{52 \times 17}$.

Since 260 is greater that 153, $\frac{5}{17} > \frac{9}{52}$.

2. $\frac{28}{3} \quad \text{and} \quad \frac{30}{4}$

3. $\frac{17}{20} \quad \text{and} \quad \frac{15}{19}$

4. $\frac{9}{13} \quad \text{and} \quad \frac{8}{11}$

WHOLE NUMBERS AND RATIONAL NUMBERS

Below the number line in Figure 10, we showed certain fractions that name rational numbers represented by points on the line. We arrived at the notion of these rational numbers by considering each unit figure as consisting of a certain *counting number* of congruent parts, and then taking a *whole number* of these parts. In fact, then, we *used* the notion of a counting number and the notion of a whole number in developing the notion of a rational number.

Above the number line of Figure 10 let us now put the symbol 0, naming the whole number 0, at the extreme left; and let us record the counting numerals 1, 2, 3, . . . as we count the successive unit intervals, as shown in Figure 20.

FIGURE 20

This suggests a useful *correspondence* between the whole numbers and certain rational numbers, as indicated in Figure 20. This correspondence is indicated in Table III. To each whole number there corresponds exactly one rational number (of course, each number has many names), and to

TABLE III

Whole Number Name	0	1	2	3	. . .
Rational Number Name	$\frac{0}{1}$	$\frac{1}{1}$	$\frac{2}{1}$	$\frac{3}{1}$	. . .

each rational number in the set $\left\{\frac{0}{1}, \frac{1}{1}, \frac{2}{1}, \frac{3}{1}, \ldots\right\}$ there corresponds exactly one whole number. For this reason, we say that the correspondence is one-to-one.

What is more, this identification is consistent with the relations between the elements of the set of whole numbers on the one hand, and the elements of the set $\left\{\frac{0}{1}, \frac{1}{1}, \frac{2}{1}, \ldots\right\}$ on the other, and with the operations we perform on them. Thus, for example, in the whole-number system we have

$$1 < 3,$$

and in the rational-number system we have

$$\frac{1}{1} < \frac{3}{1},$$

in accordance with the correspondence indicated in Table III. Again, in the whole-number system we have

$$1 + 2 = 3,$$

and in the rational-number system we shall presently define addition in such a way that

$$\frac{1}{1} + \frac{2}{1} = \frac{3}{1}.$$

It will be the same when we discuss multiplication.

Because of this consistency of relations and operations, we say that the system of whole numbers is *imbedded* in the system of rational numbers. Accordingly, from this point of view, the system of whole numbers can be considered as a subsystem of the system of rational numbers, and this is the view that we shall henceforth take.

SUMMARY

Up to this point we have concerned ourselves largely with investigating and developing our intuitive notion of what a rational number is. In doing this, we have found it convenient to distinguish between rational numbers and their various names. We have also distinguished between whole numbers and the corresponding rational numbers, but have pointed out how we can (and shall) consider the set of whole numbers as a subset of the set of rational numbers.

Now, however, that we are familiar with the rational numbers and want to work with them—or have them work for us—we shall call them by their familiar names. Thus we shall speak of the rational numbers two-thirds $\left(\dfrac{2}{3}\right)$ and five-fourths $\left(\dfrac{5}{4}\right)$, and even of the rational number three (3)

At this time, let us briefly review some of the things we have done, but in doing so, let us use letters to represent whole numbers.

When we name a rational number by the fraction $\dfrac{a}{b}$, where a is a whole number and b is a counting number, we think of each unit interval on the number line as being subdivided into b congruent subintervals, and of our taking the first a of these.

The number b is the denominator of the fraction $\dfrac{a}{b}$ and the number a is its numerator.

The fraction $\dfrac{a}{b}$ is the simplest fractional name of the rational number it represents, provided that a and b have no common factor greater than 1. Henceforth, however, if $b=1$, we shall ordinarily write a rather than $\dfrac{a}{1}$.

The simplest fractional name is not always the most useful one for a particular purpose. The name $\dfrac{n \times a}{n \times b}$, where n is a counting number, is often more useful for a particular purpose than is a given name $\dfrac{a}{b}$.

For example, to compare

$$\frac{a}{b} \quad \text{with} \quad \frac{c}{d},$$

we write

$$\frac{a}{b}=\frac{d\times a}{d\times b}=\frac{a\times d}{b\times d} \quad \text{and} \quad \frac{c}{d}=\frac{b\times c}{b\times d},$$

and compare

$$\frac{a\times d}{b\times d} \quad \text{with} \quad \frac{b\times c}{b\times d}.$$

But now the denominators are equal, and so (remember the number line!) we have only to compare the numerators; that is, we have to compare

$$a\times d \quad \text{with} \quad b\times c.$$

Accordingly, $\frac{a}{b}$ is less than, equal to, or greater than $\frac{c}{d}$ according as $a\times d$ is less than, equal to, or greater than $b\times c$. This observation is often called the *cross-product rule.*

As we know, the symbol "$>$" is read "is greater than" or "greater than," and the symbol "$<$" is read "is less than" or "less than." With this symbolism, the results in the preceding paragraph can be written

$$\frac{a}{b}<\frac{c}{d} \text{ if, and only if, } a\times d<b\times c,$$

$$\frac{a}{b}=\frac{c}{d} \text{ if, and only if, } a\times d=b\times c,$$

$$\frac{a}{b}>\frac{c}{d} \text{ if, and only if, } a\times d>b\times c.$$

The relations $>$ and $<$ are transitive; thus, if

$$\frac{a}{b}<\frac{c}{d} \quad \text{and} \quad \frac{c}{d}<\frac{e}{f}, \quad \text{then} \quad \frac{a}{b}<\frac{e}{f}.$$

THE RATIONAL NUMBERS BETWEEN 0 AND 1

It is quite instructive to try to visualize the set of points on the number line corresponding to all the rational numbers. Let us concentrate, though, on just those rational numbers between 0 and 1.

Is there a *next* rational number after 0, in the sense that 1 is the next whole number after 0? Think of it in this way: $\frac{1}{3}$ is less than $\frac{1}{2}$, $\frac{1}{4}$ is less than $\frac{1}{3}$, $\frac{1}{5}$ is less than $\frac{1}{4}$, etc., as shown in Figure 21.

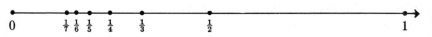

FIGURE 21

It is easier, and perhaps more suggestive, if we choose successive numbers in such a way that, each time we indicate another corresponding point, we divide the interval that has just been determined into two congruent parts, as indicated in Figure 22. Thus, $\frac{1}{2}<1, \frac{1}{4}<\frac{1}{2}, \frac{1}{8}<\frac{1}{4}, \frac{1}{16}<\frac{1}{8}$, and so on.

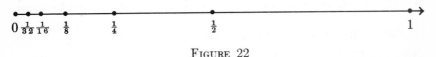

$$0 \quad \tfrac{1}{32} \tfrac{1}{16} \quad \tfrac{1}{8} \qquad \tfrac{1}{4} \qquad\qquad \tfrac{1}{2} \qquad\qquad\qquad 1$$

FIGURE 22

Accordingly, we see that there is no next rational number after 0.

Proof:

Let $\frac{a}{b}$ be any rational number other than 0, where a and b are counting numbers. Consider the fraction

$$\frac{a}{2\times b}.$$

This names a nonzero rational number because the numerator a and the denominator $2\times b$ are counting numbers. Now

$$\frac{a}{2\times b}<\frac{a}{b},$$

because

$$a\times b<2\times b\times a. \qquad \text{(See Summary, pages 21-22.)}$$

Hence, for any given nonzero rational number we have found another nonzero rational number that is less than the given number.

In a similar way, between any two given rational numbers we can find a third rational number. If between any two rational numbers there is a third, however, then between the first and third there must be a fourth, and so on. Accordingly, between any two rational numbers there must be indefinitely many rational numbers, as suggested in Figure 22 for the rational numbers 0 and 1. We describe this situation by saying that the set of rational numbers is *dense.*

Now let us try to enumerate the rational numbers between 0 and 1 in a systematic way, taking a first one, then a second one, and so on, in such a way that any given rational number ultimately will be chosen. Is this possible? We cannot do it by taking the rational numbers in their natural order, since, for example, there is no next rational number after 0.

Let us, however, first take the rational number $\frac{1}{2}$; then, those named by fractions with denominator 3 and numerators in increasing order $\left(\frac{1}{3}, \frac{2}{3}\right)$; then, those named by fractions with denominator 4 and numerators in increasing order $\left(\frac{1}{4}, \frac{2}{4}, \frac{3}{4}\right)$; and so on. But now let us omit $\frac{2}{4}$ because we have already included this number under its simplest fraction name $\frac{1}{2}$. Do you see how it is that any given rational number, say $\frac{127}{45,678}$, would ultimately be given a place in this enumeration?

Thus we have suggested a systematic method of putting the set of rational numbers that are between 0 and 1 in *one-to-one correspondence with the set of counting numbers* (Fig. 23). From this we see that, in this

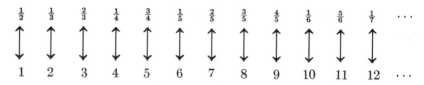

FIGURE 23

sense, there are just as many rational numbers between 0 and 1 as there are elements in the set of counting numbers.

OPERATIONS ON THE RATIONAL NUMBERS

We have observed that it is convenient to use the numerals for the whole numbers as alternative names for special rational numbers,

$$0 = \frac{0}{1}, \qquad 1 = \frac{1}{1}, \qquad 2 = \frac{2}{1}, \qquad 3 = \frac{3}{1}, \qquad \text{etc.;}$$

and even to consider the set of whole numbers as a subset of the set of rational numbers.

This identification would be quite awkward if, when we get around to defining addition for the rational numbers, we should have, for example,

$$\frac{1}{1} + \frac{3}{1} = \frac{2}{1},$$

for then we would have

$$1 + 3 = 2.$$

when the symbols "1", "3", and "2" represent rational numbers, but we would have

$$1+2=3$$

when they represent whole numbers.

Fortunately, though, this is not the case. Addition is defined for the rational numbers in such a way that

$$1+2=3,$$

whether these symbols stand for whole numbers or for the corresponding rational numbers.

Thus, as we shall see, the use of the familiar numerals for the whole numbers as symbols for these particular rational numbers is consistent in regard to the fundamental operations of addition and multiplication and the inverse operations of subtraction and division. We have already seen that it is consistent in regard to the comparison of numbers.

It should not be surprising that this is so, since *we shall always appeal to our notions regarding the whole numbers in defining what is meant by operations on rational numbers.* Thus consistency will be virtually automatic. We could define operations on the rationals in whatever way we choose, but in fact we do choose to let the system of whole numbers and our intuitive notions regarding it be our model.

For this reason, it would be advantageous for the reader now to review the definitions of addition and multiplication of whole numbers, and also their properties of closure, associativity, etc., as discussed in Booklet No. 2: *The Whole Numbers.*

ADDITION OF RATIONAL NUMBERS

From a mathematical point of view, it would be quite in order to start with a formal definition of addition of rational numbers. In other words, we could write in general terms what we shall mean by the addition of two rational numbers $\frac{a}{b}$ and $\frac{c}{d}$.

From an intuitive point of view, however, this would be an unsatisfactory approach. It is preferable to take a look once again at the number line to see if we can get any ideas of how we think two rational numbers should be added. Also we should remind ouselves of the system of whole numbers as a model. We already know about addition of whole numbers. Thus,

$$6+7=13$$

is a familiar addition fact involving three whole numbers. Also, 6 and 7 are names for rational numbers. We want to be sure that the sum of these rational numbers is the rational number named by 13.

If we proceed along these lines, we will be *led* to a definition of addition of rational numbers that will have the various properties we would want it to have, such as commutativity and associativity.

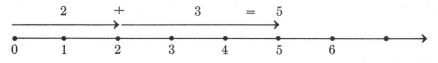

FIGURE 24

The sum $2+3$ can be illustrated on the number line, as shown in Figure 24. The point corresponding to 2 is located by counting off two unit segments starting at the point 0. Then three unit segments are counted off to the right from the point corresponding to 2, and the point corresponding to 5 is reached. Of course, we could have located the point corresponding to 3 first and then counted off two unit segments to the right from this point, again arriving at the point corresponding to 5, as shown in Figure 25.

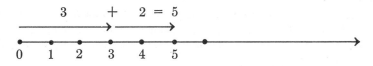

FIGURE 25

Let us use the number line to see what point should correspond to the sum of the rational numbers $\frac{7}{7}$ and $\frac{2}{7}$. See Figure 26. The first two unit

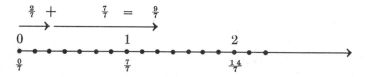

FIGURE 26

segments have been separated into seven congruent parts each. The point corresponding to $\frac{2}{7}$ is located first by counting off two of the congruent parts. From this point, seven of the congruent parts $\left(\text{representing } \dfrac{7}{7}\right)$ are counted off to the right. The point reached corresponds to $\dfrac{9}{7}$. This means that from number-line considerations we would want the sum of $\dfrac{2}{7}$ and $\dfrac{7}{7}$ to be $\dfrac{9}{7}$, and we would write

$$\frac{2}{7} + \frac{7}{7} = \frac{9}{7}.$$

It is worth mentioning that just as the phrase $7+3$ is itself a numeral, rather than a command to "do some arithmetic," the phrase $\dfrac{2}{7} + \dfrac{7}{7}$ is a numeral when its meaning is defined as suggested above: $\dfrac{2}{7} + \dfrac{7}{7}$ then represents a rational number. The numeral $\dfrac{9}{7}$ is a simpler name for the number. Much of the work done in carrying out arithmetical computations really amounts to finding a simple name for a number expressed by a complicated numeral.

What point on the number line should correspond to the sum $\dfrac{7}{5} + \dfrac{3}{5}$? From Figure 27, we see that the desired point is the point corresponding to the

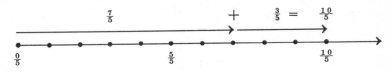

FIGURE 27

number $\dfrac{10}{5}$ (which has the simpler name, 2). Similarly, we could use the number line to show that we would want $\dfrac{3}{5} + \dfrac{7}{5}$ to name the same rational number, $\dfrac{10}{5}$.

The two examples given above have something in common. The expression $\dfrac{2}{7} + \dfrac{7}{7}$ involves two fractions with the same denominator, 7. In the expression $\dfrac{3}{5} + \dfrac{7}{5}$, both fractions have the number 5 as denominator. Notice that

$$\frac{2}{7} + \frac{7}{7} = \frac{9}{7} \quad \text{can be written} \quad \frac{2}{7} + \frac{7}{7} = \frac{2+7}{7},$$

and

$$\frac{3}{5}+\frac{7}{5}=\frac{10}{5} \quad \text{can be written} \quad \frac{3}{5}+\frac{7}{5}=\frac{3+7}{5}.$$

The numerator of the fraction $\frac{2+7}{7}$ is the sum of the numerators of the fractions $\frac{2}{7}$ and $\frac{7}{7}$, and the denominator of $\frac{2+7}{7}$ is the same as the common denominator of $\frac{2}{7}$ and $\frac{7}{7}$. Similarly, the fraction $\frac{3+7}{5}$ has the same denominator as the fractions $\frac{3}{5}$ and $\frac{7}{5}$, and its numerator is the sum of the numerators of $\frac{3}{5}$ and $\frac{7}{5}$.

From this, we are led to the following generalization: We define the *sum* of the rational numbers $\frac{a}{b}$ and $\frac{c}{b}$ to be $\frac{a+c}{b}$, no matter what whole numbers a and c are, and what counting number b is. More compactly, this can be written

$$\frac{a}{b}+\frac{c}{b}=\frac{a+c}{b},$$

where a and c are any whole numbers and b is any counting number.

Each of the following is a true sentence:

$$\frac{3}{11}+\frac{15}{11}=\frac{18}{11},$$

$$\frac{2}{2}+\frac{3}{2}=\frac{5}{2},$$

$$\frac{0}{8}+\frac{7}{8}=\frac{7}{8},$$

$$\frac{19}{100}+\frac{81}{100}=\frac{100}{100}.$$

Now let us find the sum of the rational numbers named by the fractions $\frac{2}{3}$ and $\frac{5}{7}$. The denominators of these fractions are not the same, and so it seems as if the definition that we have given in the preceding paragraph does not apply here. Remember, however, that we add rational numbers, not their names, and that any two rational numbers can be renamed by fractions with the same denominator. Thus we have

$$\frac{2}{3}=\frac{7\times2}{7\times3}=\frac{14}{21} \quad \text{and} \quad \frac{5}{7}=\frac{3\times5}{3\times7}=\frac{15}{21}.$$

We see that the fractions $\frac{14}{21}$ and $\frac{15}{21}$ can be used instead of $\frac{2}{3}$ and $\frac{5}{7}$ to name the two rational numbers whose sum we are seeking. Now the definition, as expressed by

$$\frac{a}{b}+\frac{c}{b}=\frac{a+c}{b},$$

can be applied:

$$\frac{14}{21}+\frac{15}{21}=\frac{14+15}{21}$$

$$=\frac{29}{21}.$$

The sum of the rational numbers named by the fractions $\frac{2}{3}$ and $\frac{5}{7}$ is the rational number named by $\frac{29}{21}$. The procedure in this example can be shown more compactly as follows:

$$\frac{2}{3}+\frac{5}{7}=\frac{7\times2}{7\times3}+\frac{3\times5}{3\times7}$$

$$=\frac{14}{21}+\frac{15}{21}$$

$$=\frac{14+15}{21}$$

$$=\frac{29}{21}.$$

You should note that

$$\frac{2}{3}+\frac{5}{7}, \quad \frac{7\times2}{7\times3}+\frac{3\times5}{3\times7}, \quad \frac{14}{21}+\frac{15}{21}, \quad \frac{14+15}{21}, \quad \text{and} \quad \frac{29}{21}$$

are all names for the same number, the last being the simplest name. Notice that $\frac{2}{3}+\frac{5}{7}$ was replaced by the more complicated name, $\frac{7\times2}{7\times3}+\frac{3\times5}{3\times7}$. There was a good reason for this: We wanted fractions with the same denominator.

The sum of the rational numbers $\frac{3}{4}$ and $\frac{7}{6}$ can be obtained in the same way:

$$\frac{3}{4}+\frac{7}{6}=\frac{6\times3}{6\times4}+\frac{4\times7}{4\times6}$$

$$=\frac{18}{24}+\frac{28}{24}$$

$$=\frac{18+28}{24}$$

$$=\frac{46}{24}.$$

The rational number $\frac{46}{24}$ is the sum of the rational numbers $\frac{3}{4}$ and $\frac{7}{6}$. The simplest name for this sum is $\frac{23}{12}$; the name is obtained by dividing both numerator and denominator of the fraction $\frac{46}{24}$ by 2.

There is really no compelling reason, however, for insisting that one must always write the simplest name for a sum.

Another agreement concerning language in speaking of rational numbers will be helpful. We allow ourselves to say, for example, that the sum of $\frac{3}{4}$ and $\frac{7}{6}$ is $\frac{46}{24}$. In such a statement, it is understood that we mean the rational number $\frac{3}{4}$, the rational number $\frac{7}{6}$, and the rational number $\frac{46}{24}$, not their fraction names, for names are not added.

Let $\frac{a}{b}$ and $\frac{c}{d}$ be rational numbers—where a and c are whole numbers, and b and d are counting numbers. The sum of $\frac{a}{b}$ and $\frac{c}{d}$ can be found by the same procedure used in the two preceding examples. Thus, we have

$$\frac{a}{b}+\frac{c}{d}=\frac{a\times d}{b\times d}+\frac{b\times c}{b\times d}$$

$$=\frac{(a\times d)+(b\times c)}{b\times d}.$$

This not only shows that we can apply our definition to find the sum of any two rational numbers, but it provides us with a rule for finding the sum quickly. Let us illustrate this in finding the sum of $\frac{7}{9}$ and $\frac{5}{6}$. We have

$$\frac{7}{9}+\frac{5}{6}=\frac{(7\times 6)+(9\times 5)}{9\times 6}$$

$$=\frac{42+45}{54}$$

$$=\frac{87}{54}.$$

With some practice, we can learn to find some of these sums without the use of pencil and paper.

The last example can be worked by using a smaller common denominator:

$$\frac{7}{9}+\frac{5}{6}=\frac{2\times 7}{2\times 9}+\frac{3\times 5}{3\times 6}$$

$$=\frac{14}{18}+\frac{15}{18}$$

$$=\frac{14+15}{18}$$

$$=\frac{29}{18}.$$

Here, we have used the least common multiple (see Booklet No. 5: *Numbers and Their Factors*) of 6 and 9 as denominator. It should be kept in mind, however, that the fraction $\frac{87}{54}$ is just as good a name for the sum of $\frac{7}{9}$ and $\frac{5}{6}$ as is the fraction $\frac{29}{18}$.

The numerals 7 and $\frac{14}{2}$, as noted earlier, are names for the same rational number. Also the numerals 3 and $\frac{21}{7}$ are names for the same rational number. The sum of 7 and 3 should, therefore, be the same as the sum of $\frac{14}{2}$ and $\frac{21}{7}$. We have

$$\frac{14}{2}+\frac{21}{7}=\frac{(14\times 7)+(2\times 21)}{2\times 7}$$

$$=\frac{98+42}{14}$$

$$=\frac{140}{14}$$

$$=\frac{140\div 14}{14\div 14}$$

$$=\frac{10}{1}$$

$$=10.$$

This is just an illustration of the fact that, in addition, when the numerals for whole numbers are treated as numerals for rational numbers, no inconsistencies occur, for we also have

$$7+3=10$$

when the numerals represent whole numbers.

To look in a more geometric way at the addition of two rational numbers named by fractions having different denominators, let us consider the number line with reference to the problem of finding a simpler name for the sum $\frac{3}{4}+\frac{5}{6}$. On line (a) in Figure 28, points corre-

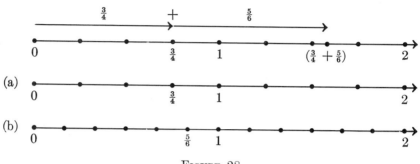

FIGURE 28

sponding to fourths are shown, and the point for $\frac{3}{4}$ is labeled. Line (b) shows points corresponding to sixths, and the point for $\frac{5}{6}$ is labeled.

To find a name for $\frac{3}{4}+\frac{5}{6}$, a number line is needed on which the set of separation points marking the subintervals of the unit interval will contain the point $\frac{3}{4}$ and the point $\frac{5}{6}$. How can a suitable number of subintervals be found?

Suppose that in Figure 28 each subinterval on line (a) is now separated into six congruent parts [see line (c), Fig. 29] and each subinterval on line (b) is separated into four congruent parts [see line (d), Fig. 29]. On (c) there will be 4×6 subintervals with the point $\frac{3}{4}$ labeled $\frac{18}{24}$; on (d) there will be 6×4 subintervals with the point $\frac{5}{6}$ labeled $\frac{20}{24}$. On line (e) there are 24 subintervals in each unit interval, and the sum $\frac{3}{4}+\frac{5}{6}=\frac{18}{24}+\frac{20}{24}=\frac{38}{24}$ is represented.

Is 24 the smallest number of subintervals that could be used? In Figure 29 (f), we see that these subintervals could have been grouped in twos, and the points for $\frac{3}{4}$ and $\frac{5}{6}$ would still have been separation points.

In the foregoing discussion, we have based our definition of the addition of rational numbers on our knowledge of the addition of whole numbers, and have leaned heavily on our intuition concerning the corre-

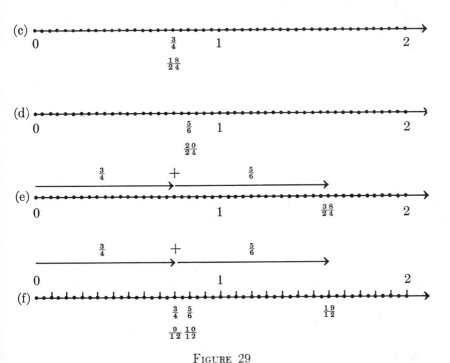

F<small>IGURE</small> 29

spondence between rational numbers and points on the number line. To review this definition and to reinforce your familiarity with it, you might also think of various physical quantities in place of points on the number line.

Thus, suppose Tom walked $\frac{1}{3}$ of a mile from his own home to his friend's home, and then $\frac{1}{2}$ of a mile more to the store. How far did he walk in all?

Suppose it took him $\frac{1}{4}$ of an hour to walk to his friend's home, he stayed there $\frac{1}{2}$ of an hour, and it took him $\frac{1}{4}$ of an hour more to walk to the store from his friend's home. What was the total elapsed time?

He spent $\frac{1}{10}$ of a dollar for candy, $\frac{3}{4}$ of a dollar for vegetables, and $\frac{9}{4}$ of a dollar for meat. How much did he spend in all?

PROPERTIES OF ADDITION FOR RATIONAL NUMBERS

It will be recalled that, in Booklet No. 2: *The Whole Numbers,* we pointed out that the set of whole numbers is closed under addition; that is, that if a and b are whole numbers then $a+b$ is also a whole number. Further properties that were established for the whole numbers are the following:

$$a+b=b+a \qquad \text{(Commutative property of addition),}$$
$$a+(b+c)=(a+b)+c \qquad \text{(Associative property of addition),}$$
$$a+0=0+a=a \qquad \text{(Identity element for addition).}$$

Do analogous properties hold for the rational numbers? They do, as we shall now indicate.

First, though, let us note that these are properties of the *numbers,* not of their names. In particular, *in dealing with more than one rational number, we might just as well name all the numbers by fractions having the same denominator,* as indicated earlier.

Next, let us note that to establish these properties, we have our choice of two methods, as follows:

In the first method we proceed, as we did for the whole numbers, from first principles. This is illustrated, for the commutative law of addition for rational numbers, in Figure 30.

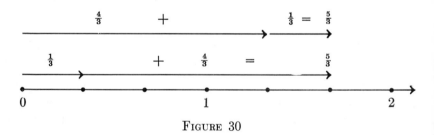

FIGURE 30

In the second method, which is the one we shall follow, *we establish the properties of addition for rational numbers by appealing to our knowledge of the analogous properties for whole numbers.*

Verification of Properties of Rational Numbers

1. *Closure Property of Addition.* By definition, for any rational numbers $\frac{a}{b}$ and $\frac{c}{b}$ (for convenience, we have named them by fractions having the same denominator, as we always can do), we have

$$\frac{a}{b}+\frac{c}{b}=\frac{a+c}{b}.$$

Now a, b, and c are whole numbers with $b \neq 0$. Hence the numerator of the right-hand member of this equation is a whole number, since the system of whole numbers is closed under addition, and the denominator also is a nonzero whole number. Thus the right-hand member names a rational number, as desired. For example:

$$\frac{1}{3} + \frac{4}{3} = \frac{1+4}{3} = \frac{5}{3}.$$

2. *Commutative Property of Addition.* By definition, we have

$$\frac{a}{b} + \frac{c}{b} = \frac{a+c}{b},$$

$$\frac{c}{b} + \frac{a}{b} = \frac{c+a}{b}$$

But

$$a + c = c + a \qquad \text{(Commutative property of addition of whole numbers).}$$

Hence

$$\frac{a}{b} + \frac{c}{b} = \frac{a+c}{b} = \frac{c+a}{b} = \frac{c}{b} + \frac{a}{b}.$$

For example:

$$\frac{1}{3} + \frac{4}{3} = \frac{1+4}{3} = \frac{5}{3} \text{ and } \frac{4}{3} + \frac{1}{3} = \frac{4+1}{3} = \frac{5}{3}.$$

3. *Associative Property of Addition.* By definition, we have

$$\frac{a}{b} + \left(\frac{c}{b} + \frac{d}{b}\right) = \frac{a}{b} + \frac{c+d}{b} = \frac{a+(c+d)}{b},$$

$$\left(\frac{a}{b} + \frac{c}{b}\right) + \frac{d}{b} = \frac{a+c}{b} + \frac{d}{b} = \frac{(a+c)+d}{b}$$

But

$$a + (c+d) = (a+c) + d \qquad \text{(Associative property of addition of whole numbers).}$$

Hence,

$$\frac{a}{b} + \left(\frac{c}{b} + \frac{d}{b}\right) = \frac{a+(c+d)}{b} = \frac{(a+c)+d}{b} = \left(\frac{a}{b} + \frac{c}{b}\right) + \frac{d}{b}.$$

For example:

$$\frac{1}{3} + \left(\frac{4}{3} + \frac{2}{3}\right) = \frac{1}{3} + \frac{4+2}{3} = \frac{1}{3} + \frac{6}{3} = \frac{7}{3},$$

and

$$\left(\frac{1}{3} + \frac{4}{3}\right) + \frac{2}{3} = \frac{1+4}{3} + \frac{2}{3} = \frac{5}{3} + \frac{2}{3} = \frac{7}{3}.$$

You will recall that addition was defined only for pairs of rational numbers. Accordingly,

$$\frac{a}{b} + \frac{c}{b} + \frac{e}{b}$$

is taken to mean

$$\left(\frac{a}{b}+\frac{c}{b}\right)+\frac{e}{b}$$

in which the first two numbers are added first, then their sum and the third number. By the associative property, however, the second and third addends may be added first. In fact, when we also consider the commutative property, we see that a sum can be computed in any order whatsoever without altering the result.

4. *Identity Element for Addition.* If $\frac{a}{b}$ is a rational number, then since

$$\frac{0}{b}=0,$$

we have

$$\frac{a}{b}+0=\frac{a}{b}+\frac{0}{b}$$

$$=\frac{a+0}{b} \qquad \text{(definition of addition)}$$

$$=\frac{a}{b}, \qquad \begin{array}{l}\text{(since 0 is the identity}\\ \text{element for addition for}\\ \text{the system of whole numbers)}\end{array}$$

and similarly,

$$0+\frac{a}{b}=\frac{0}{b}+\frac{a}{b}$$

$$=\frac{0+a}{b}$$

$$=\frac{a}{b}.$$

Now that we have completed the formal verification of these properties of the rational numbers, we should test our understanding of them by applying them to various physical situations.

In the preceding section we discussed a hypothetical boy, Tom. We expressed the distance he walked to his friend's home, and the distance he walked from there to the store, by means of rational numbers. What did we use to express the total distance he walked? We used a rational number. What property does this illustrate?

We found that he walked $\frac{5}{6}$ of a mile in all. Retracing his steps, from the store to his friend's home, and then to his own home, how far did he walk? Again, $\frac{5}{6}$ of a mile. Name the property that this illustrates.

How much did he spend in all if he first purchased the candy, then the vegetables and meat? How much did he spend if he first purchased the candy and vegetables, then the meat? What property have we now illustrated?

If he bought no shoe strings, how much did he spend on candy and shoe strings together? What property does the last answer illustrate?

Exercise Set 4

1. Explain each step in the following computation.

$$\left(\frac{3}{7}+\frac{5}{6}\right)+\frac{4}{7}=\frac{3}{7}+\left(\frac{5}{6}+\frac{4}{7}\right) \quad \text{(a)} \underline{\hspace{3cm}}$$

$$=\frac{3}{7}+\left(\frac{4}{7}+\frac{5}{6}\right) \quad \text{(b)} \underline{\hspace{3cm}}$$

$$=\left(\frac{3}{7}+\frac{4}{7}\right)+\frac{5}{6} \quad \text{(c)} \underline{\hspace{3cm}}$$

$$=\frac{7}{7}+\frac{5}{6} \quad \text{(d)} \underline{\hspace{3cm}}$$

$$=\frac{6}{6}+\frac{5}{6} \quad \text{(e)} \underline{\hspace{3cm}}$$

$$=\frac{11}{6} \quad \text{(f)} \underline{\hspace{3cm}}$$

2. Find the simplest name for each of the following sums.

(a) $5+\frac{1}{7}+\frac{1}{3}+\frac{5}{7}+\frac{5}{3}$ (b) $\frac{2}{3}+4+\frac{3}{5}+\frac{4}{3}+\frac{1}{5}$

3. Show the sum of $\frac{5}{8}$ and $\frac{1}{8}$ on a number line.

4. Using squares as unit figures, and dividing them into congruent regions by vertical line segments, as indicated in Figure 31, illustrate each of the following.

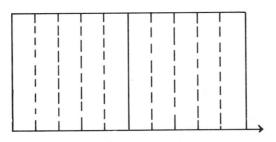

FIGURE 31

(a) Closure for addition, by considering $\frac{2}{5}+\frac{4}{5}$.

(b) Commutativity for addition, by considering $\frac{2}{5}+\frac{4}{5}$ and $\frac{4}{5}+\frac{2}{5}$.

(c) Associativity for addition, by considering $\left(\frac{2}{5}+\frac{4}{5}\right)+\frac{3}{5}$ and $\frac{2}{5}+\left(\frac{4}{5}+\frac{3}{5}\right)$.

(d) The identity element for addition, by considering $\frac{2}{5}+\frac{0}{5}$ and $\frac{0}{5}+\frac{2}{5}$.

SUBTRACTION OF RATIONAL NUMBERS

You will recall that in Booklet No. 2: *The Whole Numbers*, the operation of subtraction was defined as the inverse of the operation of addition. What did we mean by $7-3$? Thinking in terms of sets, we considered a set A having seven elements and a set B having three elements, and sought a set C, disjoint from B, such that $B \cup C$ matched A in one-to-one correspondence; the set C had to have four elements, and we wrote $7-3=4$. Thinking in terms of subsets, we asked for the number of elements remaining when a subset of A that matched B was removed from A; again we obtained $7-3=4$. Finally, thinking directly in terms of addition, we said that $7-3=4$ because 4 is the simplest name of the number that when added to 3 gives 7.

All of this can, of course, be illustrated on the number line, as in Figure 32.

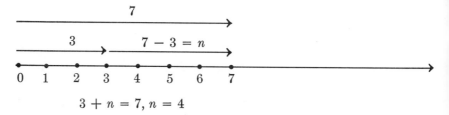

$$3+n=7, n=4$$

FIGURE 32

For given rational numbers $\frac{a}{b}$ and $\frac{c}{d}$, where $\frac{a}{b}$ is not less than $\frac{c}{d}$, we define

$$\frac{a}{b}-\frac{c}{d}$$

to be the rational number $\frac{e}{f}$ such that

$$\frac{c}{d}+\frac{e}{f}=\frac{a}{b}.$$

Our problem is to determine $\frac{e}{f}$ so that this latter equation is true.

Let us see by example how we go about doing this. We are not content, of course, with the name $\frac{a}{b} - \frac{c}{d}$; we want a fraction name, $\frac{e}{f}$.

What is a fraction name, n, for the rational number $\frac{7}{5} - \frac{3}{5}$? Since

$$\frac{3}{5} + \frac{4}{5} = \frac{3+4}{5}$$

$$= \frac{7}{5},$$

we have

$$n = \frac{7}{5} - \frac{3}{5} = \frac{4}{5}.$$

Taking advantage of our familiarity with the subtraction of whole numbers, we write

$$\frac{7}{5} - \frac{3}{5} = \frac{7-3}{5} = \frac{4}{5}.$$

Thus, $\frac{4}{5}$ is the fraction name for the rational number $\frac{7}{5} - \frac{3}{5}$.

What is a fraction name for the rational number $\frac{7}{5} - \frac{3}{4}$? This appears to be a rather different problem from the preceding one, since the denominators are different. We recall, however, that any two rational numbers can be represented by fractions having the same denominator, and write

$$\frac{7}{5} = \frac{28}{20}, \qquad \frac{3}{4} = \frac{15}{20},$$

so that

$$\frac{7}{5} - \frac{3}{4} = \frac{28}{20} - \frac{15}{20}$$

$$= \frac{28-15}{20}$$

$$= \frac{13}{20}.$$

In general, then, if a is not less than c, we have

$$\frac{a}{b} - \frac{c}{b} = \frac{a-c}{b}.$$

Similarly, if $a \times d$ is not less than $b \times c$, we obtain

$$\frac{a}{b} - \frac{c}{d} = \frac{d \times a}{d \times b} - \frac{b \times c}{b \times d}$$
$$= \frac{(a \times d) - (b \times c)}{b \times d}.$$

Since $(a \times d) - (b \times c)$ is always a whole number, and $b \times d$ is always a counting number (remember that neither b nor d can be 0), this latter expression always represents a rational number.

Exercise Set 5

1. Represent the following rational numbers by fractions having the same denominator.

   (a) $\frac{3}{4}, \frac{2}{3},$ and $\frac{5}{6}$ (c) $\frac{5}{2}, \frac{7}{4},$ and $\frac{11}{5}$

   (b) $\frac{5}{17}$ and $\frac{23}{51}$ (d) $\frac{9}{7}, \frac{13}{21},$ and $\frac{19}{42}$

2. Perform the following subtractions by renaming the rational numbers with fractions that have the same denominator.

   (a) $\frac{4}{3} - \frac{1}{2}$ (d) $\frac{59}{7} - \frac{144}{35}$

   (b) $\frac{43}{14} - \frac{13}{8}$ (e) $\frac{26}{2} - \frac{21}{8}$

   (c) $\frac{33}{5} - \frac{57}{20}$ (f) $\frac{5}{4} - \frac{4}{5}$

MULTIPLICATION OF RATIONAL NUMBERS

In the preceding sections, to explain what we meant by the addition of rational numbers, we used illustrations involving such things as unit figures, the number line, and everyday experiences. Neither these illustrations nor any other illustrations, however, could prove what is meant by the sum of two rational numbers; this is of necessity a matter of definition. We did, however, decide to use the system of whole numbers as a model in determining what we would take the sum of two rational numbers to mean, and in particular we sought a definition consistent with the definition of addition for whole numbers.

Let us proceed in the same way for multiplication. We defined the product of two whole numbers by an array. For example:

$$\begin{array}{c|c} & 3 \\ \hline 2 & \begin{matrix} \bullet & \bullet & \bullet \\ \bullet & \bullet & \bullet \end{matrix} \end{array}$$

the product 2×3 is the number of elements in an array having two rows and three columns.

We can also illustrate the product 2×3 by means of unit regions as in Figure 33.

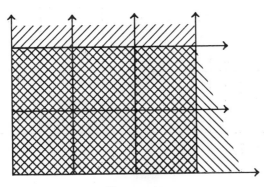

FIGURE 33

Note that there are two rows and three columns of unit regions.

Figure 34 (a) shows each unit region divided by vertical lines into four congruent regions with three of them shaded. Figure 34 (b) shows each unit region divided by horizontal lines into two congruent regions (think of a *vertical* number line), and one of them is shaded.

Now let us put these two figures together, as in Figure 34 (c). The double shading (cross-hatching) shows the set of congruent regions that we shall say corresponds to the product of $\frac{1}{2} \times \frac{3}{4}$, just as the cross-hatched region in Figure 33 shows the product $2 \times 3 = 6$. Note that each unit region is separated into eight congruent subregions, of which three are cross-hatched. So $\frac{1}{2} \times \frac{3}{4} = \frac{3}{8}$.

Similarly, Figure 35 (a) illustrates the set of congruent regions which we say corresponds to $\frac{1}{2} \times \frac{2}{3}$, and we see that $\frac{1}{2} \times \frac{2}{3} = \frac{2}{6}$. Figure 35 (b) illustrates that $2 \times \frac{1}{3} = \frac{2}{3}$, and Figure 35 (c) illustrates that $\frac{3}{2} \times \frac{11}{6} = \frac{33}{12}$.

Let us examine these illustrations to see how the product of any two rational numbers should be defined.

In Figure 34 (c), we note that the lines forming the congruent regions separate the vertical side of each unit region into two congruent segments and the horizontal side into four congruent segments. Thus there are in

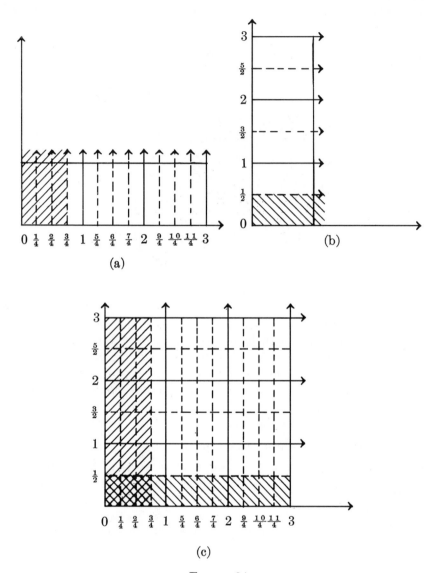

FIGURE 34

each unit region two rows and four columns, and the unit region is separated into 2×4, or 8, congruent regions. In the cross-hatched region there
are one row and three columns, or 1×3 congruent regions. Thus, the prod-
uct $\frac{1}{2} \times \frac{3}{4} = \frac{1 \times 3}{2 \times 4}$, or $\frac{3}{8}$, is represented by shading 1×3 of the 2×4 con-

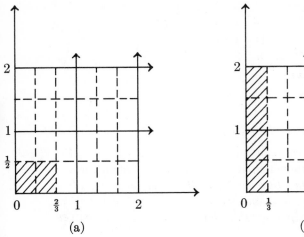 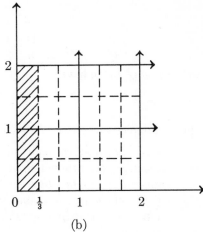

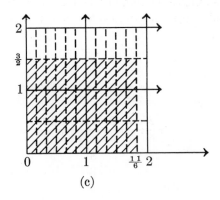

(c)

FIGURE 35

gruent regions into which the unit region is divided. From this we get

$$\frac{1}{2} \times \frac{3}{4} = \frac{1 \times 3}{2 \times 4}$$

$$= \frac{3}{8}.$$

Figure 35 suggests the relations:

$$\text{(a)} \quad \frac{1}{2} \times \frac{2}{3} = \frac{1 \times 2}{2 \times 3} = \frac{2}{6},$$

$$\text{(b)} \quad 2 \times \frac{1}{3} = \frac{2}{1} \times \frac{1}{3} = \frac{2 \times 1}{1 \times 3} = \frac{2}{3},$$

$$\text{(c)} \quad \frac{3}{2} \times \frac{11}{6} = \frac{3 \times 11}{2 \times 6} = \frac{33}{12},$$

and in Figure 33 we have

$$\frac{2}{1} \times \frac{3}{1} = \frac{2 \times 3}{1 \times 1} = \frac{6}{1}.$$

These examples suggest the following definition:

> *Given any two rational numbers named by fractions, the product of the rational numbers is named by a fraction whose numerator can be obtained by multiplying the numerators of the given fractions and whose denominator can be obtained by multiplying the denominators of the given fractions.*

That this is a reasonable definition may be seen from the following example, which is easily pictured on the number line.

Recall that when multiplication of whole numbers is defined by arrays, it follows that multiplication can also be thought of as addition of equal addends. We have

$$2+2+2+2=8,$$

whence we write

$$4 \times 2 = 8.$$

With rational numbers,

$$\frac{2}{3} + \frac{2}{3} + \frac{2}{3} + \frac{2}{3} = \frac{2+2+2+2}{3}$$

$$= \frac{8}{3},$$

whence by analogy we write

$$4 \times \frac{2}{3} = \frac{8}{3}.$$

This is illustrated in Figure 36 (a) and (b)

Alan drank $\frac{2}{3}$ of a quart of milk for each of his three meals and the same amount at bedtime. How much did he drink in all? Looking at Figure 36 (b), we write

$$4 \times \frac{2}{3} = \frac{8}{3}.$$

This can be written as

$$\frac{4}{1} \times \frac{2}{3} = \frac{8}{3};$$

(a)

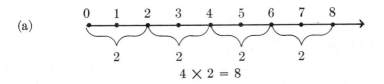

$$4 \times 2 = 8$$

(b)

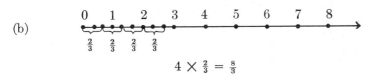

$$4 \times \tfrac{2}{3} = \tfrac{8}{3}$$

FIGURE 36

and we notice that 8 is the product of the numerators 4 and 2, and 3 is the product of the denominators 1 and 3.

On his paper route, John walks $\frac{5}{4}$ of a mile in an hour. At that rate, how far would he walk in 2 hours? In $\frac{1}{2}$ hour? In $\frac{2}{3}$ hour? Figure 37 (a) shows by means of arrows the distances John walks in 1 hour, 2 hours, $\frac{1}{2}$ hour, and $\frac{2}{3}$ hour.

Dotted lines are used to project the tips of the arrows onto the number line in Figure 37 (a). It is easy to see that in 2 hours John walks $\frac{10}{4}$ miles. The point reached in $\frac{1}{2}$ hour is seen to be midway between the points corresponding to $\frac{2}{4}$ and $\frac{3}{4}$. If each of the quarter-unit segments of the line in Figure 37 (a) is divided into two congruent parts (this means that the unit interval is now divided into eight congruent parts), then the point reached in $\frac{1}{2}$ hour is one of the division points as seen on the line given in Figure 37 (b). In fact, we can see that this point corresponds to the number $\frac{5}{8}$. John walks $\frac{5}{8}$ mile in $\frac{1}{2}$ hour.

What number corresponds to the point reached in $\frac{2}{3}$ hour? The point is seen to be between the points corresponding to $\frac{3}{4}$ and $\frac{4}{4}$ on the line in Figure 37 (a). The line in Figure 37 (c) shows each of the quarter-unit segments of the line in Figure 37 (a) to be divided into three congruent

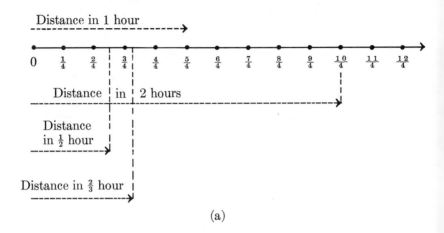

(a)

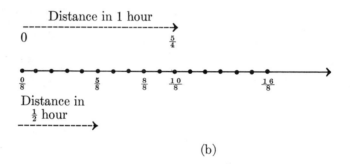

(b)

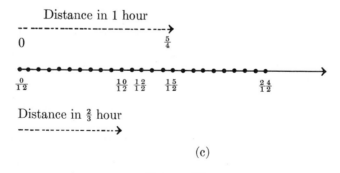

(c)

FIGURE 37

parts (this means that the unit interval is now divided into 12 congruent parts), and we see that the point reached by John in $\frac{2}{3}$ hour corresponds to the number $\frac{10}{12}$. John walks $\frac{10}{12}$ mile in $\frac{2}{3}$ hour.

Now by our notion of what the product of two rational numbers should be, we can write

$$2 \times \frac{5}{4} = \frac{2}{1} \times \frac{5}{4}$$
$$= \frac{10}{4},$$

$$\frac{1}{2} \times \frac{5}{4} = \frac{1 \times 5}{2 \times 4}$$
$$= \frac{5}{8},$$

$$\frac{2}{3} \times \frac{5}{4} = \frac{2 \times 5}{3 \times 4}$$
$$= \frac{10}{12}.$$

Thus we see that the number of miles John would walk in 2 hours, in $\frac{1}{2}$ hour, or in $\frac{2}{3}$ hour can be expressed as a product.

We are accustomed to saying, for example, that if John walks $\frac{5}{4}$ miles in one hour, then in $\frac{1}{2}$ hour he walks one-half as far, or $\frac{1}{2}$ of $\frac{5}{4}$ miles, which is $\frac{5}{8}$ mile. Thus we could write

$$\frac{1}{2} \text{ of } \frac{5}{4} = \frac{5}{8},$$

to mean the same as

$$\frac{1}{2} \times \frac{5}{4} = \frac{5}{8}.$$

Similarly,

$$\frac{2}{3} \text{ of } \frac{5}{4} = \frac{10}{12}$$

is another way of saying that

$$\frac{2}{3} \times \frac{5}{4} = \frac{10}{12}.$$

Sometimes it seems more natural to say "times" when talking about a product of rational numbers, and sometimes it seems more natural to say "of," but we mean the same thing in either case.

Earlier we arrived at the notion of what the product of two rational numbers seems to be. For example:

$$\frac{2}{3} \times \frac{4}{5} = \frac{2 \times 4}{3 \times 5}$$

$$= \frac{8}{15}.$$

We have seen that this idea is supported by representation of products on the number line and is consistent with the results obtained by multiplication of whole numbers (the product of 3 and 5 considered as rational numbers is $\frac{3}{1} \times \frac{5}{1} = \frac{3 \times 5}{1 \times 1} = \frac{15}{1} = 15$). Thus, we adopt the following definition:

If $\frac{a}{b}$ and $\frac{c}{d}$ are any two rational numbers, their product is defined to be

$$\frac{a}{b} \times \frac{c}{d} = \frac{a \times c}{b \times d}.$$

Exercise Set 6

1. Write a number sentence that describes the shaded area in the unit regions.

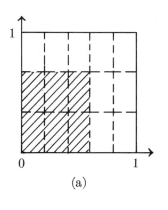

(a)

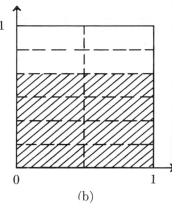

(b)

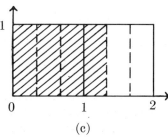

(c)

2. Use congruent subregions of unit regions to illustrate the multiplication of the following rational numbers.

(a) $\frac{3}{4}\times\frac{2}{3}$ (b) $\frac{3}{2}\times\frac{1}{5}$ (c) $\frac{5}{6}\times\frac{3}{8}$

3. Use the number lines below to illustrate (a) $\frac{2}{3}\times\frac{3}{2}$; (b) $\frac{3}{2}\times\frac{2}{3}$.

(a)

(b)

4. Illustrate each of the following products on a number line.

(a) $\frac{1}{3}\times\frac{5}{6}$ (b) $\frac{3}{4}\times\frac{2}{3}$ (c) $\frac{3}{2}\times\frac{9}{8}$

PROPERTIES OF MULTIPLICATION FOR RATIONAL NUMBERS

In Booklet No. 2: *The Whole Numbers*, the following properties of multiplication for the whole numbers $a, b, c \ldots$, were explained:

$a \times b$ is a whole number	(Closure property of multiplication)
$a \times b = b \times a$	(Commutative property of multiplication)
$a \times (b \times c) = (a \times b) \times c$	(Associative property of multiplication)
$a \times 1 = 1 \times a = a$	(Identity element for multiplication)
$a \times (b+c) = (a \times b) + (a \times c)$	(Distributive property of multiplication over addition)

It was also pointed out that 0 (the identity element for addition) has a special property with respect to multiplication of whole numbers, namely

$$a \times 0 = 0 \times a = 0.$$

We now use these known properties for the whole numbers to show that the properties hold also for the rational numbers.

1. *Closure Property of Multiplication.* By definition, for any rational number $\frac{a}{b}$ and $\frac{c}{d}$, we have

$$\frac{a}{b}\times\frac{c}{d}=\frac{a\times c}{b\times d}.$$

Now, by the closure property of multiplication of whole numbers, $a \times c$ and $b \times d$ are whole numbers. Further, since $b \neq 0$, and $d \neq 0$, we have $b \times d \neq 0$. Hence, $\dfrac{a \times c}{b \times d}$ represents a rational number, as desired.

2. *Commutative Property of Multiplication.* By definition, we have

$$\frac{a}{b} \times \frac{c}{d} = \frac{a \times c}{b \times d}, \qquad \frac{c}{d} \times \frac{a}{b} = \frac{c \times a}{d \times b}.$$

But $a \times c = c \times a$ and $b \times d = d \times b$ by the commutative property of multiplication of whole numbers. Hence

$$\frac{a}{b} \times \frac{c}{d} = \frac{a \times c}{b \times d} = \frac{c \times a}{d \times b} = \frac{c}{d} \times \frac{a}{b}.$$

3. *The Associative Property of Multiplication.* You should now be able to justify the steps in the following proof:

$$\frac{a}{b} \times \left(\frac{c}{d} \times \frac{e}{f} \right) = \frac{a}{b} \times \frac{c \times e}{d \times f}$$

$$= \frac{a \times (c \times e)}{b \times (d \times f)}$$

$$= \frac{(a \times c) \times e}{(b \times d) \times f}$$

$$= \frac{a \times c}{b \times d} \times \frac{e}{f}$$

$$= \left(\frac{a}{b} \times \frac{c}{d} \right) \times \frac{e}{f}.$$

4. *Identity Element for Multiplication.*

$$\frac{a}{b} \times 1 = \frac{a}{b} \times \frac{1}{1} \qquad \left(\text{since } 1 = \frac{1}{1} \right)$$

$$= \frac{a \times 1}{b \times 1} \qquad \text{(definition of multiplication of rational numbers)}$$

$$= \frac{a}{b} \qquad \text{(since } a \text{ and } b \text{ are whole numbers,} \quad a \times 1 = a, \text{ and } b \times 1 = b).$$

Similarly, it can be shown that

$$1 \times \frac{a}{b} = \frac{a}{b}.$$

5. *Distributive Property of Multiplication over Addition.* Justify for yourself all the steps in the following derivation:

$$\frac{a}{b} \times \left(\frac{c}{d} + \frac{e}{d} \right) = \frac{a}{b} \times \frac{c+e}{d}$$

$$= \frac{a \times (c+e)}{b \times d}$$

$$= \frac{(a \times c) + (a \times e)}{b \times d}$$

$$= \left(\frac{a \times c}{b \times d} \right) + \left(\frac{a \times e}{b \times d} \right)$$

$$= \left(\frac{a}{b} \times \frac{c}{d} \right) + \left(\frac{a}{b} \times \frac{e}{d} \right).$$

You might note that it is only in the demonstration of the validity of the distributive law that we now find it advantageous to use our prerogative of representing rational numbers by fractions having the same denominator.

6. Multiplication by Zero.

$$\frac{a}{b} \times 0 = \frac{a}{b} \times \frac{0}{1} \qquad \left(\text{since } 0 = \frac{0}{1} \right)$$

$$= \frac{a \times 0}{b \times 1} \qquad \text{(definition of multiplication of rational}$$
$$\qquad\qquad\qquad \text{numbers)}$$

$$= \frac{0}{b}$$

$$= 0. \qquad \text{(since } a \text{ is a whole number, } a \times 0 = 0\text{)}$$

Similarly it can be shown that

$$0 \times \frac{a}{b} = 0.$$

We use these properties of multiplication for rational numbers, like the properties of addition for rational numbers, routinely in our everyday calculations, often hardly taking formal cognizance of the fact that we are doing so. Thus, for example, we ordinarily take

$$\frac{a}{b} \times \frac{c}{d} \times \frac{e}{f} \quad \text{to mean} \quad \left(\frac{a}{b} \times \frac{c}{d} \right) \times \frac{e}{f}$$

in order that this triple product should have a meaning (multiplication is basically defined as an operation on only two numbers), but by the associative law of multiplication we would get the same answer if we take it to mean

$$\frac{a}{b} \times \left(\frac{c}{d} \times \frac{e}{f} \right),$$

and so we ordinarily omit the parentheses.

In addition to the six properties discussed in this section, the rational numbers have one additional property not shared by the whole numbers.

MULTIPLICATIVE-INVERSE PROPERTY OF RATIONAL NUMBERS

Observe each of the following products.

$$\text{(a)} \ \frac{5}{7} \times \frac{7}{5} = \frac{5 \times 7}{7 \times 5} \qquad \text{(b)} \ \frac{4}{9} \times \frac{9}{4} = \frac{4 \times 9}{9 \times 4} \qquad \text{(c)} \ \frac{4}{1} \times \frac{1}{4} = \frac{4 \times 1}{1 \times 4}$$
$$=1 \qquad\qquad\qquad =1 \qquad\qquad\qquad =1$$

In each case, the product of the factors is 1. Why is this so? When the numerators of the fractions $\frac{5}{7}$ and $\frac{7}{5}$ are multiplied, the product is 5×7. When the denominators of these fractions are multiplied, the product is 7×5. By the commutative property of multiplication, $5 \times 7 = 7 \times 5$, and thus $\frac{5}{7} \times \frac{7}{5} = 1$.

If the product of two numbers is 1, each number is called the *reciprocal*, or multiplicative inverse, of the other number. Thus $\frac{5}{7}$ is the reciprocal of $\frac{7}{5}$, and $\frac{7}{5}$ is the reciprocal of $\frac{5}{7}$; $\frac{4}{9}$ is the reciprocal of $\frac{9}{4}$, and $\frac{9}{4}$ is the reciprocal of $\frac{4}{9}$; 4 is the reciprocal of $\frac{1}{4}$, and $\frac{1}{4}$ is the reciprocal of 4.

For any rational number, except 0, there is another rational number such that the product of the numbers is 1. Each number is called the reciprocal, or multiplicative inverse, of the other.

The numbers 0 and 1 possess special properties in mathematics. One of these properties is that, for any number n,

$$0 \times n = 0.$$

Since there is no rational number n such that $0 \times n = 1$, the number 0 has no reciprocal.

Notice that

$$1 \times 1 = 1.$$

The number 1 is the only nonnegative rational number that is its own multiplicative inverse. It is also the only whole number whose multiplicative inverse is also a whole number.

The reciprocal property, also called the multiplicative-inverse property, is a property possessed by the rational numbers and not by the whole numbers. Each rational number, except 0, has a reciprocal that is also a rational number. Thus for each rational number a, $a \neq 0$, there is another rational number b such that

$$a \times b = 1.$$

Exercise Set 7

1. For each sentence, find a number n which makes the sentence true.

(a) $\dfrac{5}{6} \times n = 1$

(d) $1 \times n = 1$

(b) $\dfrac{7}{13} \times n = 1$

(e) $\dfrac{3}{5} \times \left(\dfrac{2}{3} \times \dfrac{3}{2} \right) = n$

(c) $4 \times n = 1$

(f) $n \times \left(\dfrac{6}{7} \times \dfrac{7}{6} \right) = \dfrac{3}{8}$

2. Name the reciprocals of the following numbers.

(a) $\dfrac{5}{6}$

(d) 1

(b) $\dfrac{7}{3}$

(e) 6

(c) $\dfrac{4}{5}$

(f) $\dfrac{5}{2}$

3. Here are some division sentences. For each one write a multiplication sentence that expresses the same relationship.

EXAMPLE: $35 \div n = 7$

$n \times 7 = 35$

(a) $36 \div n = 3$

(d) $n \div \dfrac{3}{5} = \dfrac{5}{6}$

(b) $24 \div 8 = n$

(e) $1 \div 11 = n$

(c) $17 \div n = 17$

4. For each multiplication sentence below. write two division sentences which state the same relationship.

EXAMPLE: $\dfrac{3}{5} \times \dfrac{5}{3} = 1$

$1 \div \dfrac{3}{5} = \dfrac{5}{3}$

$1 \div \dfrac{5}{3} = \dfrac{3}{5}$

(a) $\dfrac{3}{2} \times \dfrac{2}{3} = 1$

(c) $\dfrac{7}{18} \times \dfrac{18}{7} = 1$

(b) $\dfrac{16}{3} \times \dfrac{3}{16} = 1$

(d) $\dfrac{41}{9} \times \dfrac{9}{41} = 1$

5. Complete the following sequence of equivalent sentences.

$$\frac{3}{4} \times n = \frac{2}{5}$$

(a) $\frac{4}{3} \times \left(\frac{3}{4} \times n \right) = \underline{\hspace{1cm}} \times \frac{2}{5}$

(b) $\left(\frac{4}{3} \times \frac{3}{4} \right) \times n = \underline{\hspace{1cm}} \times \frac{2}{5}$

(c) $\underline{\hspace{1cm}} \times n = \underline{\hspace{1cm}} \times \frac{2}{5}$

(d) $n = \underline{\hspace{1cm}} \times \frac{2}{5}$ or $\underline{\hspace{1cm}}$

6. Complete each sentence.

$$\frac{5}{4} \div \frac{3}{7} = n$$

(a) $n \times \underline{\hspace{1cm}} = \frac{5}{4}$

(b) $n \times 1 = n \times \left(\frac{3}{7} \times \underline{\hspace{1cm}} \right)$

(c) $\left(n \times \frac{3}{7} \right) \times \underline{\hspace{1cm}} = \frac{5}{4} \times \underline{\hspace{1cm}}$ (same number in both blanks)

(d) $n \times 1 = \underline{\hspace{1cm}} \times \underline{\hspace{1cm}}$

(e) $n = \underline{\hspace{1cm}}$

(f) $\frac{5}{4} \div \frac{3}{7} = \underline{\hspace{1cm}}$

7. Complete each sentence to make it equivalent to the given sentence.

$$\frac{8}{5} \div n = \frac{16}{15}$$

(a) $n \times \underline{\hspace{1cm}} = \frac{8}{5}$

(b) $\left(n \times \frac{16}{15} \right) \times \underline{\hspace{1cm}} = \frac{8}{5} \times \underline{\hspace{1cm}}$ (same number in both blanks)

(c) $n \times 1 = \frac{8}{5} \times \underline{\hspace{1cm}}$

(d) $n = \frac{8}{5} \times \underline{\hspace{1cm}}$

(e) $n = \underline{\hspace{1cm}}$

(f) $\frac{8}{5} \div \underline{\hspace{1cm}} = \frac{16}{15}$

DIVISION OF RATIONAL NUMBERS

Just as the operation of subtraction is the inverse of the operation of addition, so the operation of division is the inverse of the operation of multiplication. In Booklet No. 2: *The Whole Numbers*, we said that 6 divided by 3 is 2 because 3 times 2 is 6:

$$6 \div 3 = 2 \quad \text{because} \quad 3 \times 2 = 6.$$

It was pointed out there that in the system of whole numbers some pairs of numbers do not have quotients which are whole numbers. Thus we saw that in the system of whole numbers, the division $20 \div 3$ is impossible; that is, there is no whole number n such that

$$3 \times n = 20.$$

In the system of rational numbers, the operation of division is again defined to be the inverse of the operation of multiplication. Thus the equation $\frac{2}{3} \div \frac{5}{6} = \frac{e}{f}$ means $\frac{2}{3} = \frac{5}{6} \times \frac{e}{f}$; more generally, the division sentence $\frac{a}{b} \div \frac{c}{d} = \frac{e}{f}$ means

$$\frac{a}{b} = \frac{c}{d} \times \frac{e}{f}.$$

As we shall see in the system of rational numbers, division (except by 0) is always possible.

The notion of reciprocals is basic to the definition of division of rational provided that their product is 1. For example, 2 and $\frac{1}{2}$, 1 and 1, and $\frac{3}{2}$ and $\frac{2}{3}$ are reciprocal pairs, since $2 \times \frac{1}{2} = 1$, $1 \times 1 = 1$, and $\frac{3}{2} \times \frac{2}{3} = 1$. In general, the rational numbers $\frac{c}{d}$ and $\frac{d}{c}$, where neither c nor d is 0, are reciprocals of each other, since

$$\frac{c}{d} \times \frac{d}{c} = \frac{c \times d}{d \times c} = \frac{c \times d}{c \times d} = 1.$$

Now let us consider the division $\frac{3}{4} \div \frac{2}{5}$. Assuming that there is a rational number n such that $\frac{3}{4} \div \frac{2}{5} = n$, how can we go about finding n?

Recall that $\frac{3}{4} \div \frac{2}{5} = n$ means that

$$\frac{2}{5} \times n = \frac{3}{4}.$$

The reciprocal of $\frac{2}{5}$ is $\frac{5}{2}$ because $\frac{5}{2} \times \frac{2}{5} = 1$. Multiplying both $\frac{2}{5} \times n$ and $\frac{3}{4}$ by $\frac{5}{2}$, we obtain

$$\frac{5}{2} \times \left(\frac{2}{5} \times n\right) = \frac{5}{2} \times \frac{3}{4},$$

$$\left(\frac{5}{2} \times \frac{2}{5}\right) \times n = \frac{5}{2} \times \frac{3}{4}, \qquad \text{(associative property of multiplication)}$$

$$1 \times n = \frac{5}{2} \times \frac{3}{4}, \qquad \left(\frac{5}{2} \times \frac{2}{5} = 1\right)$$

$$1 \times n = \frac{5 \times 3}{2 \times 4}, \qquad \text{(definition of multiplication)}$$

$$n = \frac{15}{8}. \qquad \left(1 \times n = n \text{ and } \frac{5 \times 3}{2 \times 4} = \frac{15}{8}\right)$$

So far we have shown that if there is a rational number n, such that $\frac{3}{4} \div \frac{2}{5} = n$, then $n = \frac{5 \times 3}{2 \times 4} = \frac{15}{8}$. Can we show that $\frac{15}{8}$ is a correct result? That is, can we show that $\frac{2}{5} \times \frac{15}{8} = \frac{3}{4}$? By the definition of multiplication of rational numbers,

$$\frac{2}{5} \times \frac{15}{8} = \frac{2 \times 15}{5 \times 8}$$

$$= \frac{30}{40}$$

$$= \frac{3}{4}.$$

Therefore, the one and only rational number n that makes $\frac{3}{4} \div \frac{2}{5} = n$ true is $\frac{15}{8}$.

If you look back over the steps, you notice that $\frac{15}{8}$ was obtained by multipliying $\frac{3}{4}$ by $\frac{5}{2}$, the reciprocal of $\frac{2}{5}$, and you can write

$$\frac{3}{4} \div \frac{2}{5} = \frac{3}{4} \times \frac{5}{2}.$$

How would $\frac{3}{4} \div \frac{2}{5}$ be interpreted on the number line? That is, can we find, by using a number line, a rational number $\frac{a}{b}$ such that $\frac{a}{b} \times \frac{2}{5} = \frac{3}{4}$?

If the points corresponding to $\frac{3}{4}$ and $\frac{2}{5}$ are located on a number line (see Fig. 38 (a)) it is apparent that we need a set of subintervals such that the separation points include the points corresponding to $\frac{3}{4}$ and $\frac{2}{5}$.

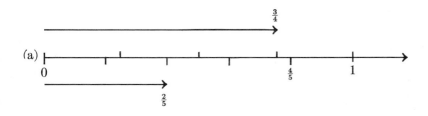

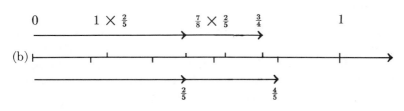

FIGURE 38

This can be accomplished by dividing unit segments (starting at 0 and continuing as far as needed) into 20 congruent parts (see Fig. 38(b)). Line (b) suggests that

$$\frac{3}{4}=\frac{15}{8}\times\frac{2}{5}.$$

Now let $\frac{a}{b}$ and $\frac{c}{d}$ be any two rational numbers such that $\frac{c}{d}\neq0$ (this means that $c\neq0$). It can be shown in the same way as it was done for the division $\frac{3}{4}\div\frac{2}{5}$ that there is exactly one rational number $\frac{x}{y}$ such that

$$\frac{a}{b}\div\frac{c}{d}=\frac{x}{y},$$

namely,

$$\frac{a}{b}\times\frac{d}{c}.$$

Thus we have for this general case,

$$\frac{a}{b}\div\frac{c}{d}=\frac{a}{b}\times\frac{d}{c}.$$

Thus *dividing by a rational number (other than 0) gives exactly the same result as multiplying by its reciprocal.*

That division by 0 is not possible in the system of rationals can be shown to be true for the same reasons it is not possible in the system of whole numbers. For example,

$$\frac{3}{4} \div 0 = n$$

implies that $0 \times n = \frac{3}{4}$. Since the product of 0 and any rational number is 0, there is no rational number n, such that $0 \times n = \frac{3}{4}$; and therefore, there is no rational number n, such that $\frac{3}{4} \div 0 = n$.

A FRACTION AS A SYMBOL FOR DIVISION

Whereas the division of 20 by 3 is impossible in the system of whole numbers, the rational number 20 divided by the rational number 3 yields a rational number. In fact, it is clear from the definition of division of rational numbers that any rational number divided by a nonzero rational number yields a rational number. By this definition,

$$20 \div 3 = \frac{20}{1} \div \frac{3}{1}$$

$$= \frac{20}{1} \times \frac{1}{3}$$

$$= \frac{20 \times 1}{1 \times 3}$$

$$= \frac{20}{3}.$$

More generally, if p is any whole number and q is any nonzero whole number, then

$$p \div q = \frac{p}{1} \div \frac{q}{1}$$

$$= \frac{p}{1} \times \frac{1}{q}$$

$$= \frac{p \times 1}{1 \times q}$$

$$= \frac{p}{q}.$$

Thus, if p and q are whole numbers, $q \neq 0$, $p \div q$ and $\frac{p}{q}$ are names for the same rational number. This means that a fraction such as $\frac{3}{4}$, for example, can be viewed not only as a name for a rational number but also as a quotient of whole numbers, in this case $3 \div 4$. It is permissible, then, to say "the rational number $7 \div 5$" instead of saying "the rational number $\frac{7}{5}$."

What can we say about the quotient, $\frac{3}{5} \div \frac{4}{7}$? Can we write it as follows?

$$\frac{\dfrac{3}{5}}{\dfrac{4}{7}}$$

Recall that fractions, as we have used them, have been symbols of the form $\frac{p}{q}$, where p and q denote whole numbers, with $q \neq 0$. Suppose that we want to extend our notion of fraction to include expressions such as $\dfrac{\dfrac{3}{5}}{\dfrac{4}{7}}$ and,

more generally, $\dfrac{\dfrac{a}{b}}{\dfrac{c}{d}}$, where $b \neq 0$, $c \neq 0$, and $d \neq 0$.

Will these new fractions that are of the form $\frac{r}{s}$, where the numerator r is a rational number and the denominator s is a nonzero rational number, have the same properties as the fractions with which we are familiar?

The answer to the above question is yes. We can compute with these new fractions according to the rules that we have learned to use with such fractions as $\frac{2}{3}$ and $\frac{7}{5}$. Let us illustrate by means of examples that the following statements are true.

(a) $\dfrac{m \times r}{m \times s} = \dfrac{r}{s}$,   where m, r, and s are rational numbers with $m \neq 0$ and $s \neq 0$.

(b) $\dfrac{a}{b} \times \dfrac{c}{d} = \dfrac{a \times c}{b \times d}$,   where a, b, c, and d are rational numbers, with $b \neq 0$, $d \neq 0$.

To illustrate statement (a), we shall show that

$$\frac{\dfrac{3}{2} \times \dfrac{2}{5}}{\dfrac{3}{2} \times \dfrac{3}{4}} = \frac{\dfrac{2}{5}}{\dfrac{3}{4}}.$$

By the definition of multiplication and division of rational numbers,

$$\frac{\frac{3}{5}\times\frac{2}{5}}{\frac{3}{2}\times\frac{3}{4}}=\frac{\frac{6}{10}}{\frac{9}{8}}$$

$$=\frac{6}{10}\div\frac{9}{8}$$

$$=\frac{6}{10}\times\frac{8}{9}$$

$$=\frac{48}{90}$$

$$=\frac{48\div6}{90\div6}$$

$$=\frac{8}{15}.$$

Now let us find the simplest name for $\dfrac{\frac{2}{5}}{\frac{3}{4}}$:

$$\frac{\frac{2}{5}}{\frac{3}{4}}=\frac{2}{5}\div\frac{3}{4}$$

$$=\frac{2}{5}\times\frac{4}{3}$$

$$=\frac{8}{15}.$$

Thus we have shown what we set out to show.

As an illustration of statement (b) we shall show that

$$\frac{\frac{2}{3}}{\frac{1}{2}}\times\frac{\frac{4}{7}}{\frac{3}{5}}=\frac{\frac{2}{3}\times\frac{4}{7}}{\frac{1}{2}\times\frac{3}{5}}$$

is a true statement. We will be in a position to show this if we find the

simplest names for $\dfrac{\frac{2}{3}}{\frac{1}{2}}\times\dfrac{\frac{4}{7}}{\frac{3}{5}}$ and $\dfrac{\frac{2}{3}\times\frac{4}{7}}{\frac{1}{2}\times\frac{3}{5}}.$

For the first of these, we have

$$\frac{\frac{2}{3}}{\frac{1}{2}} \times \frac{\frac{4}{7}}{\frac{3}{5}} = \left(\frac{2}{3} \div \frac{1}{2}\right) \times \left(\frac{4}{7} \div \frac{3}{5}\right)$$

$$= \left(\frac{2}{3} \times \frac{2}{1}\right) \times \left(\frac{4}{7} \times \frac{5}{3}\right)$$

$$= \frac{4}{3} \times \frac{20}{21}$$

$$= \frac{4 \times 20}{3 \times 21}$$

$$= \frac{80}{63}.$$

For the second expression, we have

$$\frac{\frac{2}{3} \times \frac{4}{7}}{\frac{1}{2} \times \frac{3}{5}} = \frac{\frac{8}{21}}{\frac{3}{10}}$$

$$= \frac{8}{21} \div \frac{3}{10}$$

$$= \frac{8}{21} \times \frac{10}{3}$$

$$= \frac{80}{63}.$$

Thus the desired equality has been established.

It is possible, also, to show that the other procedures developed for working with rational numbers named by fractions with whole-number numerators and denominators may be used when the fractions have rational numerators and denominators.

Statement (a), demonstrated on page 59, is sometimes used as the basis for an alternative procedure for finding the quotient of two rational numbers. For example:

$$\frac{5}{8} \div \frac{3}{4} = n,$$

$$n = \frac{5}{8} \div \frac{3}{4}$$

$$= \frac{\frac{5}{8}}{\frac{3}{4}}$$

$$= \frac{\frac{5}{8} \times \frac{8}{1}}{\frac{3}{4} \times \frac{8}{1}}$$

$$= \frac{\frac{40}{8}}{\frac{24}{4}},$$

$$n = \frac{5}{6}.$$

Exercise Set 8

1. Show that $\frac{15}{7} \div \frac{2}{3} = \frac{15}{7} \times \frac{3}{2}$ by supplying appropriate numbers to fill the blanks.

$$\frac{15}{7} \div \frac{2}{3} = n$$

$$\frac{15}{7} = n \times \frac{2}{3}$$

(a) $\frac{15}{7} \times \underline{\hspace{1cm}} = \left(n \times \frac{2}{3} \right) \times \underline{\hspace{1cm}}$ (Same number in both blanks)

(b) $\frac{15}{7} \times \underline{\hspace{1cm}} = n \times \left(\frac{2}{3} \times \underline{\hspace{1cm}} \right)$ (Same numbers as above)

(c) $\frac{15}{7} \times \underline{\hspace{1cm}} = n \times 1$

(d) $\frac{15}{7} \times \underline{\hspace{1cm}} = n$

(e) $\frac{15}{7} \times \underline{\hspace{1cm}} = \frac{15}{7} \div \frac{2}{3}$

2. Show by the method for dividing rational numbers that each of the following statements is true.

(a) $15 \div 8 = \frac{15}{8}$ (c) $2586 \div 450 = \frac{2586}{450}$

(b) $3 \div 10 = \frac{3}{10}$ (d) $2 \div 3 = \frac{2}{3}$

3. Complete each statement to make a true sentence.

(a) A property of the rational numbers which whole numbers do not have is that every rational number (except _____) has a _____.

(b) The product of a nonnegative rational number and its _____
is _____.

(c) The only nonnegative rational number which is its own _____
is _____.

4. Find the simplest name for $\dfrac{\frac{21}{40}}{\frac{13}{60}}$ by use of the following methods:

(a) Using the division process to find $\dfrac{21}{40} \div \dfrac{13}{60}$.

(b) Using the property $\dfrac{m \times \frac{a}{b}}{m \times \frac{c}{d}} = \dfrac{\frac{a}{b}}{\frac{c}{d}}$. (Let $m = 120$.)

SUMMARY

A rational number is an abstraction (as is a whole number), which may be illustrated by the separation of a unit region into a counting number of congruent subregions, and then considering a whole number of these subregions. Instead of a unit region, a unit interval on the number line, separated into congruent subintervals, or a set of discrete objects separated into equivalent subsets, may be used for illustration.

A fraction, $\dfrac{a}{b}$, where b represents the number of congruent subregions (or congruent subintervals or equivalent subsets) and a represents the number of subregions (or subintervals or subsets) considered, is a numeral for a rational number. The number a is the numerator of the fraction, and the number b is the denominator.

Many fractions (called equivalent fractions) name the same rational number: $\dfrac{m \times a}{m \times b} = \dfrac{a}{b}$, where m is a counting number. Consequently, any two rational numbers may be named by fractions with the same denominator.

The rational numbers are ordered. For any two rational numbers $\dfrac{a}{b}$ and $\dfrac{c}{d}$, either

$$\frac{a}{b} < \frac{c}{d}, \quad \text{or} \quad \frac{a}{b} = \frac{c}{d}, \quad \text{or} \quad \frac{a}{b} > \frac{c}{d},$$

accordingly as

$$a \times d < b \times c, \quad a \times d = b \times c, \quad \text{or} \quad a \times d > b \times c.$$

The set of whole numbers may be regarded as a proper subset of the set of rational numbers.

Operations on rational numbers have been defined as follows:

$$\frac{a}{b} + \frac{c}{b} = \frac{a+c}{b},$$

$$\frac{a}{b} - \frac{c}{b} = \frac{a-c}{b}, \text{ if } c \text{ is not greater than } a,$$

$$\frac{a}{b} \times \frac{c}{d} = \frac{a \times c}{b \times d},$$

$$\frac{a}{b} \div \frac{c}{d} = \frac{a}{b} \times \frac{d}{c}.$$

The definitions for addition and subtraction yield

$$\frac{a}{b} + \frac{c}{d} = \frac{ad+bc}{bd},$$

$$\frac{a}{b} - \frac{c}{d} = \frac{ad-bc}{bd},$$

if bc is not greater than ad.

Alternatively and equivalently, subtraction and division were defined as inverse operations to addition and multiplication, respectively. The operations on rational numbers have the same properties as the operations on whole numbers.

The operation of division is closed in the set of rational numbers (except for division by zero). This is not true of the set of whole numbers.

The set of rational numbers is dense; that is, between any two rational numbers there is a third rational number. This is not true of the set of whole numbers.

The fraction symbol $\frac{a}{b}$ may be used as a symbol for the division $a \div b$ (a and b whole numbers, $b \neq 0$). A similar form, $\dfrac{\frac{a}{b}}{\frac{c}{d}}$, may be used as the symbol for $\frac{a}{b} \div \frac{c}{d}$; and the laws for performing computations by means of fractions continue to hold. Since division is closed in the set of rational numbers, $\dfrac{\frac{a}{b}}{\frac{c}{d}}$ (where $b, c, d \neq 0$) is a name for a rational number.

ANSWERS TO EXERCISES

Exercise Set 1

1. (a) (1, 5)   (c) (4, 3)

   (b) (3, 4)   (d) (5, 16)

2. (a) (4, 5)   (c) (2, 3)

   (b) (1, 4)   (d) (11, 16)

3. (a) Each unit segment on the number line is divided into seven congruent segments, and $\frac{0}{7}$ corresponds to the left-hand endpoint of
   the first unit segment. This means that a set of no congruent
   segments is being considered.

   (b) A unit region is divided into nine congruent subregions, and five
   of the subregions are being considered.

   (c) It is impossible to have 0 discrete objects and then consider 8 of
   of them.

4.

5.

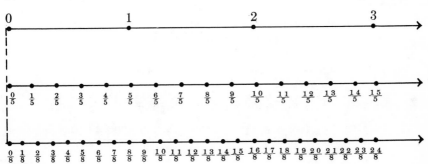

Exercise Set 2

1. $\dfrac{2}{3}$ 2. $\dfrac{4}{6}$

3. (a) 2   (b) Yes   (c) Yes

4. (a) 5×7 (b) 7×7 (c) 7   (d) $\dfrac{5}{7}$

5. $\dfrac{12}{52} = \dfrac{4 \times 3}{4 \times 13} = \dfrac{3}{13}$

   $\dfrac{30}{130} = \dfrac{3 \times 10}{13 \times 10} = \dfrac{3}{13}$

   $\dfrac{3}{13} = \dfrac{3}{13}$

Exercise Set 3

1. Example

3. $\dfrac{17}{20} = \dfrac{17 \times 19}{20 \times 19} = \dfrac{323}{20 \times 19}$

   $\dfrac{15}{19} = \dfrac{15 \times 20}{19 \times 20} = \dfrac{300}{19 \times 20}$

   $\dfrac{17}{20} > \dfrac{15}{19}$

2. $\dfrac{28}{3} = \dfrac{28 \times 4}{3 \times 4} = \dfrac{112}{3 \times 4}$

   $\dfrac{30}{4} = \dfrac{30 \times 3}{4 \times 3} = \dfrac{90}{4 \times 3}$

   $\dfrac{28}{3} > \dfrac{30}{4}$

4. $\dfrac{9}{13} = \dfrac{9 \times 11}{13 \times 11} = \dfrac{99}{11 \times 13}$

   $\dfrac{8}{11} = \dfrac{8 \times 13}{11 \times 13} = \dfrac{104}{11 \times 13}$

   $\dfrac{9}{13} < \dfrac{8}{11}$

Exercise Set 4

1. (a) Associative property of addition
   (b) Commutative property of addition
   (c) Associative property of addition
   (d) Definition of addition of rational numbers
   (e) Equivalent fractions
   (f) Definition of addition of rational numbers

2. (a) $\dfrac{1}{3} + \dfrac{5}{3} + 5 + \dfrac{1}{7} + \dfrac{5}{7} = \dfrac{6}{3} + 5 + \dfrac{6}{7} = 2 + 5 + \dfrac{18}{21} = \dfrac{14}{7} + \dfrac{35}{7} + \dfrac{6}{7} = \dfrac{55}{7}$

   (b) $\dfrac{2}{3} + \dfrac{4}{3} + \dfrac{3}{5} + \dfrac{1}{5} + 4 = \dfrac{6}{3} + \dfrac{4}{5} + 4 = 2 + 4 + \dfrac{4}{5} = \dfrac{10}{5} + \dfrac{20}{5} + \dfrac{4}{5} = \dfrac{34}{5}$

3.

$$\frac{5}{8} \ + \ \frac{1}{8}$$

| $\frac{0}{8}$ | $\frac{1}{8}$ | $\frac{2}{8}$ | $\frac{3}{8}$ | $\frac{4}{8}$ | $\frac{5}{8}$ | $\frac{6}{8}$ | $\frac{7}{8}$ | $\frac{8}{8}$ | $\frac{9}{8}$ | $\frac{10}{8}$ | $\frac{11}{8}$ | $\frac{12}{8}$ | $\frac{13}{8}$ | $\frac{14}{8}$ | $\frac{15}{8}$ | $\frac{16}{8}$ |

4.

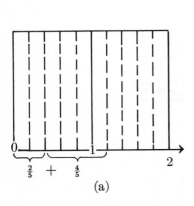

(a)

$$\frac{2}{5} \ + \ \frac{4}{5}$$

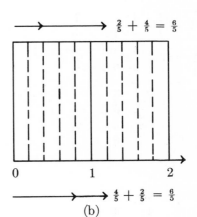

$$\frac{2}{5} + \frac{4}{5} = \frac{6}{5}$$

$$\frac{4}{5} + \frac{2}{5} = \frac{6}{5}$$

(b)

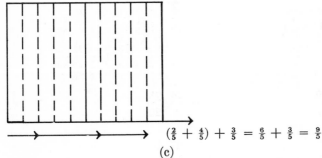

$$\frac{2}{5} + \left(\frac{4}{5} + \frac{3}{5}\right) = \frac{2}{5} + \frac{7}{5} = \frac{9}{5}$$

$$\left(\frac{2}{5} + \frac{4}{5}\right) + \frac{3}{5} = \frac{6}{5} + \frac{3}{5} = \frac{9}{5}$$

(c)

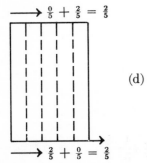

$$\frac{0}{5} + \frac{2}{5} = \frac{2}{5}$$

(d)

$$\frac{2}{5} + \frac{0}{5} = \frac{2}{5}$$

Exercise Set 5

1. (a) $\dfrac{9}{12}, \dfrac{8}{12},$ and $\dfrac{10}{12}$

   (b) $\dfrac{15}{51}, \dfrac{23}{51}$

   (c) $\dfrac{50}{20}, \dfrac{35}{20}, \dfrac{44}{20}$

   (d) $\dfrac{54}{42}, \dfrac{26}{42}, \dfrac{19}{42}$

2. (a) $\begin{aligned}\dfrac{4}{3} &= \dfrac{8}{6}\\ -\dfrac{1}{2} &= \dfrac{3}{6}\\ \hline &\ \ \dfrac{5}{6}\end{aligned}$

   (d) $\begin{aligned}\dfrac{59}{7} &= \dfrac{295}{35}\\ \dfrac{144}{35} &= \dfrac{144}{35}\\ \hline &\ \dfrac{151}{35}\end{aligned}$

   (b) $\begin{aligned}\dfrac{43}{13} &= \dfrac{172}{56}\\ \dfrac{13}{8} &= \dfrac{91}{56}\\ \hline &\ \dfrac{81}{56}\end{aligned}$

   (e) $\begin{aligned}\dfrac{26}{2} &= \dfrac{104}{8}\\ \dfrac{21}{8} &= \dfrac{21}{8}\\ \hline &\ \dfrac{83}{8}\end{aligned}$

   (c) $\begin{aligned}\dfrac{33}{5} &= \dfrac{132}{20}\\ \dfrac{57}{20} &= \dfrac{57}{20}\\ \hline &\ \dfrac{75}{20} = \dfrac{15}{4}\end{aligned}$

   (f) $\begin{aligned}\dfrac{5}{4} &= \dfrac{25}{20}\\ \dfrac{4}{5} &= \dfrac{16}{20}\\ \hline &\ \dfrac{9}{20}\end{aligned}$

Exercise Set 6

1. (a) $\dfrac{2}{3} \times \dfrac{3}{5} = \dfrac{6}{15}$ (b) $\dfrac{4}{6} \times \dfrac{2}{2} = \dfrac{8}{12}$ (c) $\dfrac{2}{2} \times \dfrac{4}{3} = \dfrac{8}{6}$

2.

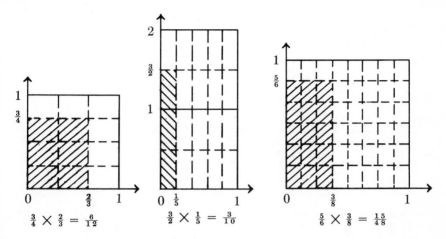

$$\frac{3}{4} \times \frac{2}{3} = \frac{6}{12} \qquad \frac{3}{2} \times \frac{1}{5} = \frac{3}{10} \qquad \frac{5}{6} \times \frac{3}{8} = \frac{15}{48}$$

3.

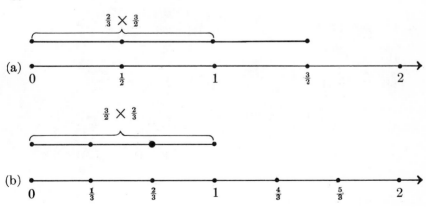

4.

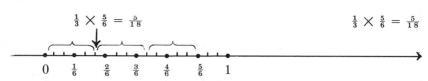

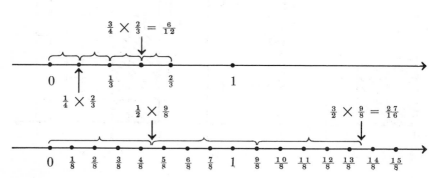

Exercise Set 7

1. (a) $\dfrac{6}{5}$ (b) $\dfrac{13}{7}$ (c) $\dfrac{1}{4}$ (d) 1   (e) $\dfrac{3}{5}$ (f) $\dfrac{3}{8}$

2. (a) $\dfrac{6}{5}$ (b) $\dfrac{3}{7}$ (c) $\dfrac{5}{4}$ (d) 1   (e) $\dfrac{1}{6}$ (f) $\dfrac{2}{5}$

3. (a) $n \times 3 = 36$ (d) $\dfrac{3}{5} \times \dfrac{5}{6} = n$

   (b) $8 \times n = 24$ (e) $11 \times n = 1$

   (c) $n \times 17 = 17$ (f) $2 \times 3 = n$

4. (a) $1 \div \dfrac{2}{3} = \dfrac{3}{2}$ $1 \div \dfrac{3}{2} = \dfrac{2}{3}$ (c) $1 \div \dfrac{18}{7} = \dfrac{7}{18}$ $1 \div \dfrac{7}{18} = \dfrac{18}{7}$

   (b) $1 \div \dfrac{3}{16} = \dfrac{16}{3}$ $1 \div \dfrac{16}{3} = \dfrac{3}{16}$ (d) $1 \div \dfrac{9}{41} = \dfrac{41}{9}$ $1 \div \dfrac{41}{9} = \dfrac{9}{41}$

5. (a) $\dfrac{4}{3} \times \dfrac{2}{5}$ (c) $1 \times n = \dfrac{4}{3} \times \dfrac{2}{5}$

   (b) $\dfrac{4}{3} \times \dfrac{2}{5}$ (d) $n = \dfrac{4}{3} \times \dfrac{2}{5} = \dfrac{8}{15}$

6. (a) $n \times \dfrac{3}{7} = \dfrac{5}{4}$ (d) $n \times 1 = \dfrac{5}{4} \times \dfrac{7}{3}$

(b) $n \times 1 = n \times \left(\dfrac{3}{7} \times \dfrac{7}{3}\right)$ (e) $n = \dfrac{35}{12}$

(c) $\left(n \times \dfrac{3}{7}\right) \times \dfrac{7}{3} = \dfrac{5}{4} \times \dfrac{7}{3}$ (f) $\dfrac{5}{4} \div \dfrac{3}{7} = \dfrac{35}{12}$

7. (a) $n \times \dfrac{16}{15} = \dfrac{8}{5}$ (d) $n = \dfrac{8}{5} \times \dfrac{15}{16}$

(b) $\left(n \times \dfrac{16}{15}\right) \times \dfrac{15}{16} = \dfrac{8}{5} \times \dfrac{15}{16}$ (e) $n = \dfrac{120}{80}$ or $\dfrac{3}{2}$

(c) $n \times 1 = \dfrac{8}{5} \times \dfrac{15}{16}$ (f) $\dfrac{8}{5} \div \dfrac{3}{2} = \dfrac{16}{15}$

Exercise Set 8

1. (a) $\dfrac{15}{7} \times \dfrac{3}{2} = \left(n \times \dfrac{2}{3}\right) \times \dfrac{3}{2}$ (d) $\dfrac{15}{7} \times \dfrac{3}{2} = n$

(b) $\dfrac{15}{7} \times \dfrac{3}{2} = n \times \left(\dfrac{2}{3} \times \dfrac{3}{2}\right)$ (e) $\dfrac{15}{7} \times \dfrac{3}{2} = \dfrac{15}{7} \div \dfrac{2}{3}$

(c) $\dfrac{15}{7} \times \dfrac{3}{2} = n \times 1$

2. (a) $15 \div 8 = \dfrac{15}{1} \div \dfrac{8}{1}$ (c) $2586 \div 450 = \dfrac{2586}{1} \div \dfrac{450}{1}$

$\qquad = \dfrac{15}{1} \times \dfrac{1}{8}$ $\qquad = \dfrac{2586}{1} \times \dfrac{1}{450}$

$\qquad = \dfrac{15 \times 1}{1 \times 8}$ $\qquad = \dfrac{2586 \times 1}{1 \times 450}$

$\qquad = \dfrac{15}{8}$ $\qquad = \dfrac{2586}{450}$

(b) $3 \div 10 = \dfrac{3}{1} \div \dfrac{10}{1}$ (d) $2 \div 3 = \dfrac{2}{1} \div \dfrac{3}{1}$

$\qquad = \dfrac{3}{1} \times \dfrac{1}{10}$ $\qquad = \dfrac{2}{1} \times \dfrac{1}{3}$

$\qquad = \dfrac{3 \times 1}{1 \times 10}$ $\qquad = \dfrac{2 \times 1}{1 \times 3}$

$\qquad = \dfrac{3}{10}$ $\qquad = \dfrac{2}{3}$

3. (a) zero, reciprocal   (b) reciprocal, one   (c) reciprocal, one

4. (a) $\dfrac{21}{40} \div \dfrac{13}{60} = \dfrac{21}{40} \times \dfrac{60}{13}$

$\qquad = \dfrac{21 \times 60}{40 \times 13}$

$\qquad = \dfrac{21 \times 3 \times 20}{2 \times 20 \times 13}$

$\qquad = \dfrac{21 \times 3}{2 \times 13}$

$\qquad = \dfrac{63}{26}$

(b) $\dfrac{\dfrac{21}{40}}{\dfrac{13}{60}} = \dfrac{\dfrac{120}{1} \times \dfrac{21}{40}}{\dfrac{120}{1} \times \dfrac{13}{60}}$

$\qquad = \dfrac{\dfrac{120 \times 21}{1 \times 40}}{\dfrac{120 \times 13}{1 \times 60}}$

$\qquad = \dfrac{\dfrac{3 \times 40 \times 21}{1 \times 40}}{\dfrac{2 \times 60 \times 13}{1 \times 60}}$

$\qquad = \dfrac{3 \times 21}{2 \times 13}$

$\qquad = \dfrac{63}{26}$

BOOKLET NUMBER SEVEN:

NUMERATION SYSTEMS FOR THE RATIONAL NUMBERS

INTRODUCTION

In Booklet No. 6: *The Rational Numbers*, we investigated and developed our intuitive notion of what rational numbers are, and we studied the meaning and properties of the basic operations on these numbers. For this purpose, we used fractions of the form $\frac{a}{b}$, where a and b are whole numbers with $b \neq 0$, as names for the rational numbers.

The rational numbers, like the whole numbers, have been given many different systems of names. Partly this is a result of the historical development of our number notions. More, though, it is a matter of convenience; one numeration system is more suggestive and useful for one purpose, and another is preferable for another purpose.

In this booklet we shall investigate several numeration systems for the rational numbers and shall make evident some of the benefits to be derived from alternative representations.

RATIONAL NUMBERS

Let us begin by briefly surveying the properties of the rational number system. Of course, to do this we shall have to use some system of numeration; that is, some kind of symbols to represent the rational numbers. Since fractions such as $\frac{3}{4}$ and $\frac{9}{5}$ are convenient for the purpose, let us employ them.

If we assume that there is a set of numbers in which each whole number when divided by any whole number other than 0 yields a number for a quotient, then we are postulating the existence of the set of rational numbers. To be more precise about it, we are assuming the existence of the set of nonnegative rational numbers; and since we do not wish to deal with negative numbers in this booklet, let us now agree that unless otherwise explicitly stated none of the numbers discussed herein will be negative.

By assuming that we can always divide one whole number by another nonzero whole number, we now have numbers such as $\frac{3}{5}$, $\frac{7}{3}$, and $\frac{0}{9}$, as well as rational numbers that can be identified with the familiar whole numbers: $\frac{16}{4}$ (4), $\frac{18}{3}$ (6), and $\frac{100}{4}$ (25). Thus the set of whole numbers can be viewed as a subset of the set of rational numbers.

In what way or ways do the rational numbers differ from the whole numbers in behavior under the familiar operations of addition and multiplication? To answer this question, let us first turn the matter about and see how they do *not* differ:

1. The system of rational numbers and the system of whole numbers are both *closed* with respect to addition and multiplication. That is, the sum or product of any two rational numbers is a rational number, just as the sum or product of two whole numbers is a whole number.

2. Addition and multiplication are *commutative* operations in the system of rational numbers as well as in the system of whole numbers. The order in which the addends appear in the sum of two rational numbers (or whole numbers), or the order in which the factors occur in the product of two rational numbers (or whole numbers) has no effect on the sum or product, respectively. For example, $\frac{2}{3} + \frac{3}{7}$ is equal to $\frac{3}{7} + \frac{2}{3}$, just as $2 + 3 = 3 + 2$.

3. Addition and multiplication are *associative* operations both in the system of rational numbers and in the system of whole numbers. The addends in a sum or the factors in a product can, in either case, be grouped as desired. For example,

$$\frac{2}{3} + \frac{1}{2} + \frac{3}{4}$$

can be viewed as meaning

$$\left(\frac{2}{3} + \frac{1}{2}\right) + \frac{3}{4}$$

or as meaning

$$\frac{2}{3} + \left(\frac{1}{2} + \frac{3}{4}\right),$$

where the parentheses indicate the numbers whose sum is considered first; the sum is the same in the two cases. This is, of course, true for whole numbers as well: $2 + 3 + 7$ can be viewed as $(2 + 3) + 7$ or as $2 + (3+7)$. Also, $\left(\frac{2}{3} \times \frac{1}{2}\right) \times \frac{3}{4} = \frac{2}{3} \times \left(\frac{1}{2} \times \frac{3}{4}\right)$ and $(2 \times 3) \times 7 = 2 \times (3 \times 7)$.

4. Multiplication *distributes* over addition in both systems. Thus,

$$\frac{1}{2} \times \left(\frac{2}{3} + \frac{3}{5}\right)$$

denotes the same number as

$$\left(\frac{1}{2} \times \frac{2}{3}\right) + \left(\frac{1}{2} \times \frac{3}{5}\right),$$

just as $2 \times (3+5)$ is equal to $(2 \times 3) + (2 \times 5)$.

5. Both systems have *additive identity* elements. An additive identity element is simply an element in a number system that is "neutral" as an addend in a sum. In the system of rational numbers, 0 plays this role just as it does in the system of whole numbers. Thus,

$$\frac{1}{2} + 0 = \frac{1}{2},$$

just as

$$8 + 0 = 8.$$

6. Both systems have *multiplicative identity* elements. A multiplicative identity element is an element that is "neutral" as a factor in a product. The number one plays this role both in the rational number system and in the system of whole numbers. For instance,

$$\frac{2}{3} \times 1 = \frac{2}{3},$$

just as

$$5 \times 1 = 5.$$

It is evident that the system of rational numbers and the system of whole numbers have a number of fundamental properties in common. Indeed, there is but one basic way in which they differ: Each nonzero element in the set of rational numbers has a *multiplicative inverse*, or *reciprocal* as it is sometimes called. A multiplicative inverse b for a given number a is a number such that the product of the two numbers a and b is the multiplicative identity element. For example, the multiplicative inverse of the rational number $\frac{3}{4}$ is the rational number $\frac{4}{3}$, because $\frac{3}{4} \times \frac{4}{3} = 1$. Note that the existence of a reciprocal for each element (except 0) in the system of rational numbers is a feature not shared by the system of whole numbers. For example, there is no whole number whose product with 3 is 1. That is, there is no whole number n such that $3 \times n = 1$.

The properties of the rational numbers discussed above are fundamental in the sense that they govern all of our operations with rational numbers, and therefore—perhaps more importantly from the standpoint of an elementary school teacher—all the operations we perform with the fractions and other symbols that name these numbers.

In passing, let us make a brief comment about *negative numbers*. We note that both in the system of whole numbers and in the system of rational numbers we have an additive identity element (0) and a multiplicative identity element (1). The multiplicative inverse b for a given number a is a number such that the *product* of the two numbers is the identity element for *multiplication:* $a \times b = 1$. By analogy, then, the *additive inverse* for a given number c should be a number such that the *sum* of the two numbers is the identity element for *addition:* $c + d = 0$. The system of (nonnegative) rational numbers might be looked on as extending the system of whole numbers to a system in which each number (other than 0) has a multiplicative inverse. In the same way, the system of integers

$$\{ \ldots, \ -2, \ -1, \ 0, \ 1, \ 2, \ \ldots \}$$

extends the system of whole numbers to a system in which each number has an *additive* inverse, and the entire system of rational numbers similarly extends the system of nonnegative rational numbers with which we are concerned in this booklet.

NUMBERS AND THEIR NAMES

A rational number, like a whole number, is an abstraction. We can talk about rational numbers by giving them names just as we do with the whole numbers. The names and symbols used to represent rational numbers, however, occur in greater variety than do those used for whole numbers. Also, when studying rational numbers and their properties, we are almost as much concerned with the properties of the names we use as we are with the numbers themselves.

Among the various representations of rational numbers in use today we find the following:

1. Fractions, such as $\dfrac{2}{3}$, $\dfrac{7}{5}$, and $\dfrac{23}{2}$;

2. Ordered pairs, such as $(2, 3)$, $(1, 7)$, and $(15, 6)$;

3. Mixed numerals, such as $1\dfrac{5}{7}$, $23\dfrac{1}{2}$, and $4\dfrac{5}{8}$;

4. Decimal numerals, such as 0.217, 0.333, and 5.5.

Each of these forms of numeration has some useful aspects, and each lends itself to certain specific applications better than any of the others. Let us examine each of these forms of symbolism in more detail.

FRACTIONS

The symbol $\frac{3}{5}$, which is used to denote the rational number three-fifths, is an example of a fraction. The whole number represented by the upper part of the fraction is called the *numerator* of the fraction, and the counting number represented by the lower part is called the *denominator* of the fraction. Observe that a fraction is defined here as a *symbol* (numeral), whereas the numerator and denominator are defined as *numbers*. This is done because we wish to talk about operations involving numerators and denominators, and our operations are defined only for numbers, not symbols. Indeed, the use of the word "fraction" itself will be kept to a minimum, since we are really interested in working with the rational number represented by a fraction rather than with the fraction itself.

Conceptually, fractions with whole-number numerators and nonzero whole-number denominators can be thought of as denoting quotients of whole numbers (see Booklet No. 6: *The Rational Numbers*). According to this view, "numerator" and "dividend" are synonymous, as are "denominator" and "divisor." Thus, $\frac{3}{5}$ is the rational number that is the quotient when 3 is divided by 5. Furthermore, if rational numbers are defined as quotients of whole numbers, the set of whole numbers becomes a proper subset of the set of rational numbers. This is true since, for any whole number a, the quotient when a is divided by 1 is a; and hence every whole number can be viewed as the quotient of two whole numbers. In fact, every whole number is the quotient of two whole numbers in an endless number of ways. Since

$$\frac{2}{1}=2, \ \frac{4}{2}=2, \ \frac{6}{3}=2, \ \frac{8}{4}=2,$$

and so on, the fractions $\frac{2}{1}, \frac{4}{2}, \frac{6}{3},$ and $\frac{8}{4}$ all denote the same number, the whole number 2.

In general, *fractions are preferred as names for rational numbers when these numbers are being used as quotients of whole numbers.*

Figure 1 shows a number line with several names for some rational numbers listed on it. In this figure, names associated with the same point are names for the same number.

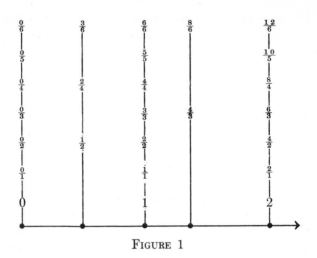

FIGURE 1

The criterion that enables us to identify fractions denoting the same rational number is the following:*

If a, b, c, and d are whole numbers,
and b and d are not 0, then

$$\frac{a}{b} = \frac{c}{d}$$

if, and only if, $a \times d = b \times c$.

Thus $\frac{12}{28} = \frac{18}{42}$ since $12 \times 42 = 28 \times 18$. Note that this test depends on the fact that, for example,

$$\frac{12}{28} = \frac{42 \times 12}{42 \times 28} \quad \text{and} \quad \frac{18}{42} = \frac{18 \times 28}{42 \times 28}.$$

More generally: $\frac{a}{b}$ is less than, equal to, or greater than $\frac{c}{d}$ according as $a \times d$ is less than, equal to, or greater than $b \times c$.

Exercise Set 1

1. Name the property illustrated by each of the following true sentences.

---

* For a more extensive discussion of the properties of rational numbers discussed in terms of fractions, see Booklet No. 6: *The Rational Numbers.*

SENTENCE	PROPERTY
$\dfrac{3}{4}+\dfrac{1}{3}=\dfrac{1}{3}+\dfrac{3}{4}$	_____
$\dfrac{5}{6}\times\dfrac{3}{7}=\dfrac{3}{7}\times\dfrac{5}{6}$	_____
$\dfrac{7}{8}\times 1=\dfrac{7}{8}$	_____
$\dfrac{9}{11}+0=\dfrac{9}{11}$	_____
$2\times\left(6+\dfrac{1}{2}\right)=(2\times 6)+\left(2\times\dfrac{1}{2}\right)$	_____
$\dfrac{7}{8}\times\dfrac{8}{7}=1$	_____
$\left(\dfrac{3}{5}+\dfrac{5}{7}\right)+\dfrac{5}{9}=\dfrac{3}{5}+\left(\dfrac{5}{7}+\dfrac{5}{9}\right)$	_____

2. Complete the following statements.

   (a) The rational numbers named by $\dfrac{6}{7}$ and $\dfrac{8}{9}$ can be renamed by fractions having the same denominator. $\dfrac{6}{7}=$ _____ and $\dfrac{8}{9}=$ _____.

   (b) Using the fractions with the same denominator in Exercise 2 (a), we can state that _____ < _____.

   (c) Using only the numerators of the fractions in Exercise 2 (b), we can state that _____ < _____.

   (d) This means that to test whether or not $\dfrac{6}{7}<\dfrac{8}{9}$, it is sufficient to test whether or not _____ < _____.

3. Complete the following statements.

   (a) The rational numbers named by $\dfrac{3}{5}$ and $\dfrac{4}{7}$ can be renamed by fractions having the same denominator. $\dfrac{3}{5}=$ _____ and $\dfrac{4}{7}=$ _____.

   (b) Using the fractions with the same denominator in Exercise 3 (a), we can state that _____ > _____.

   (c) Using only the numerators of the fractions in Exercise 3 (b), we can state that _____ > _____.

   (d) This means that to test whether or not $\dfrac{3}{5}>\dfrac{4}{7}$ it is sufficient to test whether or not _____ > _____.

4. The fractions $\dfrac{2}{6}$ and $\dfrac{5}{15}$ name the same rational number because _____ × _____ = _____ × _____.

5. Fill in the following blanks with $=$, $>$, or $<$ so that true statements result; and use the "cross-product method" of testing, shown in Exercises 2, 3, and 4.

(a) $\dfrac{2}{3}$————$\dfrac{3}{4}$ (c) $\dfrac{5}{11}$————$\dfrac{3}{7}$ (e) $\dfrac{5}{2}$————$\dfrac{15}{6}$

(b) $\dfrac{4}{9}$————$\dfrac{12}{27}$ (d) $\dfrac{7}{3}$————$\dfrac{11}{5}$ (f) $\dfrac{8}{13}$————$\dfrac{5}{17}$

ORDERED PAIRS

A second means of representing rational numbers is available through the notion of an *ordered pair* of whole numbers. An ordered pair of whole numbers is simply a pair of whole numbers for which the order in which the numbers appear is of importance. Ordered pairs are denoted by symbols like $(2, 3)$, where the parentheses and comma denote that the numbers are to be considered in order, first 2 and then 3. The numbers in an ordered pair are called the *components* of the pair. In the ordered pair $(2, 3)$, 2 is the first component, and 3 the second component.

One means by which mathematicians define a rational number is in terms of ordered pairs of whole numbers in which no ordered pair has a second component that is zero. In this view, the rational number denoted by the fraction $\dfrac{3}{5}$ could also be denoted by the ordered pair $(3, 5)$. The first component of the ordered pair corresponds to the numerator of the fraction, and the second component to the denominator. Since this is an abstract idea, when one is reading about rational numbers discussed in terms of ordered pairs, it is helpful to give the same kind of interpretation to such pairs as one would to the representation of such numbers by fractions. For example, $(3, 5)$ can be thought of in terms of "three of five congruent parts of a whole," or as "the quotient when 3 is divided by 5," or in some other similar way.

Just as many fractions denote the same rational number, many ordered pairs also correspond to the same rational number. We can define two ordered pairs to be equal (representatives of the same rational number) in a manner analogous to that used for fractions. For example, we have $\dfrac{2}{3} = \dfrac{6}{9}$, because $2 \times 9 = 3 \times 6$. Similarly, in terms of ordered pairs, we would have $(2, 3) = (6, 9)$, because $2 \times 9 = 3 \times 6$; that is, the products of the first component of each pair and the second component of the other are equal. Formally, this can be expressed as follows:

If a, b, c, and d are whole numbers,
and neither b nor d is 0, then

$$(a, b) = (c, d)$$

if, and only if, $a \times d = b \times c$.

These products can be depicted schematically by a diagram as shown in Figure 2, where the lines connect the factors in the separate products.

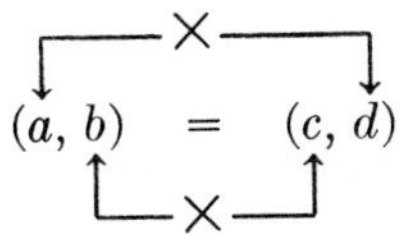

FIGURE 2

Now, if we want to know whether or not $(3, 21) = (9, 56)$ is a true statement, we form the products 3×56 and 21×9 and see whether or not they are equal. Since $3 \times 56 = 168$ and $21 \times 9 = 189$, the statement is false.

More generally, (a, b) is less than, equal to, or greater than (c, d) according as $a \times d$ is less than, equal to, or greater than $b \times c$.

Table I shows the operations of addition, subtraction, multiplication, and division for some specific examples as they appear when the rational numbers involved are represented by fractions and when they are represented by ordered pairs.

For a more general comparison of the two forms of representing

TABLE I

Operation	Fractions	Ordered Pairs
+	$\dfrac{1}{7} + \dfrac{3}{7} = \dfrac{1+3}{7} = \dfrac{4}{7}$	$(1, 7) + (3, 7) = (1+3, 7) = (4, 7)$
−	$\dfrac{13}{17} - \dfrac{7}{17} = \dfrac{13-7}{17} = \dfrac{6}{17}$	$(13, 17) - (7, 17) = (13-7, 17) = (6, 17)$
+	$\dfrac{1}{3} + \dfrac{3}{5} = \dfrac{5}{15} + \dfrac{9}{15} = \dfrac{14}{15}$	$(1, 3) + (3, 5) = (5, 15) + (9, 15) = (14, 15)$
−	$\dfrac{8}{7} - \dfrac{2}{3} = \dfrac{24}{21} - \dfrac{14}{21} = \dfrac{10}{21}$	$(8, 7) - (2, 3) = (24, 21) - (14, 21) = (10, 21)$
×	$\dfrac{3}{5} \times \dfrac{2}{7} = \dfrac{3 \times 2}{5 \times 7} = \dfrac{6}{35}$	$(3, 5) \times (2, 7) = (3 \times 2, 5 \times 7) = (6, 35)$
÷	$\dfrac{3}{5} \div \dfrac{2}{7} = \dfrac{3 \times 7}{5 \times 2} = \dfrac{21}{10}$	$(3, 5) \div (2, 7) = (3 \times 7, 5 \times 2) = (21, 10)$

rational numbers, see Table II where some basic properties are listed in both forms. In all cases, a, b, c, and d represent whole numbers.

TABLE II

Fractions	Ordered Pairs
$\dfrac{a}{b} = \dfrac{a \times c}{b \times c}$ $(b,\ c \neq 0)$	$(a, b) = (a \times c, b \times c)$ $(b,\ c \neq 0)$
$\dfrac{a}{b} + \dfrac{c}{b} = \dfrac{a+c}{b}$ $(b \neq 0)$	$(a, b) + (c, b) = (a+c, b)$ $(b \neq 0)$
$\dfrac{a}{b} - \dfrac{c}{b} = \dfrac{a-c}{b}$ $(b \neq 0)$	$(a, b) - (c, b) = (a-c, b)$ $(b \neq 0)$
$\dfrac{a}{b} + \dfrac{c}{d} = \dfrac{(a \times d) - (b \times c)}{b \times d}$ $(b,\ d \neq 0)$	$(a, b) + (c, d) = [(a \times d) + (b \times c), b \times d]$ $(b,\ d \neq 0)$
$\dfrac{a}{b} - \dfrac{c}{d} = \dfrac{(a \times d) + (b \times c)}{b \times d}$ $(b,\ d \neq 0)$	$(a, b) - (c, d) = [(a \times d) - (b \times c), b \times d]$ $(b,\ d \neq 0)$
$\dfrac{a}{b} \times \dfrac{c}{d} = \dfrac{a \times c}{b \times d}$ $(b,\ d \neq 0)$	$(a, b) \times (c, d) = (a \times c, b \times d)$ $(b,\ d \neq 0)$
$\dfrac{a}{b} \div \dfrac{c}{d} = \dfrac{a}{b} \times \dfrac{d}{c} = \dfrac{a \times d}{b \times c}$ $(b,\ c,\ d \neq 0)$	$(a, b) \div (c, d) = (a, b) \times (d, c) = (a \times d, b \times c)$ $(b,\ c,\ d \neq 0)$

In general, *ordered pairs are preferred as names for rational numbers when we are investigating the formal algebraic structure of this system.*

Exercise Set 2

1. The rational numbers in Table III are represented by fractions. Represent them as ordered pairs.

2. If we want to know whether or not $(5, 12) = (4, 11)$ is a true statement, we form the products (5×11) and (12×4) to see if they are equal. Rename the rational numbers represented by $(5, 12)$ and $(4, 11)$ by fractions and use the fractions to write a true equation or inequality.

3. Rename by fractions the rational numbers represented by ordered pairs in Table IV; and perform the basic operations indicated, using the fractions.

Table III

Fractions	Ordered Pairs
$\dfrac{4}{7}$	
$\dfrac{9}{5}$	
$\dfrac{3}{1}$	
$\dfrac{0}{8}$	
$\dfrac{5}{9}$	
$\dfrac{3}{8}$	

Table IV

Ordered Pairs	Fractions
$(2,7) + (3,7) = (2+3,7) = (5,7)$	
$(3,4) - (2,3) = (9-8,12) = (1,12)$	
$(6,5) \times (1,7) = (6\times1, 5\times7) = (6,35)$	
$(3,4) \div (5,11) = (3\times11, 4\times5) = (33,20)$	

RATIONAL NUMBERS AS EQUIVALENCE CLASSES

Before turning our attention to another representation for rational numbers, let us make a somewhat deeper approach to the definition of a rational number by using ordered pairs, an approach based on set concepts. (For a discussion of the set concepts and the notation used here, see Booklet No. 1: *Sets*.)

First, let us define *equivalent* ordered pairs:

The ordered pair (a, b), $b \neq 0$, *is equivalent to the ordered pair* (c, d) $d \neq 0$, *if, and only if,* $a \times d = b \times c$.

Thus (2, 3) is equivalent to (6, 9) because $2 \times 9 = 3 \times 6$. Notice that this is the same condition we imposed earlier for the equality of rational numbers represented by the ordered pairs. Now, however, we wish to call (2, 3) and (6, 9) equivalent ordered pairs.

Next, consider the set of ordered pairs

$$\{(1, 2), (2, 4), (3, 6), (4, 8), \ldots\},$$

where the three dots within the braces indicate that the list of these ordered pairs continues indefinitely. Notice that each of the ordered pairs in this set is equivalent to every other ordered pair in the set. Thus (1, 2) is equivalent to (3, 6) because $1 \times 6 = 2 \times 3$; (1, 2) is equivalent to (4, 8) because $1 \times 8 = 2 \times 4$; (2, 4) is equivalent to (3, 6) because $2 \times 6 = 4 \times 3$, and so on. Such a set of equivalent ordered pairs is called an *equivalence class*. Another equivalence class is

$$\{(3, 4), (6, 8), (9, 12), (12, 16), \ldots\},$$

and another is

$$\{(7, 3), (14, 6), (21, 9), (28, 12), \ldots\}.$$

Note, however, that the second component of an ordered pair in an equivalence class is never zero.

It is now possible to define a rational number as follows:

> *A rational number is an equivalence class of ordered pairs of whole numbers.*

Does this seem quite abstract? Think of it this way: The set of all ordered pairs of whole numbers with nonzero second components can be sorted into classes. Imagine a moving belt passing in front of a person. Carried along on the belt as it moves are ordered pairs (a, b) of whole numbers, with $b \neq 0$. As each ordered pair passes in front of the person (call him the "sorter"), he inspects it and then tosses it into a bin. Each such ordered pair goes into some bin. Figure 3 depicts this situation. Of course, the analogy we want to develop here is not complete, because there would have to be infinitely many bins, and the belt would never cease producing ordered pairs, but conceptually this depicts the separation of the set of all ordered pairs of whole numbers with nonzero second components into separate and distinct subsets. Each of the bins corresponds to an equivalence class, and the sorter determines the appropriate bin into which to toss a given ordered pair by noting the ordered pairs to which it is equivalent. The contents of each bin is what we have defined to be a rational number.

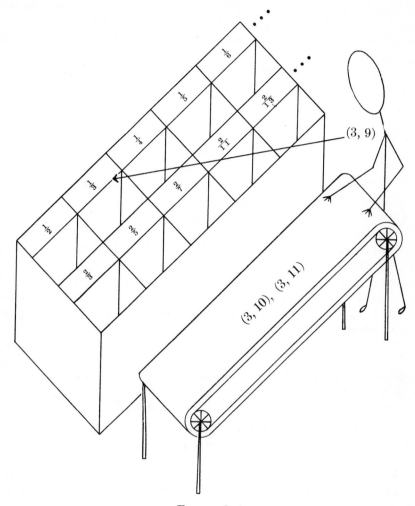

FIGURE 3

Any member (ordered pair) of an equivalence class (rational number) can be used to name the equivalence class. For example, you can name the rational number containing $(1, 2)$ by using $(1, 2)$ or by using $(2, 4)$, $(3, 6)$, or any other ordered pair in that class. A statement such as

$$(1, 2) = (6, 12)$$

is simply an assertion that "$(1, 2)$" and "$(6, 12)$" name the same rational number.

This viewpoint of a rational number as an equivalence class of ordered pairs does not alter anything we said earlier about operations with rational numbers, but simply gives a more precise meaning to the term "rational number."

Indeed, there is no reason the ordered pairs in an equivalence class cannot be displayed in fraction form. Thus

$$\left\{\frac{1}{2}, \frac{2}{4}, \frac{3}{6}, \frac{4}{8}, \ldots\right\}$$

denotes the same equivalence class as

$$\{(1, 2), (2, 4), (3, 6), (4, 8), \ldots\}.$$

MIXED NUMERALS

The rational numbers are *ordered*. That is, of any two distinct rational numbers it can always be said that one is less than the other (see Booklet No. 6: *The Rational Numbers*). Thus, we can separate the set of rational numbers into two disjoint subsets, one containing those rational numbers less than one, and the other containing those rational numbers greater than or equal to one. Figure 4 shows these subsets as represented on the number line.

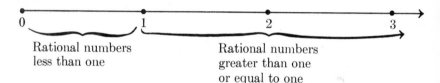

FIGURE 4

We can distinguish between fractions (or ordered pairs) naming rational numbers less than one and those naming rational numbers greater than or equal to one by observing whether or not the numerator (or first component) is less than the denominator (or second component). A fraction with a numerator less than its denominator names a rational number less than one. Such fractions were formerly called *proper fractions*, though this phrase now appears to be passing into disuse. A fraction with numerator greater than or equal to its denominator names a rational number greater than or equal to one; such fractions were formerly called *improper fractions*.

Every rational number that is named by a fraction in which the numerator is greater than or equal to the denominator is either a whole number or a number that can be expressed as the sum of a whole number and a rational number less than one. For instance,

$$\frac{28}{3}=\frac{27}{3}+\frac{1}{3}=9+\frac{1}{3},$$

$$\frac{108}{15}=\frac{105}{15}+\frac{3}{15}=7+\frac{3}{15},$$

and

$$\frac{13}{7}=\frac{7}{7}+\frac{6}{7}=1+\frac{6}{7}$$

are all examples of rational numbers that are such sums, whereas

$$\frac{24}{3}=8, \qquad \frac{19}{19}=1, \qquad \text{and} \qquad \frac{24}{6}=4$$

are examples of fractions naming whole numbers. Of course, just as there are indefinitely many fractions naming a given rational number greater than one, so are there indefinitely many ways to denote the sums we are discussing. Thus, $4+\frac{1}{3}$ can also be written as $4+\frac{2}{6}$, $4+\frac{3}{9}$, and so on.

A rational number greater than 2, such as $\frac{10}{3}$, can be thought of as the sum of a whole number and a rational number in more than one way. Thus, for $\frac{10}{3}$: not only can we write $3+\frac{1}{3}$, $3+\frac{2}{6}$, or any other variation of this expression; but also we can write $2+\frac{4}{3}$, or $1+\frac{7}{3}$, or any other variations of these. In any event, sums of this kind are usually abbreviated by simply writing the addends adjacent to each other and omitting the sign of operation. Thus, $3+\frac{1}{3}$ can be written $3\frac{1}{3}$, $2+\frac{4}{3}$ can be written $2\frac{4}{3}$ and $1+\frac{7}{3}$ can be written $1\frac{7}{3}$. Symbols such as $3\frac{1}{3}$, $2\frac{4}{3}$, and $1\frac{7}{3}$ are called *mixed numerals*, and are names for rational numbers greater than one.

One familiar problem confronting us when working with rational numbers greater than one is trying to find a fraction equivalent to (naming the same rational number as) a given mixed numeral, or conversely, finding a mixed numeral equivalent to a given fraction naming a rational number greater than one. Consider the rational number named by the mixed numeral $4\frac{1}{6}$. By definition, this is a shorthand notation for $4+\frac{1}{6}$. Since another name for 4 is $\frac{24}{6}$, we can write

$$4+\frac{1}{6}=\frac{24}{6}+\frac{1}{6}$$

$$=\frac{25}{6};$$

and $\dfrac{25}{6}$ names the same number as $4\dfrac{1}{6}$. Conversely, $\dfrac{25}{6}$ can be written as the sum $\dfrac{24}{6}+\dfrac{1}{6}$; and we can retrace the previous steps to obtain $4\dfrac{1}{6}$. We could, however, if we wished, write

$$\dfrac{25}{6} \quad \text{as} \quad \dfrac{18}{6}+\dfrac{7}{6} \quad \text{or} \quad \dfrac{12}{6}+\dfrac{13}{6} \quad \text{or even} \quad \dfrac{6}{6}+\dfrac{19}{6},$$

and obtain the mixed numerals

$$3\dfrac{7}{6}, \qquad 2\dfrac{13}{6}, \qquad \text{and} \qquad 1\dfrac{19}{6},$$

respectively, all of which are equivalent to $4\dfrac{1}{6}$. In practice, the simplest form for a mixed numeral is generally considered to be the form with the name of the largest possible whole number as one part and a fraction in simplest form as the other part. Thus, $4\dfrac{1}{6}$ would be the simplest form of a mixed numeral for the rational number it names, rather than $3\dfrac{7}{6}, 2\dfrac{13}{6}, 1\dfrac{19}{6}$, or $4\dfrac{2}{12}$.

In the addition and subtraction algorithms sometimes used to work with mixed numerals, however, forms other than the simplest are often encountered and, in some cases, actually to be preferred. For example, in finding another name for the number $8\dfrac{1}{3}-5\dfrac{2}{3}$, the numeral $8\dfrac{1}{3}$ can effectively be replaced by the equivalent mixed numeral $7\dfrac{4}{3}$, whence by inspection

$$7\dfrac{4}{3}-5\dfrac{2}{3} \text{ is equal to } 2\dfrac{2}{3}.$$

The mixed numeral to be employed in any given situation is a matter of choice, and this choice is generally governed by expediency. That is, one uses the numeral most appropriate to the situation. Except in rare instances, mixed numerals should probably be avoided when working with expressions involving products and quotients, since fractions usually provide better and simpler means for working with such expressions.

In general, *mixed numerals are preferred as names for rational numbers when we are using these numbers to express physical measurements*, as in $23\dfrac{7}{16}$ inches, $4\dfrac{1}{2}$ pounds, $3\dfrac{1}{4}$ hours, and the like.

Exercise Set 3

1. Fill in three more fractions, or ordered pairs, in each equivalence class in the following.

   (a) $\{(2, 3),\ (4, 6),\ \underline{\hphantom{xxx}},\ \underline{\hphantom{xxx}},\ \underline{\hphantom{xxx}},\ \ldots\}$

   (b) $\{(3, 5),\ (6, 10),\ \underline{\hphantom{xxx}},\ \underline{\hphantom{xxx}},\ \underline{\hphantom{xxx}},\ \ldots\}$

   (c) $\left\{\dfrac{5}{6},\ \dfrac{10}{12},\ \underline{\hphantom{xxx}},\ \underline{\hphantom{xxx}},\ \underline{\hphantom{xxx}},\ \ldots\right\}$

   (d) $\left\{\dfrac{4}{3},\ \dfrac{8}{6},\ \underline{\hphantom{xxx}},\ \underline{\hphantom{xxx}},\ \underline{\hphantom{xxx}},\ \ldots\right\}$

2. Employ three different ways to express each of the following numbers as the sum of a whole number and a rational number.

   (a) $4\dfrac{1}{3}$ as $\underline{\hphantom{xxx}},\ \underline{\hphantom{xxx}},\ \underline{\hphantom{xxx}}.$

   (b) $6 + \dfrac{2}{6}$ as $\underline{\hphantom{xxx}},\ \underline{\hphantom{xxx}},\ \underline{\hphantom{xxx}}.$

   (c) $\dfrac{22}{3}$ as $\underline{\hphantom{xxx}},\ \underline{\hphantom{xxx}},\ \underline{\hphantom{xxx}}.$

3. State the simplest mixed numeral to name the rational number represented by

   (a) $\dfrac{11}{3},\ \dfrac{22}{6},$ and $2\dfrac{5}{3}$ (c) $\dfrac{20}{7},\ \dfrac{40}{14},$ and $1\dfrac{13}{7}$

   (b) $\dfrac{22}{5},\ 3\dfrac{7}{5},$ and $2\dfrac{12}{5}$

BASIC FRACTIONS

A fraction with denominator that is a power of 10, for example $\dfrac{1}{10^0}, \dfrac{1}{10^1},$ or $\dfrac{1}{10^2},$ might for brevity be called a *basic fraction*. You will recall that $10^0 = 1.$ Some examples of basic fractions are

$$\frac{15}{1},\ \frac{3}{10},\ \frac{71}{100},\ \frac{3}{1000},\ \text{and}\ \frac{173,512}{10,000}.$$

The base-ten numeration system, which was developed to name the whole numbers (see Booklet No. 3: *Numeration Systems for the Whole Numbers*), can be extended to provide convenient names for the rational numbers named by basic fractions. (Indeed, this system can be extended further to provide names for *every* rational number; but let us first focus our attention on just those named by basic fractions.)

Recall that "437" is a shorthand expression naming the sum $400 + 30 + 7$, each addend of which is, in turn, the product of a number from the set of *digits*

$$\{0, 1, 2, 3, 4, 5, 6, 7, 8, 9\}$$

and a power of ten. Thus, $400 + 30 + 7$ can be written

$$(4 \times 100) + (3 \times 10) + (7 \times 1), \quad \text{or} \quad (4 \times 10^2) + (3 \times 10^1) + (7 \times 10^0).$$

The powers of 10 employed in this notation are called the *place values* of the positions occupied by the digits 4, 3, and 7. It seems natural, therefore, to extend this notation to include sums such as

$$\frac{4}{10} + \frac{3}{100} + \frac{7}{1000},$$

where each addend is the product of a number from the set of digits

$$\{0, 1, 2, 3, 4, 5, 6, 7, 8, 9\}$$

and the *reciprocal* of a power of ten. Thus, we can write the sum

$$\frac{4}{10} + \frac{3}{100} + \frac{7}{1000} \quad \text{as} \quad \left(4 \times \frac{1}{10^1}\right) + \left(3 \times \frac{1}{10^2}\right) + \left(7 \times \frac{1}{10^3}\right).$$

If we now agree that this sum can be abbreviated by the symbol "437", we would have an exact counterpart for the notation we developed for the whole numbers, this time assigning place values $\frac{1}{10}$, $\frac{1}{100}$, and $\frac{1}{1000}$ to the positions occupied by "4", "3", and "7", respectively. We cannot, however, use the numeral "437" to denote both

$$(4 \times 10^2) + (3 \times 10^1) + (7 \times 10^0) \quad \text{and} \quad \left(4 \times \frac{1}{10^1}\right) + \left(3 \times \frac{1}{10^2}\right) + \left(7 \times \frac{1}{10^3}\right).$$

without creating confusion.* Therefore, to indicate whether we wish to denote the place values as powers of ten or as reciprocals of powers of ten, we use a period (called a *decimal point*) to separate them—all positions occupied by digits to the right of the period having as place values reciprocals of powers of ten. Thus, "437" will mean

$$(4 \times 10^2) + (3 \times 10^1) + (7 \times 10^0),$$

whereas 0.437 will mean

$$\left(4 \times \frac{1}{10^1}\right) + \left(3 \times \frac{1}{10^2}\right) + \left(7 \times \frac{1}{10^3}\right).$$

---

*It might be worthwhile to observe that this is just what the ancient Babylonians did in the numeration system they employed, although they used 60 for the base. Thus, the Babylonian symbol V was used for 60, 1, or $\frac{1}{60}$, as well as other powers of 60, and the reader of their writings is left to determine the intent from context. The extent to which this confused Babylonians is not recorded.

Moreover, mixed numerals whose fractional parts are basic fractions can be denoted very efficiently by using the foregoing powers. For instance, $17\frac{9}{10}$ can be written $17+\frac{9}{10}$. This in turn can be written 17.9, because we have agreed that $\frac{9}{10}$ can be denoted by 0.9; and our numeration system has a built-in assumption concerning the addition of consecutive multiples of powers of ten. (Note that we have written 0.9 here rather than .9, to be sure that the decimal point will not be overlooked.) Thus,

$$17.9 = (1 \times 10^1) + (7 \times 10^0) + \left(9 \times \frac{1}{10^1}\right).$$

Not all basic fractions have numerators from the set

$$\{0, 1, 2, 3, 4, 5, 6, 7, 8, 9\}.$$

Consider the basic fraction $\frac{27}{100}$. The agreement we have made concerning expanded notation such as

$$\left(4 \times \frac{1}{10^1}\right) + \left(3 \times \frac{1}{10^2}\right) + \left(7 \times \frac{1}{10^3}\right)$$

or, equivalently,

$$\left(4 \times \frac{1}{10}\right) + \left(3 \times \frac{1}{100}\right) + \left(7 \times \frac{1}{1000}\right)$$

is to the effect that one of the factors of each product involved must be named by a one-digit numeral. This means that we cannot write $\left(27 \times \frac{1}{100}\right)$ directly, because "27" contains two digits. It is a fact, however, that $\frac{27}{100}$ is expressible as $\frac{20}{100} + \frac{7}{100}$, and that $\frac{20}{100}$ can be replaced by $\frac{2}{10}$ (which is another name for the same rational number), so that $\frac{27}{100}$ is equivalent to $\frac{2}{10} + \frac{7}{100}$. By definition, then,

$$\frac{27}{100} = \frac{2}{10} + \frac{7}{100} = 0.27.$$

For another example, consider the fraction $\frac{37}{1000}$, which is equivalent to $\frac{30}{1000} + \frac{7}{1000}$, or $\frac{3}{100} + \frac{7}{1000}$. This last expression can be written

$$\left(0 \times \frac{1}{10}\right) + \left(3 \times \frac{1}{100}\right) + \left(7 \times \frac{1}{1000}\right).$$

Note that a multiple of $\frac{1}{10}$ is not an addend in the expression $\left(3 \times \frac{1}{100}\right) +$ $\left(7 \times \frac{1}{1000}\right)$, but, since our numeration system makes mandatory the inclusion of a numeral with place value $\frac{1}{10}$, we envisage $0 \times \frac{1}{10}$ as an addend. Then

$$\left(0 \times \frac{1}{10}\right) + \left(3 \times \frac{1}{100}\right) + \left(7 \times \frac{1}{1000}\right)$$

is equivalent to 0.037. Similarly, the fraction $\frac{327}{1000}$ can be shown to be equivalent to the decimal numeral 0.327, $\frac{432}{10,000}$ to 0.0432, and $27\frac{389}{1000}$ to 27.389.

Look again at the examples in the preceding paragraph and observe, for example, that:

In the fraction $\frac{27}{100}$ there are two 0's in the numeral for the denominator, and in the decimal numeral 0.27 there are two digits to the right of the decimal point.

In the fraction $\frac{432}{10,000}$ there are four 0's in the numeral for the denominator, and in the decimal numeral 0.0432 there are four digits to the right of the decimal point.

In each case, the number of 0's in the numeral for the denominator of the basic fraction is the same as the number of digits to the right of the decimal point in the decimal numeral.

Basic fractions naming numbers that are greater than one and that are not whole numbers, are equivalent to decimal numerals with nonzero digits on both sides of the decimal point. For example,

$$\frac{2357}{100} = \frac{2300}{100} + \frac{57}{100}$$

$$= 23 + \frac{57}{100}$$

$$= 23.57.$$

Conversely, for a given terminating decimal numeral, it is also possible to find an equivalent basic fraction. By "terminating" is meant that the decimal numeral has a last nonzero digit. The decimal numeral 0.333 . . . , for example, is not a terminating numeral since we envisage the digit 3 as being repeated endlessly. If a decimal numeral does terminate, however, then the basic fraction to which it corresponds can be written directly. Thus,

$$0.237 = \frac{237}{1000}, \quad 0.0812 = \frac{812}{10,000}, \quad \text{and } 3.79 = \frac{379}{100}.$$

Rewriting 0.237 as $\frac{237}{1000}$ is justified by the fact that 0.237 can be written in expanded form as

$$\left(2 \times \frac{1}{10}\right) + \left(3 \times \frac{1}{100}\right) + \left(7 \times \frac{1}{1000}\right),$$

which, in turn, is equivalent to

$$\frac{2}{10} + \frac{3}{100} + \frac{7}{1000}.$$

By the usual procedure involved in writing sums such as this, the first two fractions are replaced with equivalent fractions having 1000 for denominator, so that we have

$$\frac{200}{1000} + \frac{30}{1000} + \frac{7}{1000},$$

from which we obtain

$$\frac{200 + 30 + 7}{1000}, \quad \text{or } \frac{237}{1000}.$$

We shall not go through this process in the general case, but it is true that any terminating decimal numeral denoting a rational number less than one can be written directly as a basic fraction. The fraction will have as numerator the whole number denoted by the digits in the decimal numeral (i.e., 237 for 0.0237, 54 for 0.0054, or 3 for 0.3). It will have as denominator the power of 10 that is the denominator of the place value for the position occupied by the last digit in the decimal numeral (e.g., 10,000 for 0.0237, 10,000 for 0.0054, and 10 for 0.3). Thus,

$$0.72 \text{ is equivalent to } \frac{72}{10^2}, \quad \text{or } \frac{72}{100};$$

$$0.0302 \text{ is equivalent to } \frac{302}{10^4}, \quad \text{or } \frac{302}{10,000};$$

$$\text{and } 0.00004 \text{ is equivalent to } \frac{4}{10^5}, \quad \text{or } \frac{4}{100,000}.$$

The equivalence between basic fractions $\left(\text{such as } \frac{16}{100}\right)$ and decimal numerals (such as 0.16) provides us with a guide to reading decimal numerals for rational numbers less than one. The words "tenths," "hundredths," "thousandths," and so on are assigned to the appropriate place value, and to read such a decimal numeral we need only consult its last digit, which may be, but generally is not, zero. Thus, 0.023 is read "twenty-three thousandths," because the last digit has as place value $\frac{1}{1000}$. Sometimes, for one reason or another, decimal numerals are written to terminate in one or more zeros, in which case these zeros must be included in the reading of the numeral. In the foregoing example, had the numeral 0.0230 been written in place of 0.023, it would be read "two hundred thirty ten-thousandths" rather than "twenty-three thousandths," although both numerals name the same rational number. Figure 5 shows place-value names for several positions to the right of the decimal point in a decimal numeral.

.   1   2   3   4   5   6   7   8   9

decimal point	tenths	hundredths	thousandths	ten-thousandths	hundred-thousandths	millionths	ten-millionths	hundred-millionths	billionths

FIGURE 5

In general, decimal numerals are preferred as names for rational numbers in scientific works and in orderly computations.

FRACTIONS EQUIVALENT TO BASIC FRACTIONS

There is another class of fractions each member of which, though not a basic fraction, is equivalent to a basic fraction, that is, to a fraction having a power of 10 as denominator. These are the fractions whose denominators contain only the numbers 2 and 5 as factors. Some examples are

$$\frac{1}{2}, \quad \frac{3}{5}, \quad \frac{7}{20}, \quad \frac{11}{40}, \quad \frac{1}{50}, \quad \frac{113}{80}, \quad \text{and } \frac{211}{160}.$$

Now

$$\frac{7}{20} \text{ is equivalent to } \frac{7}{2 \times 2 \times 5}, \text{ or } \frac{7}{2^2 \times 5};$$

$\dfrac{11}{40}$ is equivalent to $\dfrac{11}{2\times2\times2\times5}$, or $\dfrac{11}{2^3\times5}$;

$\dfrac{1}{50}$ is equivalent to $\dfrac{1}{2\times5\times5}$, or $\dfrac{1}{2\times5^2}$;

$\dfrac{13}{80}$ is equivalent to $\dfrac{13}{2\times2\times2\times2\times5}$, or $\dfrac{13}{2^4\times5}$;

and $\dfrac{211}{160}$ is equivalent to $\dfrac{211}{2\times2\times2\times2\times2\times5}$, or $\dfrac{211}{2^5\times5}$.

We can always find basic fractions equivalent to such fractions by supplying each of the factors 2 and 5 an appropriate number of times to their denominators.

In order to do this, however, it is first necessary to recall that if the numerator and denominator of a given fraction are multiplied by the same counting number, the result will be a fraction equivalent to the given fraction. For example,

$$\frac{3}{5}=\frac{3\times5}{5\times5}=\frac{15}{25}, \quad \frac{1}{2}=\frac{1\times2}{2\times2}=\frac{2}{4}, \quad \text{and} \quad \frac{5}{8}=\frac{5\times2}{8\times2}=\frac{10}{16}.$$

Now we can find a basic fraction equivalent to $\dfrac{1}{2}$ by multiplying both numerator and denominator by 5 to obtain the equivalent fraction $\dfrac{5}{10}$. If we wish to obtain a basic fraction equivalent to $\dfrac{11}{40}$, we write

$$\frac{11}{40}=\frac{11}{2\times2\times2\times5}=\frac{11}{2^3\times5},$$

and then observe that there are, in this denominator, three factors 2 but only one factor 5. By multiplying both numerator and denominator of $\dfrac{11}{2^3\times5}$ by 5^2, or 25, we obtain $\dfrac{11\times25}{2^3\times5\times25}$, or $\dfrac{275}{1000}$, which is a basic fraction. We have, in a manner of speaking, "introduced" two factors 5 into the denominator of $\dfrac{11}{2^3\times5}$ to produce a denominator $2^3\times5^3$, which is 10^3, or 1000. Indeed we should observe that if a number is to be a power of 10, it must contain an equal number of factors 2 and 5. To find a basic fraction equivalent to $\dfrac{1}{50}$, for example, we note that

$$\frac{1}{50}=\frac{1}{2\times5^2};$$

and we need to introduce an additional factor 2 here in order that the resulting denominator will be $2^2\times5^2$, or 100. Accordingly, we multiply the numerator and denominator of $\dfrac{1}{50}$ by 2 to obtain $\dfrac{1 \times 2}{50 \times 2}$, or $\dfrac{2}{100}$, which is a basic fraction.

As a last example of this process, let us find a basic fraction equivalent to $\dfrac{13}{80}$. The denominator, 80, can be written in factored form as $2^4 \times 5$, and lacks three factors 5 of being a power of ten. Therefore, we multiply the numerator and denominator of $\dfrac{13}{80}$ by 5^3 to obtain

$$\frac{13 \times 5^3}{80 \times 5^3} = \frac{13 \times 125}{80 \times 125},$$

which, in turn, in equivalent to $\dfrac{1625}{10,000}$.

Since fractions with denominators which are products of powers of 2 and 5 are equivalent to basic fractions, they can be expressed as decimal numerals. For example, we observed above that $\dfrac{1}{2}$ is equivalent to $\dfrac{5}{10}$, so we can write

$$\frac{1}{2} = \frac{5}{10} = 0.5;$$

similarly, we have

$$\frac{11}{40} = \frac{275}{1000} = 0.275,$$

$$\frac{1}{50} = \frac{2}{100} = 0.02,$$

and

$$\frac{13}{80} = \frac{1625}{10,000} = 0.1625.$$

Conversely, every terminating decimal numeral is equivalent to a fraction with denominator containing as factors powers of 2 and 5, only; and such a fraction can be found for each such numeral by simply writing the numeral as a basic fraction. For example, we have

$$0.176 = \frac{176}{1000} = \frac{176}{2^3 \times 5^3} = \frac{2^4 \times 11}{2^3 \times 5^3} = \frac{2 \times 11}{5^3} = \frac{22}{125}$$

and

$$0.25 = \frac{25}{100} = \frac{25}{2^2 \times 5^2} = \frac{1}{2^2} = \frac{1}{4}.$$

Exercise Set 4

1. Express each of the following numbers in expanded notation, using exponents.

Example: $0.327 = \left(3 \times \frac{1}{10^1}\right) + \left(2 \times \frac{1}{10^2}\right) + \left(7 \times \frac{1}{10^3}\right)$

(a) 21.47   (c) 80.1089

(b) 165.036   (d)   0.807

2. Write the basic fraction that corresponds to each of the following terminating decimal numerals.

(a) 0.417   (c) 0.06   (e) 14.12

(b) 3.208   (d)   8.005   (f) 10.075

3. Write the decimal numeral for the number represented by each of the following basic fractions.

(a) $\dfrac{169}{10^3}$ (c) $\dfrac{24}{10^3}$ (e) $\dfrac{105}{10^1}$

(b) $\dfrac{205}{10^4}$ (d) $\dfrac{7}{10^2}$ (f) $\dfrac{19}{10^5}$

4. Rename the following numbers as products of primes.

(a) 40   (c) 160   (e) 20

(b) 80   (d) 800   (f) 50

5. Express the following numbers as basic fractions if possible, and then as decimal numerals.

Example:

$$\frac{7}{40} = \frac{7}{2 \times 2 \times 2 \times 5}$$

$$= \frac{7}{2^3 \times 5}$$

$$= \frac{7}{2^3 \times 5} \times \frac{5^2}{5^2}$$

$$= \frac{7 \times 5^2}{2^3 \times 5^3}$$

$$= \frac{175}{1000}$$

$$= 0.175$$

(a) $\dfrac{3}{50}$ (c) $\dfrac{9}{40}$ (e) $\dfrac{13}{20}$

(b) $\dfrac{13}{80}$ (d) $\dfrac{11}{25}$ (f) $\dfrac{7}{120}$

DECIMAL NUMERALS AND THE DIVISION ALGORITHM

The division algorithm that we used in finding quotients of whole numbers (see Booklet No. 4: *Algorithms for Operations with Whole Numbers*) can also be used to find decimal numerals for rational numbers equivalent to basic fractions, that is, fractions with a power of 10 as denominator. To see how this is done, let us recall that each rational number can be viewed as the quotient of a pair of whole numbers. That is, the fraction $\dfrac{a}{b}$ denotes the quotient when the whole number a is divided by the nonzero whole number b. The division algorithm is used to find other names for such quotients. For example, another name for $\dfrac{85}{5}$ can be found as follows:

$$
\begin{array}{r}
17 \\
5\ \overline{)\ 85} \\
5 \\
\hline
35 \\
35 \\
\hline
0
\end{array}
$$

where "17" is the desired name. Again, $\dfrac{87}{5}$, when subjected to the same treatment, yields

$$
\begin{array}{r}
17 \\
5\ \overline{)\ 87} \\
5 \\
\hline
37 \\
35 \\
\hline
2
\end{array}
$$

where we have a remainder of 2, and hence

$$
\frac{87}{5} = 17\frac{2}{5}.
$$

Recall that $\dfrac{87}{5} = \dfrac{85}{5} + \dfrac{2}{5} = 17 + \dfrac{2}{5}$.

In decimal numeration, $17\dfrac{2}{5}$ is expressed as 17.4.

Now, let us consider the problem of seeking a decimal numeral for, say, $\dfrac{3}{8}$. This time, when we set up the form for the algorithm, $8\ \overline{)\ 3}$, we find that we can obtain no useful information by the usual continuation. That is, we have

$$8 \enclose{longdiv}{3} \quad \begin{array}{c} 0 \\ \hline \\ \end{array}$$

$$\begin{array}{r} 0 \\ 8 \,)\, \overline{3} \\ \underline{0} \\ 3 \end{array}$$

and the algorithm produces nothing but $0+\frac{3}{8}$, or $\frac{3}{8}$. It is useful to observe, though, that for the rational number $\frac{3000}{8}$, which is just 1000 times $\frac{3}{8}$, the algorithm yields

$$\begin{array}{r} 375 \\ 8 \,)\, \overline{3000} \\ \underline{24} \\ 60 \\ \underline{56} \\ 40 \\ \underline{40} \\ 0 \end{array}$$

That is, $\frac{3000}{8}=375$. We know, however, that $\frac{3000}{8}$ is 1000 times the rational number $\frac{3}{8}$, so that 375 is 1000 times $\frac{3}{8}$. If, then, we *divide* 375 by 1000, the result should be $\frac{3}{8}$; that is,

$$\frac{375}{1000}=\frac{3}{8}.$$

We can check this result by noting that $375 \times 8 = 3 \times 1000$. But $\frac{375}{1000}$ can be written as the decimal numeral 0.375. Thus, we have used the algorithm to establish that $\frac{3}{8}=0.375$ by establishing that

$$\frac{3000}{8}=375.$$

Note. Using fractions, $\frac{3}{8}=\frac{3}{8}\times 1$

$$=\frac{3}{8}\times\left(\frac{1000}{1}\times\frac{1}{1000}\right)$$

$$=\left(\frac{3}{8}\times\frac{1000}{1}\right)\times\frac{1}{1000}$$

$$=\frac{3000}{8}\times\frac{1}{1000}$$

$$=\frac{375}{1}\times\frac{1}{1000}.$$

This procedure can be abbreviated by observing that

$$\frac{375}{8 \;)\; 3000}$$

is a statement, namely the statement that

$$\frac{3000}{8} = 375,$$

and that if both members here are divided by 1000 to yield

$$\frac{3.000}{8} = 0.375,$$

the corresponding algorithm has the form

$$\frac{0.375}{8 \;)\; 3.000}.$$

Thus, we could have begun with

$$8 \;)\; \overline{3.000},$$

and continued with the process

$$
\begin{array}{r}
0.375 \\
8 \;)\; \overline{3.000} \\
2\,4 \\ \hline
60 \\
56 \\ \hline
40 \\
40 \\ \hline
0
\end{array}
$$

where the machinery of the algorithm is applied to $\frac{3000}{8}$, but where the retention of the decimal point in 3.000 and the insertion of a decimal point in 0.375 renders the process applicable to $8 \;)\; \overline{3}$

Similarly, to find a decimal numeral equivalent to $\frac{13}{80}$, we could use the algorithm to find $\frac{130,000}{80}$ and divide the results by 10,000, or, as an alternative, proceed directly.

$$
\begin{array}{r}
0.1625 \\
80 \;)\; \overline{13.0000} \\
8\,0 \\ \hline
5\,00 \\
4\,80 \\ \hline
200 \\
160 \\ \hline
400 \\
400
\end{array}
$$

Notice that in this example, instead of considering 1000 times the rational number $\frac{13}{80}$, we proposed using 10,000 times the number $\frac{130,000}{80}$. How does one know the appropriate power of ten to consider as a factor in each case? The answer is that, if the algorithm is used as above, the problem takes care of itself. One need only continue to apply the algorithm until a zero remainder is attained.

Consider the problem of finding a decimal number equivalent to $\frac{19}{40}$. The algorithm can be set up in the form

$$40 \overline{) \ 19.0}$$

and continued as follows:

$$
\begin{array}{r}
0.4 \\
40 \overline{) \ 19.0} \\
16\ 0 \\
\hline
3\ 0
\end{array}
$$

Since the remainder is not zero, 19.0 is replaced by 19.00, another name for the same number, and the process is repeated:

$$
\begin{array}{r}
0.47 \\
40 \overline{) \ 19.00} \\
16\ 0 \\
\hline
3\ 00 \\
2\ 80 \\
\hline
20
\end{array}
$$

Since the remainder is still not zero, 19.00 is replaced by its equivalent 19.000 and we have

$$
\begin{array}{r}
0.475 \\
40 \overline{) \ 19.000} \\
16\ 0 \\
\hline
3\ 00 \\
2\ 80 \\
\hline
200 \\
200 \\
\hline
0
\end{array}
$$

Hence, we can assert that $\frac{19}{40} = 0.475$. It is now clear that the algorithm for whole numbers was applied to 1000 times the rational number $\frac{19}{40}$, that is to $\frac{19,000}{40}$; but the decimal point was retained in 19.000, and a decimal point was inserted preceding the digits in the numeral for the quotient. Also, the replacement of 19.0 by 19.00 and then by 19.000 need not be done as shown, it being sufficient to continue to annex 0's to the right-hand end of 19.0.

The procedure can be adapted, of course, to such quotients as $\dfrac{19}{0.04}$, in which the denominator is not a whole number but is expressed as a decimal numeral. We simply write

$$\frac{19}{0.04} = \frac{1900}{4}$$

and proceed as before.

Viewing the application of the algorithm for whole numbers to generate decimal numerals for quotients as a matter of merely multiplying by a power of ten and then dividing by the same power of ten is not the only way in which its applicability for this purpose can be justified. Indeed, the algorithm can be shown to be valid by a direct appeal to the properties of the decimal numeration system and the properties of rational numbers. The point to be made here is that the algorithm can be used to find such numerals when it is applied to suitable pairs of integers—suitable, that is, in the sense that there exists a terminating decimal numeral that names the quotient. We have seen that this will be the case whenever the divisor contains only powers of 2 and 5 as factors.

Approximating Rational Numbers

Thus far, we have discussed the determination of decimal numerals for rational numbers named either by basic fractions, that is, fractions $\left(\text{such as } \dfrac{3}{100}\right)$ whose denominators are powers of ten, or by fractions $\left(\text{such as } \dfrac{3}{5}\right)$ that are equivalent to basic fractions. However, if a fraction which is the simplest name for a rational number has a denominator which contains as a factor any counting number other than 2 or 5, then there is no equivalent basic fraction. For example, consider the fraction $\dfrac{1}{6}$, in which the denominator has as factors 2 and 3. Suppose there were a basic fraction equivalent to $\dfrac{1}{6}$; that is, suppose there were a fraction $\dfrac{a}{10^n}$, where a is a whole number and n is a natural number, such that

$$\frac{1}{6} = \frac{a}{10^n}.$$

We know this is true if and only if

$$1 \times 10^n = 6 \times a.$$

But the number represented by the left-hand member of this equation has only the prime factors 2 and 5; whereas, the right-hand member has 3 as a factor (whatever whole number a may be) because 6 has 3 as a factor. Therefore, the left-hand and right-hand members cannot possibly be equal, and we cannot find a basic fraction equivalent to $\frac{1}{6}$. An argument similar to this can be used to establish that fractions that are the simplest names for rational numbers have basic fractions as equivalents *only if* their denominators have powers of 2 and 5, exclusively, as factors. (For a more complete discussion of factors of whole numbers, see Booklet No. 5: *Numbers and Their Factors*.)

It is therefore true that we cannot always find a terminating decimal numeral equivalent to a given fraction, because such numerals may not exist. It is possible, however, to find terminating decimal numerals that "approximate" rational numbers such as $\frac{1}{6}$ as closely as desired. By "approximate," we mean that their numerals name rational numbers that differ from the rational number $\frac{1}{6}$ by an amount as small as we think desirable.

Let us examine a procedure by which we can make such approximations, using again the division algorithm for whole numbers. Suppose we wish to find an approximation for $\frac{1}{6}$ that is correct within $\frac{1}{1000}$, that is, we wish to find the name of a rational number that is different from $\frac{1}{6}$ by less than $\frac{1}{1000}$. If we consider first the problem of finding a mixed numeral for 1000 times $\frac{1}{6}$, that is for $\frac{1000}{6}$, we have

$$
\begin{array}{r}
166 \\
6\ )\ \overline{1000} \\
\underline{6} \\
40 \\
\underline{36} \\
40 \\
\underline{36} \\
4
\end{array}
$$

which means that

$$\frac{1000}{6} = 166\frac{4}{6} = 166\frac{2}{3}.$$

Now, to relate this to $\frac{1}{6}$, we must divide $166\frac{2}{3}$ by 1000. By definition,

$$166\frac{2}{3} = 166 + \frac{2}{3},$$

and we have

$$\frac{166+\dfrac{2}{3}}{1000} = \frac{166}{1000} + \frac{\dfrac{2}{3}}{1000}$$

$$= 0.166 + \frac{2}{3000}$$

$$= 0.166 + \frac{1}{1500}.$$

Since $\dfrac{1}{1500}$ is less than $\dfrac{1}{1000}$, we can be sure that 0.166 does not differ from $\dfrac{1}{6}$ by more than $\dfrac{1}{1000}$, as was required, and thus 0.166 is an acceptable approximation for $\dfrac{1}{6}$.

For a second example, consider the problem of finding an approximation in decimal numeration for $\dfrac{3}{14}$, correct to within $\dfrac{1}{10,000}$. This time let us use the abbreviated algorithm, retaining the decimal point in the dividend and inserting one in the quotient. We have

$$
\begin{array}{r}
0.2142 \\
14\ )\ \overline{3.0000} \\
2\,8 \\
\hline
20 \\
14 \\
\hline
60 \\
56 \\
\hline
40 \\
28 \\
\hline
12 \\
\end{array}
$$

Is 0.2142 a rational number differing from $\dfrac{3}{14}$ by less than $\dfrac{1}{10,000}$? The remainder in the last step above was 12. The same digits would have occurred in the remainder had we multiplied by 10,000 to obtain $\dfrac{30,000}{14}$, and then applied the algorithm to get $2142\dfrac{12}{14}$. Accordingly, upon division by 10,000, we would have $\dfrac{2142}{10,000} + \dfrac{12}{140,000}$, so that 0.2142 differs from $\dfrac{3}{41}$ by $\dfrac{12}{140,000}$. But $\dfrac{12}{140,000} = \dfrac{6}{70,000}$, which is less than $\dfrac{1}{10,000}$, and accordingly 0.2142 is acceptable as an approximation.

In practice, if accuracy is specified to within $\dfrac{1}{10^n}$ units, then the algorithm is terminated when the nth digit to the right of the decimal point has been found, and the decimal numeral obtained determines a satisfactory approximation.

Exercise Set 5

1. Which of the following fractions do not have equivalent decimal numerals? Decide by inspecting only the denominator, and state why it is sufficient to do this.

   (a) $\dfrac{5}{6}$ (b) $\dfrac{17}{40}$ (c) $\dfrac{2}{3}$ (d) $\dfrac{19}{50}$ (e) $\dfrac{8}{11}$

2. Find a terminating decimal numeral for a number that approximates each of the following rational numbers to within $\dfrac{1}{1000}$.

   (a) $\dfrac{5}{9}$ (b) $\dfrac{13}{21}$ (c) $\dfrac{7}{15}$.

REPEATING DECIMAL NUMERALS

In the preceding section we argued that, for certain rational numbers, terminating decimal numerals do not exist, and we outlined a means of obtaining satisfactory approximations for such numbers. There is, however, a property of decimal numerals for rational numbers that enables us to relate all such numerals to fractions.

Let us return to the problem of approximating $\dfrac{3}{14}$ by means of a decimal numeral. By applying the division algorithm, we obtain the following:

$$
\begin{array}{r}
0.2142857 \\
14\ )\ \overline{3.0000000} \\
2\,8 \\
\hline
20 \leftarrow \\
14 \\
\hline
60 \\
56 \\
\hline
40 \\
28 \\
\hline
120 \\
112 \\
\hline
80 \\
70 \\
\hline
100 \\
98 \\
\hline
2 \leftarrow
\end{array}
$$

Note that we have arrived at 0.2142857 as an approximation to $\frac{3}{14}$ and, in the process, have encountered again the number 2 as a remainder. The word "again" is appropriate here because the remainder we obtained after the first division was also 2. Since the result when 20 was subsequently divided by 14 was 1 with a remainder 6, the same result will be obtained if we once more divide 20 by 14. That is, the next digit in a closer decimal approximation for $\frac{3}{14}$ will be 1. Thus, we first had

$$0.2142857$$

and will next have

$$0.21428571.$$

Similarly, we can expect the remainder when 1×14 is subtracted from 20 again to be 6, and the next digit in a closer approximation will be 4; thus,

$$0.214285714.$$

Indeed, we should expect the entire sequence of digits 142857 to repeat itself, to produce the approximation

$$0.2142857\ 142857.$$

At this point, the remainder in the algorithm will again be 2, and the sequence again repeats. This, then, will continue indefinitely. That is,

$$\frac{3}{14} = 0.2142857142857\overline{142857},$$

where the bar over 142857 indicates that the group 142857 repeats endlessly. Decimal numerals having groups of digits that repeat endlessly are called *repeating decimals*.

As another example, consider the problem of finding a decimal numeral equivalent to $\frac{3}{22}$. We have

```
              0.136
      22 ) 3.000
             2 2
             ‾‾‾‾
              80  ←
              66
             ‾‾‾‾
             140
             132
             ‾‾‾‾
               8  ←
```

where we find that the remainder, 8, is a repetition of an earlier remainder. Since this remainder will initiate an exact duplication of an earlier part of the algorithm, we can expect a repetition of the appropriate group of digits in the quotient—in this case, the group 36. Hence

$$\frac{3}{22} = 0.1\overline{36},$$

where $0.1\overline{36}$ is viewed not as an approximation for $\frac{3}{22}$ but as a numeral equivalent to the fraction $\frac{3}{22}$. Further examples are

$$\frac{1}{3} = 0.\overline{3},$$

$$\frac{1}{6} = 0.1\overline{6},$$

$$\frac{14}{15} = 0.9\overline{3},$$

$$\frac{26}{111} = 0.\overline{234}.$$

A little thought about what occurs in the division algorithm should make it plausible that every rational number can be represented either by a terminating decimal numeral or by a repeating decimal. In finding a decimal numeral equivalent to a fraction $\frac{a}{b}$, where a and b are whole numbers, and b is not 0, the division algorithm is applied to divide a by b. The remainder at each step in the algorithm will be one of the whole numbers from 0 to one less than b; i.e., $b-1$. If the remainder is 0 at any step, then we have found a terminating decimal numeral equivalent to $\frac{a}{b}$. Assuming a zero remainder does not occur, then there are $b-1$ possible remainders, so within $b-1$ steps we will *have* to repeat some remainder, and once this happens, we have begun a repeating group of digits. Consider a specific example, the identification of a decimal numeral for $\frac{3}{14}$. Earlier, we found this to be $0.2\overline{142857}$. The algorithm is reproduced here for convenient reference, and the remainder at each step is circled.

$$
\begin{array}{r}
0.2\,1\,4\,2\,8\,5\,7 \\
14\ )\ \overline{3.0\,0\,0\,0\,0\,0\,0} \\
2\,8 \\
\hline
②0 \leftarrow \\
1\,4 \\
\hline
⑥0 \\
5\,6 \\
\hline
④0 \\
2\,8 \\
\hline
①②0 \\
1\,1\,2 \\
\hline
⑧0 \\
7\,0 \\
\hline
①⓪0 \\
9\,8 \\
\hline
② \leftarrow
\end{array}
$$

We could have expected, before beginning the division, that the remainder after the first subtraction would be one of the whole numbers from 1 to 13, inclusive. We would not expect 0 in this example because the divisor contains a factor other than a power of 2 or 5, namely 7. Had the first remainder been 3, then we would have as a quotient the repeating decimal $0.\overline{2}$. The actual remainder, however, was 2. If the next remainder had been either 2 or 3, then we would be entering a cycle and would have established a repeating block of digits in the quotient. The actual remainder, however, was 6. Thus, we continue the algorithm, each time obtaining as a remainder one of the whole numbers from 1 to 13, inclusive, and each time we check to see if the number is 3 or has occurred previously as a remainder. This will certainly occur within thirteen divisions, and actually occurs at the seventh, when 2 appears for the second time as a remainder and establishes the repeating block of digits, 142857. A similar situation occurs whenever one whole number is divided by another that is not zero, although the repeating block of digits may be very large.

FRACTIONS EQUIVALENT TO REPEATING DECIMALS

Given any fraction that is the simplest fraction name for a rational number with denominator containing factors other than 2 and 5, we can use the division algorithm to obtain an equivalent repeating decimal. Conversely, it is possible, given any repeating decimal, to find an equivalent fraction with whole numbers for numerator and denominator, which means that all such decimals are names for rational numbers.

Before describing in detail the procedure used to accomplish this in the general case, let us examine two specific examples. Let us assume for the moment that there is a rational number denoted by $0.23\overline{4234}$. If we let the letter n be another name for this number, then we can write

$$n = 0.234234234 \ldots$$

Now 1000 times this number can be represented by either $1000 \times n$ or $1000 \times 0.234234234 \ldots$. Since these expressions also name the same number, we have

$$1000 \times n = 1000 \times 0.234234234 \ldots ,$$

$$= 234.234234 \ldots$$

Now, since $1000 \times n$ is certainly greater than n (or $1 \times n$), we can subtract n from $1000 \times n$, just as we can subtract $0.234234234 \ldots$ from $234.234234234 \ldots$, and we can demonstrate the fact that these differences are equal by subtracting as follows:

$$
\begin{aligned}
1000 \times n &= 234.234234 \ldots \\
1 \times n &= 0.234234 \ldots \\
\hline
999 \times n &= 234.000000 \ldots ;
\end{aligned}
$$

that is, if we subtract $1 \times n$ from $1000 \times n$, by the distributive property we have as difference $999 \times n$; and if we subtract $0.234234234 \ldots$ from $234.234234234 \ldots$, we have as difference 234. Furthermore, these differences are the same, because the numbers involved in the subtractions are the same. Now if $999 \times n$ and 234 name the same number, then $999 \times n$ divided by 999 must be the same number as 234 divided by 999. That is

$$\frac{999 \times n}{999} = \frac{234}{999}.$$

But $\dfrac{999 \times n}{999}$ is another name for $\dfrac{999}{999} \times n$, and since $\dfrac{999}{999} = 1$, we have

$$1 \times n = \frac{234}{999}$$

or

$$n = \frac{234}{999}.$$

Thus we have shown that if there is a rational number n, such that

$$n = 0.\overline{234},$$

then we have

$$n = \frac{234}{999}.$$

Conversely, by the division algorithm it is easy to show that

$$\frac{234}{999} = 0.\overline{234}.$$

Thus, we have found a fraction equivalent to the repeating decimal $0.\overline{234}$. We can express $\frac{234}{999}$ in lower terms by dividing numerator and denominator by 9 to obtain $\frac{26}{111}$, which is the simplest fractional expression for n.

Let us apply the same process in a slightly modified form to find a fraction equivalent to $0.27\overline{34}$, where the block of repeating digits does not start immediately after the decimal point. We begin by letting n be another name for $0.27\overline{34}$, and write

$$n = 0.27343434 \ldots .$$

If we multiply by 100 this time, we have

$$100 \times n = 100 \times 0.27343434 \ldots$$

or

$$100 \times n = 27.34343434 \ldots .$$

In doing this, we have found a number, $100 \times n$, for which the repeating block of digits does immediately follow the decimal point. Let us now multiply *this* number by 10^2, because there are two digits in the repeating block (the *repetend*), and subtract:

$$\begin{aligned} 10{,}000 \times n &= 2734.\overline{34} \\ 100 \times n &= 27.\overline{34} \\ \hline 9900 \times n &= 2707. \end{aligned}$$

Thus,

$$n = \frac{2707}{9900},$$

and the division algorithm shows conversely that

$$\frac{2707}{9900} = 0.27\overline{34}.$$

As a final example, let us find a fraction equivalent to $0.5\overline{67}$. We first assume that there is a rational number, n, such that

$$n = 0.5\overline{67};$$

then we have

$$\begin{aligned} 10n &= 5.\overline{67} \\ 1000n &= 567.\overline{67} \\ 10n &= 5.\overline{67} \\ \hline 990n &= 562 \quad , \end{aligned}$$

whence

$$n = \frac{562}{990}.$$

Now we check that $0.5\overline{67} = \frac{562}{990}$ by the division algorithm:

```
          0.5̄6̄7̄
990 ) 562.000
      495 0
       67 00  ←
       59 40
        7 600
        6 930
          670  ←
```

The procedure in the foregoing examples is perfectly general and can be applied to find a fraction equivalent to any repeating decimal.

Exercise Set 6

1. Find the fraction, if there is one, that is equivalent to the decimal numeral by completing the steps in the following exercises.

(a) $n = 0.\overline{27}$
$100 \times n = 27.\overline{27}$
$\underline{\qquad} \times n =$
$\overline{99 \times n =}$
$n =$

(b) $n = 0.\overline{158}$
$\underline{\qquad} \times n =$
$\underline{\qquad} \times n =$
$\overline{\qquad\qquad}$
$=$
$n =$

(c) $n = 4.0\overline{17}$
$\underline{\qquad} \times n =$
$\underline{\qquad} \times n =$
$\overline{\qquad\qquad}$
$=$
$n =$

(d) $n = 0.3\overline{246}$
$\underline{\qquad} \times n =$
$10 \times n =$
$\overline{\qquad\qquad}$
$=$
$n =$

In each case, determine the simplest name for the rational number represented by the fraction.

2. Find the fraction that is the simplest name for the rational number represented by the repeating decimal numerals.

(a) $0.\overline{17}$ (b) $0.\overline{423}$ (c) $3.\overline{1265}$ (d) $0.5\overline{34}$

3. Verify your answers in Exercise 2, parts (a) and (b), by the division algorithm.

NONREPEATING DECIMAL NUMERALS

In the foregoing sections, we have seen that any rational number can be denoted either by a terminating decimal or by a repeating decimal, and conversely that any terminating or repeating decimal represents a rational number. Thus, for example, we have

$$\frac{1}{2} \quad \begin{array}{l}\text{(has equivalent}\\\text{basic fraction)}\end{array} = 0.5 \quad \text{(terminating decimal)},$$

$$\frac{1}{3} \quad \begin{array}{l}\text{(has no equivalent}\\\text{basic fraction)}\end{array} = 0.\overline{3} \quad \text{(repeating decimal)}.$$

Let us now determine the fraction naming the rational number

$$n = 0.4\overline{9}.$$

We have

$$100 \times n = 49.\overline{9}$$
$$\underline{10 \times n = \ \ 4.\overline{9}}$$
$$90 \times n = 45$$

whence

$$n = \frac{45}{90} = \frac{1}{2} = 0.5.$$

Verification of this result requires a bit of an adjustment of the division algorithm:

$$
\begin{array}{r}
0.4\overline{9} \\
2 \ ) \ \overline{1.00} \\
\underline{8} \\
20 \leftarrow \\
\underline{18} \\
2 \leftarrow.
\end{array}
$$

The number named by the repeating decimal $0.4\overline{9}$ is equal to the number named by the terminating decimal 0.5! This is hardly surprising, though, when we think of the point corresponding to $0.4\overline{9}$ on the number line. It must be to the right of the point corresponding to 0.49, or 0.499, or 0.4999, or any rational number less than 0.5; but it certainly is not to the right of the point corresponding to 0.5 itself.

Actually, any terminating decimal numeral, that is, any decimal numeral expressed by only a finite number of nonzero digits, can be considered as a special sort of repeating decimal numeral. Thus, we have

$$0.5 = 0.5000 \ . \ . \ . \ = 0.5\overline{0}, \ \text{etc.}$$

Accordingly, *every* rational number can be denoted by a repeating decimal numeral. Each fraction not equivalent to a basic fraction corresponds to just one of these, as in

$$\frac{1}{7}=0.\overline{142857}, \quad \frac{2}{3}=0.\overline{6},$$

whereas each fraction that is equivalent to a basic fraction corresponds to two of them, as in

$$\frac{1}{8}=0.125\overline{0}=0.124\overline{9},$$

$$\frac{3}{5}=0.60\overline{0} \quad =0.59\overline{9}.$$

Ordinarily, of course, we would not think of expressing a basic fraction as a repeating decimal numeral.

If, then, the set of repeating decimal numerals is thus associated with the set of rational numbers, is there such a thing as a nonrepeating (and nonterminating) decimal? If so, is it a numeral? That is, is it the name of some sort of number?

There certainly are nonrepeating decimal expressions, even rules for generating some of them. Here is one such expression:

$$0.12112111211112 \ldots ,$$

where one more 1 immediately follows each 2 than immediately precedes it. If there is a point on the number line corresponding to this expression, it lies to the right of the point corresponding to 0.1, to the right of the point corresponding to 0.12, etc. But to the left of the point corresponding to

$$0.2, \quad \text{or} \quad 0.13, \quad \text{or} \quad 0.122, \text{etc.}$$

We make the basic assumption that there is such a point, and that the point corresponds to a number which is not a rational number—since this number is denoted by a nonterminating and nonrepeating decimal numeral. We call such a number an *irrational* number.

You are acquainted with some irrational numbers. One of these is

$$\pi=3.14159 \ldots ,$$

the ratio of the length of the circumference of a circle to its diameter. Another is

$$\sqrt{2} =1.41428 \ldots .$$

In Booklet No. 6: *The Rational Numbers*, you learned that the set of rational numbers is *dense*, that is, that between any two distinct rational numbers there is a third rational number and, therefore, an indefinite number of rational numbers. The irrational numbers actually are dense on the number line, too, and in a certain sense there are even more irrational numbers than rational numbers.

The rational numbers and the irrational numbers together make up the *real number system,* an understanding of which is quite essential for performing mathematical analysis.

Why do we concern ourselves with numbers that are capable of expressing physical magnitudes more precisely than we possibly could measure them? It is a strange and wonderful fact that, on the basis of his relatively crude observations and measurements of his physical environment, the applied mathematician and scientist often makes *idealized mathematical models,* analyzes these, and then applies the results back to that environment in ways that he could never achieve and that would never occur to him through his observations and measurements alone. This has been an essential ingredient in much of our scientific progress. It affects all of us, for it is part of our culture and of our everyday life. It has released atomic energy for us, it has helped stamp out disease, and one day it will take us to the moon and to the planets.

ANSWERS TO EXERCISE SETS

Exercise Set 1

1. Commutative property of addition
   Commutative property of multiplication
   Identity element for multiplication
   Identity element for addition
   Distributive property of multiplication over addition
   Reciprocal property of rational numbers
   Associative property of addition

2. (a) $\dfrac{6}{7} = \dfrac{9 \times 6}{9 \times 7} = \dfrac{54}{63}$ and $\dfrac{8}{9} = \dfrac{7 \times 8}{7 \times 9} = \dfrac{56}{63}$

   (b) $\dfrac{9 \times 6}{9 \times 7} < \dfrac{7 \times 8}{7 \times 9}$,   or $\dfrac{54}{63} < \dfrac{56}{63}$

   (c) $9 \times 6 < 7 \times 8$,   or $54 < 56$

   (d) $9 \times 6 < 7 \times 8$

3. (a) $\dfrac{3}{5} = \dfrac{7 \times 3}{7 \times 5} = \dfrac{21}{35}$ and $\dfrac{4}{7} = \dfrac{5 \times 4}{5 \times 7} = \dfrac{20}{35}$

   (b) $\dfrac{7 \times 3}{7 \times 5} > \dfrac{5 \times 4}{5 \times 7}$,   or $\dfrac{21}{35} > \dfrac{20}{35}$

   (c) $7 \times 3 > 5 \times 4$,   or $21 > 20$

   (d) $7 \times 3 > 5 \times 4$

4. $2 \times 15 = 6 \times 5$

5. (a) $\dfrac{2}{3} < \dfrac{3}{4}$ (c) $\dfrac{5}{11} > \dfrac{3}{7}$ (e) $\dfrac{5}{2} \doteq \dfrac{15}{6}$

     (b) $\dfrac{4}{9} = \dfrac{12}{27}$ (d) $\dfrac{7}{3} > \dfrac{11}{5}$ (f) $\dfrac{8}{13} > \dfrac{5}{17}$

Exercise Set 2

1. $(4,7)$; $(9,5)$; $(3,1)$; $(0,8)$; $(5,9)$; $(3,8)$.

2. $\dfrac{5}{12} \quad \dfrac{4}{11}$

$5 \times 11 > 4 \times 12$

$\dfrac{5}{12} > \dfrac{4}{11}$

3. $\dfrac{2}{7} + \dfrac{3}{7} = \dfrac{2+3}{7} = \dfrac{5}{7}$

$\dfrac{3}{4} - \dfrac{2}{3} = \dfrac{3 \times 3}{3 \times 4} - \dfrac{4 \times 2}{4 \times 3} = \dfrac{9-8}{12} = \dfrac{1}{12}$

$\dfrac{6}{5} \times \dfrac{1}{7} = \dfrac{6 \times 1}{5 \times 7} = \dfrac{6}{35}$

$\dfrac{3}{4} \div \dfrac{5}{11} = \dfrac{3}{4} \times \dfrac{11}{5} = \dfrac{3 \times 11}{4 \times 5} = \dfrac{33}{20}$

Exercise Set 3

1. (a) $\{(2,3), (4,6), (6,9), (8,12), (10,15) \dots\}$

     (b) $\{(3,5), (6,10), (9,15), (12,20), (15,25) \dots\}$

     (c) $\left\{ \dfrac{5}{6}, \dfrac{10}{12}, \dfrac{15}{18}, \dfrac{20}{24}, \dfrac{25}{30} \dots \right\}$

     (d) $\left\{ \dfrac{4}{3}, \dfrac{8}{6}, \dfrac{12}{9}, \dfrac{16}{12}, \dfrac{20}{15} \dots \right\}$

2. (a) $4 + \dfrac{1}{3}$, $3 + \dfrac{4}{5}$, $2 + \dfrac{7}{3}$,   or $4 + \dfrac{2}{6}$, $3 + \dfrac{16}{12}$, etc.

     (b) $6 + \dfrac{1}{3}$, $5 + \dfrac{8}{6}$, $4 + \dfrac{14}{6}$,   or $6 + \dfrac{4}{12}$, $5 + \dfrac{24}{18}$, etc.

     (c) $7 + \dfrac{1}{3}$, $6 + \dfrac{4}{3}$, $5 + \dfrac{7}{3}$,   or $7 + \dfrac{3}{9}$, $6 + \dfrac{16}{12}$, etc.

3. (a) $3\dfrac{2}{3}$ (b) $4\dfrac{2}{5}$ (c) $2\dfrac{6}{7}$

Exercise Set 4

1. (a) $(2 \times 10^1) + (1 \times 10^0) + \left(4 \times \dfrac{1}{10^1}\right) + \left(7 \times \dfrac{1}{10^2}\right)$

    (b) $(1 \times 10^2) + (6 \times 10^1) + (5 \times 10^0) + \left(0 \times \dfrac{1}{10^1}\right) + \left(3 \times \dfrac{1}{10^2}\right) + \left(6 \times \dfrac{1}{10^3}\right)$

    (c) $(8 \times 10^1) + (0 \times 10^0) + \left(1 \times \dfrac{1}{10^1}\right) + \left(0 \times \dfrac{1}{10^2}\right) + \left(8 \times \dfrac{1}{10^3}\right) + \left(9 \times \dfrac{1}{10^4}\right)$

    (d) $\left(8 \times \dfrac{1}{10^1}\right) + \left(0 \times \dfrac{1}{10^2}\right) + \left(7 \times \dfrac{1}{10^3}\right)$

2. (a) $\dfrac{417}{1000}$ (b) $\dfrac{3208}{1000}$ (c) $\dfrac{6}{100}$

    (d) $\dfrac{8005}{1000}$ (e) $\dfrac{1412}{100}$ (f) $\dfrac{10,075}{1000}$

3. (a) 0.169   (b) 0.0205   (c) 0.024

    (d) 0.07   (e) 10.5   (f) 0.00019

4. (a) $2 \times 2 \times 2 \times 5$ or $2^3 \times 5$ (b) $2 \times 2 \times 2 \times 2 \times 5$ or $2^4 \times 5$

    (c) $2 \times 2 \times 2 \times 2 \times 2 \times 5$ or $2^5 \times 5$ (d) $2 \times 2 \times 2 \times 2 \times 2 \times 5 \times 5$ or $2^5 \times 5^2$

    (e) $2 \times 2 \times 5$ or $2^2 \times 5$ (f) $2 \times 5 \times 5$ or 2×5^2

5. (a) $\dfrac{3}{2 \times 5^2} = \dfrac{3}{2 \times 5^2} \times \dfrac{2}{2} = \dfrac{3 \times 2}{2^2 \times 5^2} = \dfrac{6}{100} = 0.06$ (b) $\dfrac{13}{2^4 \times 5} \times \dfrac{5^3}{5^3} = \dfrac{13 \times 125}{10,000}$

    $$= \dfrac{1625}{10,000}$$

    $$= 0.1625$$

    (c) $\dfrac{9}{2^3 \times 5} \times \dfrac{5^2}{5^2} = \dfrac{9 \times 25}{1000}$

    $$= \dfrac{225}{1000}$$

    $$= 0.225$$

    (d) $\dfrac{11}{5^2} \times \dfrac{2^2}{2^2} = \dfrac{44}{100}$

    $$= 0.44$$

    (e) $\dfrac{13}{2^2 \times 5} \times \dfrac{5}{5} = \dfrac{65}{100}$

    $$= 0.65$$

    (f) $\dfrac{7}{120} = \dfrac{7}{2^3 \times 3 \times 5}$

    Since 120 has the factor 3, the fraction $\dfrac{7}{120}$ has no equivalent basic fraction.

Exercise Set 5

1. (a)   6 has the factor 3   (c) 3 has the factor 3

(e) 11 has the factor 11

If the denominator has a factor other than 2 or 5, and the fraction is in simplest form, the fraction does not have an equivalent terminating decimal numeral.

2. (a)

$$
\begin{array}{r}
0.555 \\
9\ )\overline{\ 5.000} \\
4\,5 \\
\hline
50 \\
45 \\
\hline
50 \\
45 \\
\hline
5
\end{array}
$$

(b)

$$
\begin{array}{r}
0.619 \\
21\ )\overline{\ 13.000} \\
12\,6 \\
\hline
40 \\
21 \\
\hline
190 \\
189 \\
\hline
1
\end{array}
$$

(c)

$$
\begin{array}{r}
0.466 \\
15\ )\overline{\ 7.000} \\
6\,0 \\
\hline
1\,00 \\
90 \\
\hline
100 \\
90 \\
\hline
10
\end{array}
$$

Exercise Set 6

1. (a)

$$n = 0.\overline{27}$$
$$100 \times n = 27.\overline{27}$$
$$1 \times n = 0.\overline{27}$$
$$99 \times n = 27$$
$$n = \frac{27}{99}$$
$$\text{or } n = \frac{3}{11}$$

(b)

$$n = 0.\overline{158}$$
$$1000 \times n = 158.\overline{158}$$
$$1 \times n = 0.\overline{158}$$
$$999 \times n = 158$$
$$n = \frac{158}{999}$$

(c)

$$n = 4.\overline{017}$$
$$1000 \times n = 4017.\overline{017}$$
$$1 \times n = 4.\overline{017}$$
$$999 \times n = 4013$$
$$n = \frac{4013}{999}$$

(d)

$$n = 0.3\overline{246}$$
$$10,000 \times n = 3246.\overline{246}$$
$$10 \times n = 3.\overline{246}$$
$$9990 \times n = 3243$$
$$n = \frac{3243}{9990}$$
$$\text{or } n = \frac{1081}{3330}$$

2. (a) $\qquad n = 0.\overline{17}$

$\qquad 100 \times n = 17.\overline{17}$

$\qquad 1 \times n = 0.\overline{17}$

$\qquad 99 \times n = 17$

$\qquad n = \dfrac{17}{99}$

(b) $\qquad n = 0.\overline{423}$

$\qquad 1000 \times n = 423.\overline{423}$

$\qquad 1 \times n = 0.\overline{423}$

$\qquad 999 \times n = 423$

$\qquad n = \dfrac{423}{999}$

or $\quad n = \dfrac{47}{111}$

(c) $\qquad n = 3.\overline{1265}$

$\qquad 10{,}000 \times n = 31{,}265.\overline{1265}$

$\qquad 1 \times n = 3.\overline{1265}$

$\qquad 9999 \times n = 31262$

$\qquad n = \dfrac{31262}{9999}$

$\qquad = \dfrac{2842}{909}$

(d) $\qquad n = 0.5\overline{34}$

$\qquad 1000 \times n = 534.\overline{34}$

$\qquad 10 \times n = 5.\overline{34}$

$\qquad 990 \times n = 529$

$\qquad n = \dfrac{529}{990}$

3. (a)
$$
\begin{array}{r}
0.\overline{17} \\
99 \overline{)\ 17.00} \leftarrow \\
9\ 9 \\
\hline
7\ 10 \\
6\ 93 \\
\hline
17 \leftarrow
\end{array}
$$

(b)
$$
\begin{array}{r}
0.\overline{423} \\
111 \overline{)\ 47.0} \leftarrow \\
44\ 4 \\
\hline
2\ 60 \\
2\ 22 \\
\hline
380 \\
333 \\
\hline
47 \leftarrow
\end{array}
$$

BOOKLET NUMBER EIGHT:

NUMBER SENTENCES

THE LANGUAGE OF MATHEMATICS

Because of its abstractness, mathematics is useful in solving problems. For example, the number sentence $4+2=6$ is a mathematical description of many different and largely unrelated physical situations. A useful first step in problem solving is to isolate the conditions in the statement of the problem and translate these conditions into mathematical language.

The highly symbolic nature of the language of mathematics makes it useful as an aid not only in solving problems, but also in formulating clear statements of mathematical relations. Statements of properties of a set of numbers, such as $a+b=b+a$, where a and b are whole numbers, have definite advantage over verbal statements expressing the same idea. For these reasons it is important to be able to write clear, correct, and precise mathematical sentences.

The language of mathematics contains symbols comparable to nouns, verbs, and phrases, which are used in communicating with words. It also contains symbols similar to punctuation marks, which are used to clarify the meaning of a mathematical phrase or sentence.

Symbols used in numeration systems to represent numbers are called *numerals*. Typical examples of numerals are 4, VII, 6, and 705. There are also the four familiar symbols $+$, $\times$, $-$, and $\div$, which indicate the mathematical *operations* of addition, multiplication, subtraction, and division. A numeral may consist of a combination of symbols for numbers and symbols for operations. The phrase, 5×2, which combines symbols for numbers and the symbol for the operation of multiplication, is a numeral for the number 10. Some of the symbols used to show order relationships between numbers are $=$, $<$, $>$, $\leq$, and $\geq$. These symbols will be explained later in greater detail. Parentheses ( ), brackets [ ], and braces { } may be regarded as punctuation marks because they help to clarify the meaning of mathematical phrases and sentences. When you are directed to simplify a phrase, you are being asked to find the simplest name for the number named by the phrase.

Parentheses indicate that certain numbers are to be associated, and that the phrase enclosed is to be regarded as a symbol for a single number. Why are such devices needed? The mathematical phrase

$$5 \times 4 - 2$$

might mean

$$(5 \times 4) - 2 = 20 - 2$$
$$= 18,$$

or it might mean

$$5 \times (4 - 2) = 5 \times 2$$
$$= 10.$$

In the absence of parentheses, actual or implied, $5 \times 4 - 2$ cannot be regarded as a numeral, since it is not possible to determine what one number it names.* If parentheses had been used in the original phrase, there would be no confusion as to which association was the desired one. Note also that the entire phrase, $(5 \times 4) - 2$, is a numeral representing one number, in this particular case the number eighteen.

Brackets [ ] are also grouping symbols whose function is similar to that of parentheses. If one pair of grouping symbols has already been used in a mathematical phrase, a different pair can be used to show further grouping; and the part of the phrase enclosed in this second pair is to be considered as a name for a single number. In order to simplify a phrase involving both parentheses and brackets, we perform the operation within the innermost pairs of grouping symbols first, and then use these results to perform the operations within the outer pair of grouping symbols. For instance, to find a simple expression for the numeral $[(6+2) + (3 \times 5)] - 9$, we can simplify the mathematical phrase as follows:

$$[(6+2) + (3 \times 5)] - 9 = [8 + 15] - 9$$
$$= 23 - 9$$
$$= 14.$$

Thus, the entire phrase represents the number fourteen.

If still further grouping is needed, and parentheses and brackets have already been used, braces { } can be employed (it will be clear from the context that the phrase within the braces is not a listing of the members of a set). To simplify a phrase involving braces, brackets, and parentheses, we agree to perform the operations within the innermost grouping symbols first, and then we use these results to perform the operations

---

* Usually the convention is adopted that "multiplication and division take precedence over addition and subtraction." In this case $5 \times 4 - 2$ is taken to mean $(5 \times 4) - 2$.

within the next grouping symbols, and then use these results to perform the operations within the outmost pair of grouping symbols. For instance:

$$\{12+[(3\times2)-4]\}-(4\times3)=\{12+[6-4]\}-12$$
$$=\{12+2\}-12$$
$$=14-12$$
$$=2.$$

The entire phrase represents the number two.

Fraction bars also serve as grouping symbols. For example, in the symbol

$$\frac{3+7}{6},$$

the fraction bar groups the addends in the sum $3+7$. Thus,

$$\frac{3+7}{6}=\frac{10}{6}.$$

Exercise Set 1

Write as simple an expression as you can for each of the following.

Example: $[3+(8-3)]+5=[3+5]+5$
$$=8+5$$
$$=13$$

1. $8+(7-6)+2$

2. $6+[3+(5-1)]-2$

3. $\{6+[5+(2+6)]\}+[2\times(1+3)]$

4. $\{4+[3\times(6-1)]+2\}+[3\times(2+1)]$

5. $\dfrac{7+3}{2}+\left(2+\dfrac{3+1}{2}\right)$

6. $\left\{\left(2+\dfrac{3+1}{2}\right)+[2\times(3-1)]\right\}+2$

TRUE AND FALSE STATEMENTS

In ordinary language, there are four kinds of sentences: declarative, imperative, interrogative, and exclamatory. We shall confine our consideration to only one of these, the declarative sentence. A declarative sentence is an assertion about something. The following are examples of simple declarative sentences:

> The Queen of England in 1962 was Elizabeth II.
> There are more men than women in this room.
> The sum of six and seven is fourteen.

The first and third of these are sentences that may be labeled either "true" or "false"; the first sentence is a true statement, and the third false. We say such sentences as these have *truth value,* the truth value being "True" in one case and "False" in the other. The second sentence, however, may be either true or false, depending on what room "this room" is and what its contents are. Such a sentence does not have a truth value since it is impossible, from the information given, to determine whether it is true or false.

Sentences like the first and third examples above, which do have truth value, are called *statements.* Sentences like the second, which have no truth value but would have a truth value if indefinite nouns or pronouns were replaced by suitable definite ones, are called *open sentences.*

Some number sentences are statements. For example,

> $6+4=10$ is a true statement, while
> $7+3=12$ is a false statement.

In the language of mathematics a symbol for a verb or verb phrase is needed to form a complete number sentence. The symbol "$=$" denotes the verb "equals" or one of the verb phrases "is equal to," "names the same number as," "is the same as," or (regarding sets) "has the same members as." A simple number sentence which contains this symbol is called an *equation.* There are other symbols for verb phrases in mathematics. In the example $2<5$, the symbol "$<$" is read "is less than." In a number sentence which is true the symbol points to the lesser of the two numbers being compared. The number sentence $2<5$ (read "Two is less than five") is true. The number sentence $9<5$ (read "Nine is less than five") is an example of a false number sentence. In the number sentence $6>5$, the symbol "$>$" is read "is greater than." The number sentence $6>5$ (read "Six is greater than five") is true. Again notice that in this true statement the symbol "$>$" points to the lesser of the two numbers being compared. The number sentence $7>10$ (read "Seven is greater than ten") is a false number sentence. A number sentence containing the symbols "$<$" or "$>$" is called an *inequality.*

Since a statement is a sentence that is either true or false (but not both), a false statement can be made true by adding or removing a corresponding negative word or phrase such as "not." It is also possible to change a true statement to a false statement by appropriately supplying a negative word. The sentence, "Mr. Smith is President of the United States of America," is false. By adding the word "not," the sentence becomes the true statement, "Mr. Smith is not President of the United States of America." This same technique can be used in number sentences. In the language of mathematics, the symbol for "not" is the *slant bar, /,* when superimposed on a symbol comparable to a verb or verb phrase. The following examples show how the slant bar is used.

SENTENCE	READ	TRUTH VALUE
$7 = 4 + 2$	Seven equals four plus two.	False
$7 \neq 4 + 2$	Seven is *not* equal to four plus two.	True
$9 < 7$	Nine is less than seven.	False
$9 \nless 7$	Nine is *not* less than seven.	True
$10 > 7$	Ten is greater than seven.	True
$10 \ngtr 7$	Ten is *not* greater than seven.	False

The order symbols and comparable verb phrases introduced thus far for our number sentences are as follows:

SYMBOL	VERB PHRASE
$=$	is equal to
	is the same as
	names the same number as
$>$	is greater than
$<$	is less than
$\neq$	is not equal to
$\ngtr$	is not greater than
$\nless$	is not less than

Exercise Set 2

1. Translate the following word sentences into number sentences.

   (a) If eight is subtracted from twenty-four, the result is sixteen.
   (b) Sixteen is greater than ten.
   (c) Seventeen is not equal to the sum of eight and two.
   (d) Eighty is less than twenty.
   (e) Ten is the product of three and four.
   (f) Nine is less than eleven.
   (g) Twelve is not greater than seven.
   (h) The sum of twenty and six is greater than the product of three and eight.

2. Indicate which of the sentences in Exercise 1 are true and which are false.

3. Translate the following number sentences into word sentences.

(a) $15+3=12-3$ (d) $14 \neq 8+5$

(b) $4 \times 6 > 20$ (e) $17 \not> 11$

(c) $18 < 10+15$ (f) $30-5 \not< 10+10$

4. Indicate which of the sentences in Exercise 3 are true and which are false.

5. Label each of the following either true or false.

(a) A statement can be both true and false at the same time.

(b) "$>$" is read "is greater than."

(c) "$=$" denotes "is the same as."

(d) "$/$" is a symbol in mathematics that stands for *not* when super-imposed on a symbol for a verb or verb phrase.

(e) "$<$" is a symbol that is read "is greater than."

OPEN SENTENCES IN MATHEMATICS

Is the sentence, "He was the first President of the United States of America," true or false? Clearly, as it stands, we cannot say. It is true when the name "George Washington" is substituted for the pronoun, "he." If the pronoun, "he," is replaced by the name Dwight D. Eisenhower the statement is false. The answer to the question depends upon what name replaces the pronoun, "he." Such a sentence is called an *open sentence*.

Similarly in mathematics we use sentences that do not have truth values. An example of such an open sentence in mathematics is

$$\square + 4 = 10.$$

The symbol $\square$ stands for a definite but unspecified number. We call the symbol a *variable*. Is the sentence above true? We cannot say until the symbol $\square$ is replaced by a numeral. If $\square$ is replaced by 3, a false statement results; if $\square$ is replaced by 6, a true statement results. As it stands, then, the sentence

$$\square + 4 = 10$$

does not have a truth value, and we call it an open sentence. *A sentence that contains one or more variables is an open sentence.* The open sentences we shall consider in this booklet are number sentences, that is, sentences in which the variables represent numbers.

In the primary grades teachers often use *frames* such as $\square$, $\triangle$, $\bigcirc$, or $\bowtie$ to represent variables. In the upper grades, letters are used more often than frames for this purpose. It is unimportant whether you use a frame, a question mark, a letter, or just an empty space, so long as the student understands that *the symbol used represents an unspecified number.* Thus, the choice of a symbol for a variable is arbitrary.

A set of numbers, the members of which are the permissible replacements of the variable in an open number sentence, is called the *replacement set* or *domain of the variable.* From the replacement set, the subset of numbers that makes the sentence true is selected. This subset is called the *solution set* for the sentence, and each number in this set is said to be a *solution* of the open sentence. (See Booklet No. 1: *Sets,* for a further discussion of sets and subsets.) In this booklet the capital letter D is used to name the set that is the domain of the variable.

Consider the sentence

$$(3 \times n) + 8 = 23, \qquad D = \{1,\ 3,\ 5,\ 7\}.$$

Let us find the solution set for this sentence by trial.

Replace n by 1: $(3 \times 1) + 8 = 23$

$3 + 8 = 23$

$11 = 23$ False

1 is not a member of the solution set.

Replace n by 3: $(3 \times 3) + 8 = 23$

$9 + 8 = 23$

$17 = 23$ False

3 is not a member of the solution set.

Replace n by 5: $(3 \times 5) + 8 = 23$

$15 + 8 = 23$

$23 = 23$ True

5 is a member of the solution set.

Replace n by 7: $(3 \times 7) + 8 = 23$

$21 + 8 = 23$

$29 = 23$ False

7 is not a member of the solution set.

We see that 5 is the only number in the domain of n for which $(3 \times n) + 8 = 23$ is true; and so the solution set of the sentence is $\{5\}$.

Now consider the sentence

$$\triangle + 2 > 17, \qquad D = \{15,\ 16,\ 17,\ 18,\ 19,\ 20\}.$$

Try 15: $15 + 2 > 17$

$17 > 17$

Since this sentence is false, 15 is not a solution.

Try 16: $16 + 2 > 17$

$18 > 17$

Since this sentence is true, 16 is a solution.

Try 17: $17 + 2 > 17$

$19 > 17$

Since this sentence is true, 17 is a solution.

Similarly, we can show that 18, 19, and 20 are solutions; and so the solution set of the open sentence is

$$\{16\ 17,\ 18,\ 19,\ 20\}.$$

In the two preceding examples, both the domain of the variable and the solution set are finite sets. The two examples that follow will have a domain that is an infinite set.

Consider the sentence

$$w - 4 < 6, \qquad D = \{0,\ 1,\ 2,\ 3,\ 4,\ 5,\ \ldots\}\ .$$

(The three dots show that only part of the set is listed, and that the list continues indefinitely in the pattern indicated.)

This is an open sentence involving the variable w. Let us agree that we shall accept only those replacements for w which are such that $w - 4$ is a whole number. By what number or numbers can w be replaced to make the sentence true? If w is replaced by 10, we have $10 - 4 < 6$. This sentence is false because $10 - 4 = 6$. If w is replaced by 9, we have $9 - 4 < 6$. This sentence is true because $5 < 6$ is true. If w is replaced by 8, we have $8 - 4 < 6$. This sentence is true because $4 < 6$ is true. If w is replaced by 7, we have $7 - 4 < 6$. This is true because $3 < 6$ is true. Can you see that the sentence $w - 4 < 6$ is also true for 6, 5, and 4? The numbers 3, 2, 1, and 0 are not solutions, because for these replacements $w - 4$ is not a whole number (as specified above). For example, $3 - 4$ is not a whole number. The solution set is $\{9, 8, 7, 6, 5, 4\}$. When an open sentence involves any of the symbols $<$, $>$, $\leq$, or $\geq$, its solution set often contains more than one number.

Now consider the sentence

$$m+5>12, \qquad D=\{0, 1, 2, 3, 4, 5, \ldots\}.$$

If m is replaced by 7, the result is $7+5>12$, which is a false sentence.
If m is replaced by 8, the result is $8+5>12$, which is a true sentence.
If m is replaced by 9, the result is $9+5>12$, which is a true sentence.

Can you see now that a true sentence results if m is replaced by any number greater than 7? The solution set is $\{8, 9, 10, \ldots\}$. This set is infinite.

The domain of the variable in an open sentence can be a set of rational numbers. (See Booklet No. 6: *The Rational Numbers*.) Consider the sentence

$$6 \div m < 4, \qquad D=\left\{\frac{1}{2}, \frac{5}{6}, \frac{8}{4}, \frac{7}{3}\right\}.$$

If m is replaced by $\frac{1}{2}$, we have $6 \div \frac{1}{2} < 4$, which is a false

sentence because $6 \div \frac{1}{2} = 12$.

If m is replaced by $\frac{5}{6}$, we have $6 \div \frac{5}{6} < 4$, which is a false

sentence because $6 \div \frac{5}{6} = \frac{36}{5}$.

If m is replaced by $\frac{8}{4}$, we have $6 \div \frac{8}{4} < 4$, which is a true

sentence because $6 \div \frac{8}{4} = 3$.

If m is replaced by $\frac{7}{3}$, we have $6 \div \frac{7}{3} < 4$, which is a true

sentence because $6 \div \frac{7}{3} = \frac{18}{7}$.

The solution set for this sentence is

$$\left\{\frac{8}{4}, \frac{7}{3}\right\}.$$

Sometimes the solution set is the empty set, that is, no replacement from the domain will yield a true sentence. For example, consider the sentence

$$n+7=6,$$

in which the domain is the set of whole numbers. There is no replacement for n which yields a true sentence since there is no whole number which when added to 7 will yield 6. Thus the solution set of this sentence is the empty set.

A summary of the terms used in this section is given below.

1. A *variable* is a symbol used to represent a definite but unspecified number or numbers.

2. A sentence that contains a variable is called an *open sentence*. It has no *truth value*. When the variable is replaced by a number, the resulting sentence is either true or false.

3. The set of numbers that may be used as permissible replacements for a variable in an open sentence is called the *replacement set* or *domain of the variable*.

4. Any number in the domain (replacement set) of the variable that yields a true sentence when it replaces the variable in an open sentence is a *member* of the *solution set* of the sentence. A solution set may contain no members, one member, or more than one member. In fact, it may have indefinitely many members. Each member of the solution set is called a *solution of the open sentence*.

Exercise Set 3

1. Translate the following verbal sentences into mathematical open sentences using either a letter or a frame for the variable.

(a) Six plus this number is equal to fifteen.
(b) The sum of two and this number is greater than ten.
(c) Twenty is less than this number minus eight.
(d) This number minus nine is greater than twenty-four.

2. Translate the following mathematical open sentences into verbal sentences.

(a) $8 + k = 22$ (c) $\square + 8 > 17$

(b) $14 < \square - 5$ (d) $n - 6 \neq 13$

3. For each of the open sentences, state the number or numbers that make the sentence true; that is, find the solution set. The domain of the variable is the set of whole numbers, $W = \{0, 1, 2, 3, \ldots\}$.

(a) $m - 7 = 27$ (e) $\clubsuit - 3 = 18$

(b) $\square + 5 > 12$ (f) $\square + 2 = 2$

(c) $8 < \triangle - 2$ (g) $m - 5 < 10$

(d) $4 \times k > 20$ (h) $n + 6 > 10$

Equivalent Open Sentences

Equivalent open sentences are open sentences having the same solution set. The following are equivalent open sentences:

$$3+n=9,$$
$$n=9-3,$$

and

$$3=9-n.$$

The solution set for each of these is $\{6\}$.

The sentences

$$n=5\times 3,$$
$$n\div 5=3,$$

and

$$n\div 3=5$$

are equivalent sentences, each having $\{15\}$ as a solution set.

The following are equivalent open sentences:

$$\frac{1}{2}\times m=10,$$
$$m=2\times 10.$$

The solution set for each of these sentences is $\{20\}$.

The following are equivalent open sentences:

$$n\div\frac{4}{3}=12,$$
$$n=12\times\frac{4}{3}.$$

The solution set for each of these sentences is $\{16\}$.

When you are solving verbal problems, it is helpful to realize that more than one number sentence can be used to express the conditions of the problem in mathematical language. For example, let us consider this verbal problem:

John has three dollars. He wants to buy a pair of skates that costs nine dollars. How much more money must John save if he is to be able to buy the skates?

Let n be the number of dollars John needs to save. Then each of the following is a translation of the conditions which n must satisfy:

$3+n=9,$	$3=9-n,$
$n+3=9,$	$9-n=3,$
$9=3+n,$	$9-3=n,$
$9=n+3,$	$n=9-3.$

1. Write an open sentence equivalent to each of the following sentences.

   (a) $\square - 264 = 928$ (c) $r + 407 = 964$

   (b) $437 = n - 89$ (d) $1007 = 3986 - r$

2. Write an open sentence equivalent to each of the following sentences.

   (a) $n \times 57 = 1368$ (c) $\square \div 48 = 37$

   (b) $2240 \div z = 35$ (d) $43 = n \div 72$

COMPOUND OPEN SENTENCES

Consider these two simple English sentences:

> Mary is an elementary school teacher.
> Mary is a good cook.

These two simple English sentences can be combined to form a compound sentence. "Mary is an elementary school teacher, *and* Mary is a good cook" is one compound sentence that could be formed. When two simple sentences are joined with the connective "and," the compound sentence is defined to be true if, and only if, *both* parts are true.

We could also make this compound sentence read: "Mary is an elementary school teacher, *or* Mary is a good cook." When "or" is used as the connective, the sentence is considered true if, and only if, at least *one* part is true. If Mary is an elementary school teacher but is not a good cook then the first compound sentence is *false*, and the second compound sentence is *true*. Thus, we can see that the connectives "and" and "or" differ in their effects.

Consider these compound number sentences:

(a) $2 < 5$ and $10 = 2 \times 5$

    $2 < 5$ is a true sentence.

    $10 = 2 \times 5$ is a true sentence.

    Thus, the compound number sentence "$2 < 5$ and $10 = 2 \times 5$" is true since both parts are true.

(b) $2 < 5$ and $10 = 8$

    $2 < 5$ is a true sentence.

    $10 = 8$ is a false sentence.

    Thus, the compound number sentence "$2 < 5$ and $10 = 8$" is false since one part is false.

(c) $5 < 10$ or $10 < 15$

    $5 < 10$ is a true sentence.

    $10 < 15$ is a true sentence.

Thus, the compound number sentence "$5<10$ or $10<15$" is true since both parts are true. (It would have been adequate for only one of the parts to be true.)

(d) $5<10$ or $5=2\times3$

   $5<10$ is a true sentence.

   $5=2\times3$ is a false sentence.

Thus, the compound number sentence "$5<10$ or $5=2\times3$" is true since one of its parts is true.

(e) $6=5\times2$ or $9>10$

   $6=5\times2$ is a false sentence.

   $9>10$ is a false sentence.

Thus, the compound number sentence "$6=5\times2$ or $9>10$" is false since neither of its parts is true.

Compound number sentences can be either compound open sentences, or compound statements, or a combination of these. An example of a compound open number sentence is

$$x<5 \text{ or } x=5,$$

where the domain of the variable is the set of whole numbers.

$x<5$ is a true sentence if x is a member of the set $\{0, 1, 2, 3, 4\}$.

$x=5$ is a true sentence if x is a member of the set $\{5\}$.

The union of the two sets, $\{0, 1, 2, 3, 4, 5\}$, is the solution set for the "or" compound sentence. (See Booklet No. 1: *Sets*, for discussion of "Union of Sets.") It is important to remember that a number is a solution of an "or" sentence like $x<5$ or $x=5$ if, and only if, it makes at least one of the simple sentences true.

A short way of writing $x<5$ or $x=5$ is

$$x\leq5,$$

which is read, "x is less than 5 *or* x is equal to 5." The symbol $\leq$ can be regarded as a combination of the symbols "$<$" and "$=$", where "$<$" refers to that part of the compound sentence which is a simple "less than" sentence; and "__" refers to the part of the compound sentence which is a simple "equals" sentence.

Another example of a compound open sentence is

$$x>5 \text{ or } x=5$$

where the domain of the variable is the set of whole numbers.

$x>5$ is a true sentence if x is a member of the set $\{6, 7, 8, 9, 10, \ldots\}$.

$x=5$ is a true sentence if x is a member of the set $\{5\}$.

The union of the two sets, {5, 6, 7, 8, 9, 10, . . .}, is the solution set for the "or" compound sentence.

A short way of writing $x>5$ or $x=5$ is

$$x\geq 5,$$

which is read, "x is greater than 5 *or* x is equal to 5." The symbol $\geq$ can be regarded as a combination of the symbols ">" and "=", where ">" refers to that part of the compound sentence which is a simple "greater than" sentence, and "___" refers to that part which is a simple "equals" sentence.

A number is a solution to an "or" sentence, such as a sentence involving either the symbol $\leq$ or the symbol $\geq$ if, and only if, it makes at least one of the simple sentences true. Let us look at some examples of such sentences.

EXAMPLE 1

Find the solution set of the open sentence:
$$\square+2\geq 10, \qquad D=\{6, 7, 8, 9, 10\}.$$

If $\square$ is replaced by 6, the sentence becomes $6+2\geq 10$. This "or" sentence is false because $6+2>10$ is false and $6+2=10$ is false.

If $\square$ is replaced by 7, the sentence becomes $7+2\geq 10$, which is false because $7+2$ is neither equal to 10 nor greater than 10.

If $\square$ is replaced by 8, the sentence becomes $8+2\geq 10$, which is true because $8+2=10$ is true. Remember that a compound "or" sentence is true if at least one part is true.

If $\square$ is replaced by 9, the sentence becomes $9+2\geq 10$, which is true because $9+2$ is greater than 10.

If $\square$ is replaced by 10, the sentence becomes $10+2\geq 10$, which is true because $10+2$ is greater than 10.

The solution set is $\{8, 9, 10\}$.

EXAMPLE 2

Find the solution set of the open sentence:
$$7+x\leq 12, \qquad D=\{3, 4, 5, 6, 7, 8\}.$$

If x is replaced by 3, the sentence becomes $7+3\leq 12$, which is true because $7+3$ is less than 12.

If x is replaced by 4, the sentence becomes $7+4\leq 12$, which is true because $7+4$ is less than 12.

If x is replaced by 5, the sentence becomes $7+5\leq12$, which is true because $7+5=12$.

If x is replaced by 6, the sentence becomes $7+6\leq12$, which is not true because $7+6$ is neither less than 12 nor equal to 12.

If x is replaced by 7, the sentence becomes $7+7\leq12$, which is not true because $7+7$ is neither less than 12 nor equal to 12.

If x is replaced by 8, the sentence becomes $7+8\leq12$, which is not true because $7+8$ is neither less than 12 nor equal to 12.

Solution set $= \{3, 4, 5\}$.

Now consider this sentence: "n is a whole number between 5 and 8." This sentence asserts that n is greater than 5 *and* n is less than 8. In symbols, the sentence is written

$$5<n<8, \text{ with } D = \{0, 1, 2, 3, \ldots\}.$$

It is read, "5 is less than n, and n is less than 8," or alternatively, "n is greater than 5 and less than 8." Can you see that when n is replaced by 6 or 7, the resulting sentence is true? Any other replacement for n results in a false sentence. Remember that a compound "and" sentence is true only when both parts are true.

EXAMPLE 3

Find the solution set of the sentence:

$$8<n<12, \qquad D = \{8, 9, 10, 11, 12\}.$$

If n is replaced by 8, the sentence becomes $8<8<12$, which is not true. The number 8 makes one but not both parts of the compound sentence true; $8<8$ is a false sentence, and $8<12$ is a true sentence.

If n is replaced by 9, the sentence becomes $8<9<12$, which is true because $8<9$ is true and $9<12$ is true.

If n is replaced by 10 the sentence becomes $8<10<12$, which is true.

If n is replaced by 11, the sentence becomes $8<11<12$, which is true.

If n is replaced by 12, the sentence becomes $8<12<12$, which is not true. The number 12 makes one but not both parts of the compound sentence true; $8<12$ is a true sentence, but $12<12$ is a false sentence.

The solution set is $\{9, 10, 11\}$.

Note that the solution set for the sentence $8<n$ is $\{9, 10, 11, 12\}$, and the solution set for $n<12$ is $\{8, 9, 10, 11\}$. The solution set for the "and" compound sentence is the intersection of these two solution sets. (See Booklet No. 1: *Sets*, for discussion of "Intersection of Sets.")

In summary, an "and" sentence is true if, and only if, both of the simple sentences in the "and" sentence are true.

We have considered "and" sentences such as $5<n<8$. We have also considered "or" sentences, such as $5\leq n$. Often we encounter situations involving an even more complex set of conditions. For example, consider the sentence, "Applicants for this position must be between the ages of 25 and 35 inclusive." Suppose n represents the number of years an eligible candidate must have lived. He must be *at least* 25 ($25\leq n$) *and* not older than 35 ($n\leq 35$). This is described by the compound open sentence

$$25\leq n \quad \text{and} \quad n\leq 35,$$

which can be written in the abbreviated form

$$25\leq n\leq 35$$ (read "25 is less than or equal to n, and n is less than or equal to 35"; or, alternatively, "n is greater than or equal to 25 and less than or equal to 35").

Note that this says

"$25<n$ *or* $25=n$ *and* $n<35$ *or* $n=35$."

This is a compound sentence with the connective "and," each part of which is itself a compound sentence with the connective "or." Suppose we consider two replacements for n in the "or-and-or" sentence:

$$25\leq n\leq 35.$$

Try 25.   Does 25 make both sentences $25\leq n$ and $n\leq 35$ true? Yes; $25\leq 25$ is true because $25=25$ is true, and $25\leq 35$ is true because $25<35$ is true. Hence 25 is a solution.

Now try 38.   Does 38 make both sentences $25\leq n$ and $n\leq 35$ true? No. Although $25\leq 38$ is true, $38\leq 35$ is not true, because neither $38<35$ nor $38=35$ is true. So 38 is not a solution.

We can see that such a sentence is considered true when both parts of the "and" sentence are true.

EXAMPLE 4

Find the solution set for

$$5\leq n\leq 8, \quad D=\{5, 6, 7, 8, 9\}.$$

If n is replaced by 5, the sentence becomes $5\leq 5\leq 8$. $5\leq 5$ is true because $5=5$ is a true sentence. $5\leq 8$ is true because $5<8$ is a true sentence. Thus, $5 \leq 5 \leq 8$ is true because both parts of the "and" sentence are true. So 5 is a member of the solution set.

If n is replaced by 6, the sentence becomes $5 \leq 6 \leq 8$. $5 \leq 6$ is true because $5 < 6$ is a true sentence. $6 \leq 8$ is true because $6 < 8$ is a true sentence. Thus, $5 \leq 6 \leq 8$ is true because both parts of the "and" sentence are true. So 6 is a member of the solution set.

If n is replaced by 7, the sentence becomes $5 \leq 7 \leq 8$. $5 \leq 7$ is true because $5 < 7$ is a true sentence. $7 \leq 8$ is true because $7 < 8$ is a true sentence. Thus, $5 \leq 7 \leq 8$ is true because both parts of the "and" sentence are true. So 7 is a member of the solution set.

If n is replaced by 8, the sentence becomes $5 \leq 8 \leq 8$. $5 \leq 8$ is true because $5 < 8$ is a true sentence. $8 \leq 8$ is true because $8 = 8$ is a true sentence. Thus, $5 \leq 8 \leq 8$ is true because both parts of the "and" sentence are true. So 8 is a member of the solution set.

If n is replaced by 9, the sentence becomes $5 \leq 9 \leq 8$. $5 \leq 9$ is true because $5 < 9$ is a true sentence. $9 \leq 8$ is not true because neither $9 < 8$ nor $9 = 8$ is true. Thus $5 \leq 9 \leq 8$ is not true because both parts of the "and" sentence must be true in order for the sentence to be true. So 9 is not a member of the solution set.

The solution set for the sentence is $\{5, 6, 7, 8\}$.

Exercise Set 5

1. Translate the following verbal sentences into compound open number sentences. Use either a frame or a letter for the variable.

   (a) This number is greater than or equal to nine.
   (b) The sum of thirteen and this number is less than or equal to twenty-nine.
   (c) The sum of this number and eleven is greater than or equal to thirty.
   (d) Eight is less than this number, and this number is less than fifteen.
   (e) This number is between nine and thirty, inclusive.

2. Translate the following compound open number sentences into verbal sentences.

   (a) $n \leq 7$ (d) $2 < n < 5$
   (b) $\square + 2 \geq 3$ (e) $8 \leq t \leq 15$
   (c) $7 - x \leq 12$

3. Find the solution set for each of the following compound number sentences. The domain of the variable is the set of whole numbers, $\{0, 1, 2, 3, \ldots\}$.

(a) $8 + \square \geq 10$

(b) $x + 2 \leq 5$

(c) $3 \times n \leq 9$

(d) $4 + \triangle \geq 12$

(e) $n - 7 \geq 14$

(f) $11 + k \leq 13$

(g) $4 < n < 6$

(h) $3 < n \leq 6$

OPEN SENTENCES WITH MORE THAN ONE VARIABLE

A child is told that he may choose four balloons from a bag containing four identical round balloons and four identical long balloons. What are the possible combinations that he might choose? Since two different kinds of balloons are involved, a number sentence for this problem contains two variables. If $\bigcirc$ represents the number of round balloons he chooses, and $\bigcirc$ represents the number of long balloons he chooses, then the number sentence for this problem is

$$\bigcirc + \bigcirc = 4.$$

Because there are two variables, each solution to this problem will be an ordered pair * of numbers yielding a true sentence when the components of the ordered pair are used as replacements for the appropriate variables. The replacement set for each variable is the set $\{0, 1, 2, 3, 4\}$, since the child can choose 0, 1, 2, 3, or 4 round and 0, 1, 2, 3, or 4 long balloons. The solution set for the open sentence

$$\bigcirc + \bigcirc = 4$$

is the set of all ordered pairs the sum of whose components is four. In the sentence

$$\bigcirc + \bigcirc = 4,$$

if $\bigcirc$ is replaced by 0, a true statement results if $\bigcirc$ is replaced by 4. Thus, the ordered pair (0, 4) is a solution of (or a member of the solution set of) the open sentence.

If $\bigcirc$ is replaced by 1, a true statement results if $\bigcirc$ is replaced by 3. Thus, (1, 3) is a solution.

If $\bigcirc$ is replaced by 2, a true statement results if $\bigcirc$ is replaced by 2. Thus, (2, 2) is a solution.

If $\bigcirc$ is replaced by 3, a true statement results if $\bigcirc$ is replaced by 1. Thus, (3, 1) is a solution.

---

* Refer to Booklet No. 1: *Sets,* and to Booklet No. 2: *The Whole Numbers,* for a discussion of ordered pairs.

If ◯ is replaced by 4, a true statement results if ⬭ is replaced by 0. Thus, (4, 0) is a solution.

The members of the solution set may be listed in a table or in set notation. (See Table I.)

TABLE I

◯	⬭
0	4
1	3
2	2
3	1
4	0

$\{(0, 4), (1, 3), (2, 2), (3, 1), (4, 0)\}$

There are five ordered pairs that make the number sentence true. Because the solutions are ordered pairs, the solution (0, 4) is not the same solution as (4, 0), nor is (1, 3) the same solution as (3, 1). The solution (0, 4) represents no round balloons and four long balloons, whereas the solution (4, 0) represents four round balloons and no long balloons.

Let the set of whole numbers be the replacement set for each of the variables in the sentence:

$$\square + \triangle + \clubsuit = 12.$$

Since there are three variables in this number sentence, each solution contains three numbers, and can be regarded as an ordered triplet the sum of whose components is twelve. There are many more solutions to this number sentence than there were in the preceding sentence. Seven of the solutions are listed in Table II. Since the sum is twelve, there is no possibility of replacing any of the variables with a number greater than twelve, since such a replacement could not yield a true number sentence.

Let the set of whole numbers be the replacement set for each of the variables $\square$ and $\triangle$ in the open sentence:

$$(\square + \triangle) - \square = 6.$$

The same number must be used as a replacement for the variable $\square$ at each place it is used in the sentence. If $\triangle$ is replaced by 6, a true sentence results no matter what whole number is used as a replacement for $\square$. On the other hand, if $\triangle$ is replaced by any whole number other than 6, a false sentence results no matter what number is used as a replacement

TABLE II

	□	△	✿
(a)	5	4	3
(b)	10	1	1
(c)	12	0	0
(d)	0	7	5
(e)	0	5	7
(f)	4	3	5
(g)	1	10	1

for □. The solution set is infinite. Every solution set has the number 6 as its second component. A few of the solutions are given in Table III, and the solution set is given in set notation beside the table.

TABLE III

□	△
0	6
1	6
2	6
5	6
9	6
⋮	6

$\{(0, 6), (1, 6), (2, 6), (3, 6), (4, 6), (5, 6), \ldots\}$

If the replacement set of each of the variables in the number sentence

$$\triangle - \text{✿} = 0$$

is the set of whole numbers, a few tries should convince us that in each solution, the two components of the ordered pair are the same and that the solution set is infinite. A few of the solutions are listed in Table IV, and the solution set is given in set notation.

In the following sentence, the replacement set for each of the variables is the set of numbers represented by the numerals in the bag (Fig. 1).

TABLE IV

△	✿
7	7
3	3
8	8
9	9
0	0

$\{(0,0), (1,1), (2,2), (3,3), (4,4), (5,5), \ldots\}$

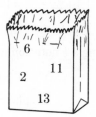

$\bigcirc \; + \; \text{✿} \quad > \quad 15.$

FIGURE 1

A solution of this sentence is an ordered pair of numbers whose components may be the same number or different numbers. Some of the replacements of $\bigcirc$ and ✿ by the components of an ordered pair of numbers yield true sentences (these ordered pairs are solutions), and some yield false sentences. The replacements are given in Table V with T indicating those yielding true sentences, and F indicating those yielding false sentences.

TABLE V

If $\bigcirc = 2$

○	✿	
2	2	F
2	6	F
2	11	F
2	13	F

If $\bigcirc = 6$

○	✿	
6	2	F
6	6	F
6	11	T
6	13	T

If $\bigcirc = 11$

○	✿	
11	2	F
11	6	T
11	11	T
11	13	T

If $\bigcirc = 13$

○	✿	
13	2	F
13	6	T
13	11	T
13	13	T

All the permissible ordered pairs for this sentence have been listed; and the solution set is

$\{(6, 11), (6, 13), (11, 6), (11, 11), (11, 13), (13, 6), (13, 11), (13, 13)\}.$

Exercise Set 6

1. Using the following set as the replacement set of each variable, list the solution sets of the following sentences in table form.

$$\{0, 1, 2, 3, 4, 5, 6, 7, 8, 9, 10\}$$

(a) $\clubsuit \times \triangle = 12$

(b) $\square + \triangle + \square = 10$

(c) $\bigcirc + \square \leq 4$

2. Using set notation, write the solution set for the following sentence.

$$(\triangle \times 5) + (\square \times 10) = 45,$$

Replacement set $= \{0, 1, 2, 3, 4, 5, 6, 7, 8, 9\}.$

EDUCATED GUESSING

One very practical means of finding solutions for some open sentences with one variable is simply to guess, or, perhaps more correctly, to use a trial-and-error process. By selecting some number as a possible solution, and then observing the result when the variable in the sentence is replaced by this selection, you can often obtain information that will help you make a second selection closer to the true solution. For example, consider the open sentence:

$$(\square + 4) - 5 = 20, \qquad \square = \{0, 1, 2, 3, \ldots\}.$$

Note. The parentheses show order of operation in this sentence; that is, the sum $(\square + 4)$ is to be computed prior to subtracting 5.

For what whole number (if any) is the sentence true? Suppose you select first the number 10 as a likely candidate. When $\square$ is replaced by 10, the resulting sentence is

$$(10 + 4) - 5 = 20,$$

or

$$9 = 20,$$

which is false. By inspection we see that the number 10 for $\square$ results in the left-hand member being much too small, so your second guess should be greater than 10. Try the number 15 for your second guess. When $\square$ is replaced by 15, the resulting sentence is

$$(15+4)-5=20,$$

or

$$14=20,$$

which is false. Should your next guess be greater than or less than 15? It must be greater than 15 because 15 still produces a left-hand member that is too small. If you have observed the pattern in the results of the first two guesses, perhaps your third guess will be correct. Let 21 be your third guess. When $\square$ is replaced by 21, we get

$$(21+4)-5=20,$$

or

$$20=20,$$

which is true; and 21 is the solution you seek.

Now consider the open sentence:

$$[2\times(\triangle-3)]+5=27.$$

By what whole number (if any) can $\triangle$ be replaced to make this sentence true? Suppose you try 20 as your first guess. When $\triangle$ is replaced by 20, you have

$$[2\times(20-3)]+5=27,$$

or

$$39=27,$$

which is false. Should your next guess be greater than or less than 20? You can see that the left-hand member is too large, so your second guess needs to be less than 20. For your second guess try 13. When $\triangle$ is replaced by 13, you get

$$[2\times(13-3)]+5=27,$$

or

$$25=27,$$

which is not true. Should your next guess be greater than or less than 13? It should be greater than 13 because 13 produces a number that is too small. Now your observations might lead you to expect that 14 will be the correct replacement. When $\triangle$ is replaced by 14, you obtain

$$[2\times(14-3)]+5=27,$$

or

$$27=27,$$

which is true. The solution set is $\{14\}$.

After many sentences are solved in this fashion, some students will find systematic ways of finding the solution sets of open sentences. Students may be assured that mathematicians often use the technique of trial and error when they solve problems of a kind they have not previously attempted.

Exercise Set 7

1. Find solutions for the following open sentences by guessing, and record your guesses and the results.

(a) $(6+\square)-5=23$ (d) $[2\times(\triangle+4)]-9=37$

(b) $(\triangle-4)+6=32$ (e) $[3\times(7+\square)]+3=63$

(c) $7+(10-\square)=9$ (f) $12+[6\times(\triangle-7)]=36$

USE OF THE NUMBER LINE WITH NUMBER SENTENCES

The number line can serve as an aid for finding solutions for open sentences involving one variable. (See Booklet No. 1: *Sets*, for a detailed discussion of the number line.)

Recall that the whole numbers can be placed in one-to-one correspondence with a set of equally spaced points on the number line, after one point has been chosen arbitrarily to correspond to 0, and another to correspond to 1.

Let us consider some problems which show how the number line can be used to picture a number relation pertaining to a verbal problem, and how, from the picture, a number sentence can be derived.

PROBLEM 1. John and Dick live on the same street on which the school is located. John lives two blocks east of the school and Dick lives seven blocks east of the school. How much farther from school does Dick live than John?

Suppose that Dick lives m miles farther from school than John; then the following picture can be drawn (Fig. 2).

The picture leads to the idea of the following number sentence:

$$2+m=7. \quad (m=7-2 \text{ is an equivalent sentence.})$$

Since this physical situation suggests a comparison, the question is answered by saying, "Dick lives five blocks *farther* from school than John does."

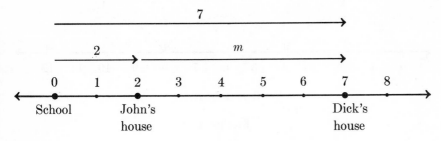

FIGURE 2

The wording in the next problem suggests the idea of removing from a set of objects a certain subset. This notion is shown on the number line (Fig. 3) by a "movement to the left."

PROBLEM 2. Bob was carrying a stack of 15 books. A friend helped him by taking 8 of the books from the stack and carrying them. How many books did Bob then carry?

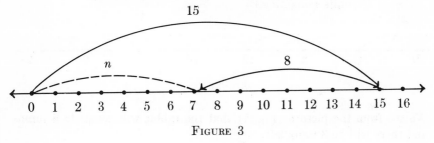

FIGURE 3

The picture suggests the following number sentence:

$$15 - 8 = n. \quad (8 + n = 15 \text{ is an equivalent sentence.})$$

The answer to the problem would be a sentence such as, "Bob then carried seven books."

Number lines can be used to illustrate products. For example, the number line below (Fig. 4) shows that the product of 3 and 4 can be viewed as the sum $4 + 4 + 4$.

It is often helpful to visualize a situation as though it were an action taking place on the number line. This idea can be employed in any situation similar to the following example:

PROBLEM 3. A "four-rabbit" jumps four units at a time. How many jumps to the right will he be able to complete if he begins at the point corresponding to zero on the number line

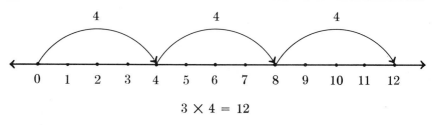

$$3 \times 4 = 12$$

FIGURE 4

(Fig. 5), but isn't allowed to go any farther than the point corresponding to 27?

As the four-rabbit is visualized hopping along at the rate of 4 units per hop, it is clear that he may not land exactly on the point corresponding to 27; some units may be left over. Thus, a number sentence expressing this situation would be $27 = (n \times 4) + r$. (The variable n represents the number of hops completed, and the variable r represents the number of units remaining.)

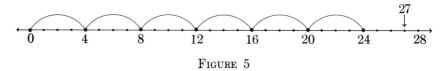

FIGURE 5

We see from the picture (Fig. 5) that the rabbit will complete 6 jumps and there will be 3 units left.

The following observation can be made concerning the use of the number line in solving problems:

1. From a picture on the number line showing the numerical relationship in a problem, more than one number sentence can be derived.
2. A number of different physical situations or problems can be pictured by the same drawing and, hence, can be described by the same number sentence.

Graphing Solution Sets

Successive points on a number line are labeled to correspond to successive whole numbers whose order has been previously established. (For a discussion of order, see Booklet No. 1: *Sets.*) The number line (Fig. 6) has been labeled so that the point corresponding to the greater of two numbers lies to the right of the point corresponding to the lesser. Thus, the truth of a statement about the equality or inequality of numbers can be checked by observing the positions of the points which correspond to the numbers in the sentence.

Is $6>5$ a true sentence?

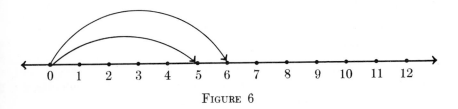

FIGURE 6

The point corresponding to the number six is to the right of the point corresponding to the number five, and the sentence $6>5$ is true.

The solution set of an open sentence involving an inequality can be pictured on the number line. Using the numbers indicated on the number line below (Fig. 7) for the domain, what is the solution set of the open sentence

$$m+2>7?$$

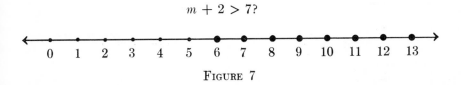

FIGURE 7

If m is replaced by 5, we get $5+2>7$, which is not true.
If m is replaced by 6, we get $6+2>7$, which is true.

True sentences also result when m is replaced by 7, 8, 9, 10, 11, 12, or 13. All numbers in the domain that correspond to points to the right of the point labeled 5 are members of the solution set. The other numbers in the domain are not members of the solution set. To picture the solution set on the number line, make a large dot at the point corresponding to each of the numbers 6, 7, 8, 9, 10, 11, 12, and 13. The solution set is {6, 7, 8, 9, 10, 11, 12, 13}. The set of points marked by large closed dots is the *graph* of the solution set.

Determine the solution set of the open sentence

$$y+3<11,$$

using as domain the set of numbers indicated on the number line below (Fig. 8).

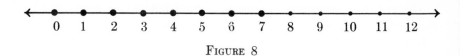

FIGURE 8

If y is replaced by 8, we get $8+3<11$ which is not true.

If y is replaced by 7, we get $7+3<11$ which is true.

All numbers in the domain that correspond to points to the left of the point labeled 8 are members of the solution set, but the other numbers in the domain are not members of the solution set. The solution set is

$$\{0, 1, 2, 3, 4, 5, 6, 7\}.$$

To graph the solution set on the number line, make large dots to mark the points corresponding to the numbers in the set $\{0, 1, 2, 3, 4, 5, 6, 7\}$, as pictured in Figure 8.

Using the set of whole numbers as the domain of the variable, determine the solution set of the open sentence

$$\square-4>7$$

on the number line below (Fig. 9).

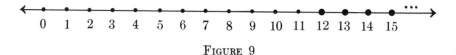

FIGURE 9

If $\square$ is replaced by 10, we get $10-4>7$, which is false.

If $\square$ is replaced by 11, we get $11-4>7$, which is false.

If $\square$ is replaced by 12, we get $12-4>7$, which is true.

If $\square$ is replaced by 13, we get $13-4>7$, which is true.

Any whole number greater than 11, then, is a member of the solution set. The other whole numbers are not members of the solution set. To graph the solution set on the number line (Fig. 9) make large dots on the points corresponding to 12, 13, 14, and 15. Then, after 15, make three raised dots indicating that all whole numbers from 15 on belong to the graph of the solution set. This solution set is an infinite set and you cannot list all of its members.

Let us find the solution set of the following "or" sentence and show the graph of this solution set on the number line (Fig. 10).

$$\square+2\geq10, \qquad D=\{6, 7, 8, 9, 10\}.$$

If □ is replaced by 6, we get $6+2\geq10$, which is false.

If □ is replaced by 7, we get $7+2\geq10$, which is false.

If □ is replaced by 8, we get $8+2\geq10$, which is true.

If □ is replaced by 9, we get $9+2\geq10$, which is true.

If □ is replaced by 10, we get $10+2\geq10$, which is true.
Solution set $= \{8, 9, 10\}$.

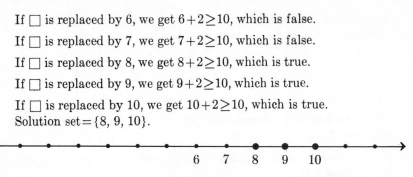

FIGURE 10

Note that only the points corresponding to the numbers which are member of the domain are labeled.

Now let us consider the "and" open sentence

$$8<n<12, \qquad D=\{8, 9, 10, 11, 12\}.$$

If n is replaced by 8, we have $8<8<12$, which is false.

If n is replaced by 9, we have $8<9<12$, which is true.

If n is replaced by 10, we have $8<10<12$, which is true.

If n is replaced by 11, we have $8<11<12$, which is true.

If n is replaced by 12, we have $8<12<12$, which is false.

Solution set $= \{9, 10, 11\}$.

The graph of the solution set is as pictured below (Fig. 11).

8   9   10   11   12

FIGURE 11

Exercise Set 8

1. Draw a number-line illustration of each number sentence. Label the points on the number line corresponding to the whole numbers from 0 to 12, inclusive.

(a) $12-7=a$ (d) $5\times2=m$

(b) $6+5=x$ (e) $□+3=10$

(c) $2\times5=m$

2. Draw a number line for each problem and label the points corresponding to the whole numbers from 0 to 12, inclusive. This set of numbers

is to be considered the domain of the variable. Draw the graph of the solution set for each open sentence.

(a) $6 + \square < 14$ (d) $\triangle \leq 4$

(b) $\square - 5 > 4$ (e) $1 < y < 6$

(c) $\square \geq 6$ (f) $1 \leq y \leq 6$

3. Write an addition sentence that is equivalent to the open sentence in Exercise 1 (a).

4. Write two subtraction sentences each equivalent to the open sentence in Exercise 1 (b).

PROBLEM SOLVING

Number sentences are useful in finding solutions of verbal problems. To write number sentences for problems, it is necessary to be able to translate verbal sentences and phrases into mathematical language. Here are some verbal phrases typical of those occurring in problems, along with their mathematical translations.

The sum of a number and 2	$n + 2$
A number increased by 10	$n + 10$
15 increased by some number	$15 + n$
36 decreased by some number	$36 - n$
A number decreased by 3	$n - 3$
A number diminished by 8	$n - 8$
The product of 3 and a number	$3 \times n$
The age of a boy two years older than Fred if Fred is n years old	$n + 2$
The cost in cents of 3 dolls costing 40 cents each	3×40
The number of cents n dolls cost if each costs 40 cents	$n \times 40$
The number of cents 3 dolls cost if each costs n cents	$3 \times n$
The number 54 is 3 times a certain number	$54 = 3 \times n$
$\frac{1}{2}$ of a number	$\frac{1}{2} \times n$ or $\frac{n}{2}$

Now consider the following situation:

Jane had 22 jacks. She can find only 8. How many are missing?
Let us list the numbers involved here:

Number of jacks Jane has now	8
Number of jacks missing	n
Number of jacks she had	$n+8$
Number of jacks she had	22.

There are two expressions for the number of jacks Jane had, $(n+8)$ and 22. So we have the number sentence $n+8=22$.

One might think a little differently, as follows:

Number of jacks she had	22
Number of jacks she has now	8
Number of jacks missing	$22-8$
Number of jacks missing	n.

Here we have two expressions for the number of jacks missing, from which we get the number sentence $n=22-8$.

We see that the number sentences $n+8=22$ and $n=22-8$ are true if n is replaced by 14 and false if n is replaced by any other number. These number sentences are equivalent to one another because they have the same solution set. Each sentence is a correct representation of the number relation in the problem. When you are solving a problem, it is important to remember that there can be more than one correct number sentence that describes the number relations of the problem.

The following examples illustrate how to translate a problem situation into an open number sentence and to use the number sentence to find the solution of a problem. In the word-statement of a problem, the domain of the variable is usually not explicitly stated, but restrictions on the domain are implied by the wording of the statement. In some cases, the nature of the problem is such that the domain is restricted to whole numbers; in others, rational numbers are permissible replacements, in fact, even required replacements.

PROBLEM 1. I have x dollars, and you have \$2.00 more than I. Together we have \$16.00. How many dollars do I have?

Solution:

Let us list the numbers involved here:

Number of dollars I have	x
Number of dollars you have	$x+2$

Number of dollars in all $x + (x + 2)$

Number of dollars in all   16

Sentence: $x + (x + 2) = 16$, $D = \{0, 1, 2, 3, \ldots\}$.

This sentence is true when x is replaced by 7 and false when x is replaced by any other number. Thus, I have $7.00.

PROBLEM 2.   You have twice as much money as I have. Together we have $24.00. How many dollars do I have?

Solution:

Number of dollars I have n

Number of dollars you have $(2 \times n)$

Number of dollars together $n + (2 \times n)$

Number of dollars together   24

Sentence: $n + (2 \times n) = 24$, $D = \{0, 1, 2, 3, \ldots\}$.

Solution set: $\{8\}$.

Thus, I have $8.00.

PROBLEM 3.   Jane bought 2 dozen rolls at 30¢ a dozen and some hot dogs. Her bill was $1.40. How many cents did the hot dogs cost?

Solution:

Let n be the number of cents the hot dogs cost.

Number of cents for 1 dozen rolls   30

Number of cents for 2 dozen rolls 2×30

Number of cents for hot dogs n

Number of cents for total bill $(2 \times 30) + n$

Number of cents for total bill   140

Sentence: $(2 \times 30) + n = 140$, $D = \{0, 1, 2, 3, \ldots\}$.

Solution set: $\{80\}$.

Thus, the hot dogs cost 80¢.

PROBLEM 4.   Bill bought 3 balls and a bat for $2.46. The bat cost $1.50. What was the price of one ball if the price was the same for each ball?

Solution:

Number of cents for one bat   150

Number of cents for one ball n

Number of cents for 3 balls $3 \times n$

Number of cents for balls and bat $(3 \times n) + 150$

Number of cents for balls and bat   246

Sentence: $(3 \times n) + 150 = 246$, $D = \{0, 1, 2, 3, \ldots\}$.

This sentence is equivalent to the sentence $3 \times n = 96$.
Solution set: $\{32\}$.
Thus, the price of each ball was 32¢.

PROBLEM 5. A public beach lies between towns A and B. The beach is
3 times as far from B as from A. The distance from A to B
is 58 miles. How many miles is it from the beach to town A?

Solution:

The required number of miles might not be a whole number.
So here we take as our domain the rational numbers.

Number of miles from beach to A n

Number of miles from beach to B $3 \times n$

Number of miles from A to B $n + (3 \times n)$

Number of miles from A to B 58

Sentence: $n + (3 \times n) = 58$, $D = \{$rational numbers$\}$.

This sentence is equivalent to

$$(1 \times n) + (3 \times n) = 58$$

which is equivalent to

$$(1 + 3) \times n = 58 \qquad \text{(Distributive property)}$$

or

$$4 \times n = 58.$$

The replacement which yields a true sentence is $\dfrac{58}{4}$ or $14\frac{1}{2}$.

Thus, the distance from the beach to town A is $14\frac{1}{2}$ miles.

Not all verbal problems can be solved by sentences involving equations.
There are verbal problems that deal with inequalities as well as equalities.
Many life situations involve the notion of inequality. Such problems,
however, can be expressed by number sentences in much the same way as
we express problems dealing with equality.

PROBLEM 6. Mary has $10.00. She buys two pairs of gloves at $3.00 a pair. She is also going to buy a blouse. How much can she spend for the blouse?

Solution:

Let s be the number of cents she spends for a blouse.

Number of cents for 1 pair of gloves	300
Number of cents for 2 pairs of gloves	(2×300)
Number of cents Mary has	1000
Number of cents Mary spends for a blouse cannot exceed	$1000 - (2 \times 300)$

Sentence: $s \leq 1000 - (2 \times 300)$, $D = \{$rational numbers$\}$.

This sentence is equivalent to the sentence $s \leq 400$. Thus we see that Mary cannot spend more than 400 cents on a blouse. Mary can spend $4.00 or any amount less than $4.00 for the blouse. If the problem had stated that Mary *must* spend all of her money, then she would have to spend $4.00. When the problem is stated: "How much *can* she spend?" the implication is that Mary has a choice. She can spend $4.00 for a blouse, or she can spend any amount less than $4.00.

PROBLEM 7. Mr. Jackson traveled 240 miles on a toll road. The minimum permissible speed was 40 miles per hour; the maximum permissible speed was 60 miles per hour. How long did it take him to travel the 240 miles if he obeyed the law throughout the trip and made no stops?

Solution:

Number of miles he had to travel	240
Minimum speed in miles per hour	40
Maximum speed in miles per hour	60
Maximum number of hours	$240 \div 40$
Minimum number of hours	$240 \div 60$
Number of hours to travel 240 miles	t

The number t must be greater than or equal to $(240 \div 60)$ *and* less than or equal to $(240 \div 40)$.

Sentence: $240 \div 60 \leq t \leq 240 \div 40$, $D = \{$rational numbers$\}$.

This sentence is equivalent to the sentence $4 \leq t \leq 6$. t can be any number from 4 to 6, inclusive. Thus, it will take Mr. Jackson from 4 to 6 hours to travel 240 miles.

There is no magic formula to ensure success in solving problems. It involves translating the verbal problem into an open number sentence, and then finding the solution set for the equation or inequality. After the solution is found, a sentence can be written which interprets the solution as the answer to the problem.

Exercise Set 9

1. Translate each of the following word phrases into number phrases.

    (a) the sum of a number and sixteen
    (b) the product of thirteen and a number
    (c) one-fifth of a number
    (d) a number divided by four
    (e) the product of five and two more than a number

2. Translate each of the following word sentences into number sentences.

    (a) The sum of six times this number and eight is equal to forty-four.
    (b) This number plus eight-is greater than fourteen.
    (c) The result of dividing this number by four is less than seventeen.
    (d) Eight decreased by this number is equal to four.
    (e) This number increased by seven is greater than three times the number.

3. Solve the following verbal problems. For each problem, list the numbers involved and write the number sentence. Find the solution set and then write a sentence to interpret your answer.

    (a) Sue had saved $3.54. She earned 75¢ more by babysitting. How much money does she still need to buy a sweater that costs $7.95?
    (b) George had $15.00. He spent $6.00 for baseball shoes and $5.00 for a baseball shirt. How much can he spend for a baseball bat?
    (c) Chicago is 2200 miles from San Diego. On a nonstop flight from San Diego to Chicago, a jet averages 535 miles per hour. How far from Chicago is the jet 3 hours after taking off from San Diego?
    (d) A college student has 93 days of summer vacation. He spends 9 days on a fishing trip. The remaining time he works as a camp counselor. How many weeks does he spend at camp?
    (e) The highest daily temperatures for 5 consecutive days in San Francisco were 70, 72, 78, 69, and 74. What was the average highest daily temperature for the 5 days?

4. Here are some open sentences. For each sentence make up a verbal problem for which the sentence expresses the number relations.

    (a) $n + 8 = 39$ (c) $(2 \times n) + 7 < 26$

    (b) $\frac{1}{4} \times n = 19$ (d) $39 \leq n \leq 45$

SUMMARY

1. Number sentences such as

$$5+2=9$$

   and

$$19>8$$

   are called *statements*. A statement is either true or false (we can say it has a *truth value* of "True" or "False"). Here $5+2=9$ is a false statement, whereas $19>8$ is a true statement.

2. A number sentence such as

$$\square+5=12, \qquad \text{Domain}=\{0, 1, 2, 3, \ldots, 12\},$$

   is called an *open number sentence*. The symbol $\square$ is called a *variable*, and it represents a definite but unspecified number from the given set of numbers, $\{0, 1, 2, 3, \ldots, 12\}$. This set of numbers is called the *domain* of the variable. When the symbol $\square$ is replaced by a numeral for a number from the domain, the resulting sentence is either true or false.

3. A number from the domain of the variable occurring in an open sentence is called a *solution* of the open sentence provided a true statement results when the variable is replaced by a numeral for that number. For example, 7 is a solution of the sentence $\square+5=12$. The set of all solutions of an open sentence is called its *solution set*.

4. A solution of an open sentence in two variables consists of an ordered pair of numbers from a specified set of ordered pairs of numbers. Again the set of all solutions is called the solution set.

5. Two open sentences in one variable are *equivalent* provided they have the same solution set. For example, $\square+5<11$ and $\square<6$ are equivalent.

6. A number sentence expressing equality of two numbers is called an *equation*.

7. A number sentence expressing inequality of two numbers is called an *inequality*.

8. Open sentences are often used in solving verbal problems. The procedure is this: First translate the numerical relation contained in the problem into an open number sentence, then find the solution set of this sentence, and finally interpret the solution, or solutions, as the answer to the problem.

9. The *number line* is a useful device both for picturing the numerical relation contained in a problem and for showing the graph of the solution of the open sentence for the problem.

ANSWERS TO EXERCISE SETS

Exercise Set 1

1. 11   **3.** 27   **5.** 9

2. 11   **4.** 30   **6.** 10

Exercise Set 2

1. (a) $24 - 8 = 16$ (e) $10 = 3 \times 4$

    (b) $16 > 10$ (f) $9 < 11$

    (c) $17 \neq 8 + 2$ (g) $12 \not> 7$

    (d) $80 < 20$ (h) $20 + 6 > 3 \times 8$

2. (a) True   (e) False

    (b) True   (f) True

    (c) True   (g) False

    (d) False   (h) True

3. (a) The sum of fifteen and three is twelve minus three.

    (b) The product of four and six is greater than twenty.

    (c) Eighteen is less than the sum of ten and fifteen.

    (d) Fourteen is not equal to the sum of eight and five.

    (e) Seventeen is not greater than eleven.

    (f) Thirty minus five is not less than the sum of ten and ten.

4. (a) False   (d) True

    (b) True   (e) False

    (c) True   (f) True

5. (a) False   (d) True

    (b) True   (e) False

    (c) True

Exercise Set 3

1. (a) $6+\square=15$ (c) $20<\triangle-8$

(b) $2+m>10$ (d) $y-9>24$

2. (a) The sum of eight and this number is equal to twenty-two.

(b) Fourteen is less than this number minus five.

(c) The sum of this number and eight is greater than seventeen.

(d) This number minus six is not equal to thirteen.

3. (a) $\{34\}$ (e) $\{21\}$

(b) $\{8, 9, 10, 11, \ldots\}$ (f) $\{0\}$

(c) $\{11, 12, 13, 14, \ldots\}$ (g) $\{5, 6, 7, 8, 9, 10, 11, 12, 13, 14\}$

(d) $\{6, 7, 8, 9, \ldots\}$ (h) $\{5, 6, 7, 8, 9, 10, \ldots\}$

Exercise Set 4

There are many possibilities. Some examples are as follows:

1. (a) $264+928=\square$ (c) $964=r+407$

$928=\square-264$ $964-407=r$

$\square-928=264$ $964-r=407$

(b) $n-89=437$ (d) $1007+r=3986$

$n=437+89$ $3986-1007=r$

$n-437=89$ $3986-r=1007$

2. (a) $1368\div57=n$ (c) $48\times37=\square$

$57=1368\div n$ $\square\div37=48$

$57\times n=1368$ $\square=37\times48$

(b) $z\times35=2240$ (d) $n=72\times43$

$z=2240\div35$ $n\div43=72$

$35=2240\div z$ $72=n\div43$

Exercise Set 5

1. (a) $m\geq9$ (d) $8<n<15$

(b) $13+y\leq29$ (e) $9\leq x\leq30$

(c) $\square+11\geq30$

2. (a) This number is less than or equal to seven.

(b) The sum of this number and two is greater than or equal to three.

(c) Seven minus this number is less than or equal to twelve.

(d) Two is less than this number, and this number is less than five.

(e) Eight is less than or equal to this number, and this number is less than or equal to fifteen.

3. (a) {2, 3, 4, . . .}   (e) {21, 22, 23, 24, . . .}

(b) {0, 1, 2, 3}   (f) {0, 1, 2}

(c) {0, 1, 2, 3}   (g) {5}

(d) {8, 9, 10, 11, . . .}   (h) {4, 5, 6}

Exercise Set 6

1. (a)

✿	△
2	6
3	4
6	2
4	3

(b)

▢	△
1	8
2	6
3	4
5	0

(c)

◯	▢
0	0
0	1
0	2
0	3
0	4
1	0
1	1
1	2
1	3
2	0
2	1
2	2
3	0
3	1
4	0

2. {(9, 0), (7, 1), (5, 2), (3, 3), (1, 4)}

Exercise Set 7

1. The answers given here are just a few of many ways to arrive at solutions:

    (a) $(6 + \square) - 5 = 23$

    Try 25 as your first guess. When $\square$ is replaced by 25, you have
    $(6 + 25) - 5 = 23$,
    $\qquad 26 = 23$,   which is false.
    Since 26 is greater than 23, the second guess should be less than 25.
    Try 22 as your second guess. When $\square$ is replaced by 22, you have
    $(6 + 22) - 5 = 23$,
    $\qquad 23 = 23$,   which is true.
    So 22 is the solution to the sentence.

    (b) $(\triangle - 4) + 6 = 32$

    Try 40 as your first guess. When $\triangle$ is replaced by 40, you find
    $(40 - 4) + 6 = 32$,
    $\qquad 42 = 32$,   which is false.
    Since 42 is greater than 32, the second guess should be less than 40.
    Try 30 as your second guess. When $\triangle$ is replaced by 30, you obtain
    $(30 - 4) + 6 = 32$,
    $\qquad 32 = 32$,   which is true.
    So 30 is the solution to the sentence.

    (c) $7 + (10 - \square) = 9$

    Try 5 as your first guess. When $\square$ is replaced by 5, you obtain
    $7 + (10 - 5) = 9$,
    $\qquad 12 = 9$,   which is false.
    Try 9 as your second guess. When $\square$ is replaced by 9, you have
    $7 + (10 - 9) = 9$,
    $\qquad 8 = 9$,   which is false.
    Try 8 as your third guess. When $\square$ is replaced by 8, you obtain
    $7 + (10 - 8) = 9$,
    $\qquad 9 = 9$,   which is true.
    Thus, 8 is the solution to the sentence.

    (d) $[2 \times (\triangle + 4)] - 9 = 37$

    Try 20 as your first guess. When $\triangle$ is replaced by 20, you have
    $[2 \times (20 + 4)] - 9 = 37$,
    $\qquad 39 = 37$,   which is false.
    Try 19 as your second guess. When $\triangle$ is replaced by 19, you obtain
    $[2 \times (19 + 4)] - 9 = 37$,
    $\qquad 37 = 37$,   which is true.
    Thus, 19 is the solution to the sentence.

(e) $[3 \times (7 + \square)] + 3 = 63$

Try 10 as your first guess. When $\square$ is replaced by 10, you have
$[3 \times (7 + 10)] + 3 = 63$,

$54 = 63$,   which is false.

Try 15 as your second guess. When $\square$ is replaced by 15, you have
$[3 \times (7 + 15)] + 3 = 63$,

$69 = 63$,   which is false.

Try 13 as your third guess. When $\square$ is replaced by 13, you obtain
$[3 \times (7 + 13)] + 3 = 63$,

$63 = 63$,   which is true.

Thus, 13 is the solution for the sentence.

(f) $12 + [6 \times (\triangle - 7)] = 36$

Try 10 as your first guess. When $\triangle$ is replaced by 10, you have
$12 + [6 \times (10 - 7)] = 36$,

$30 = 36$,   which is false.

Try 11 as your second guess. When $\triangle$ is replaced by 11, you have
$12 + [6 \times (11 - 7)] = 36$,

$36 = 36$,   which is true.

Thus, 11 is the solution for the sentence.

Exercise Set 8

In most cases there are several ways in which the problem could be illustrated on the number line. One example is given for each of the sentences.

1. (a) $12 - 7 = a$

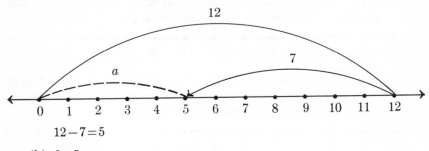

$12 - 7 = 5$

(b) $6 + 5 = x$

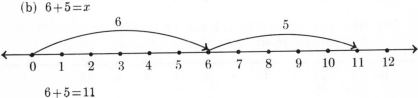

$6 + 5 = 11$

(c) $2 \times 5 = m$

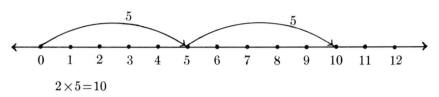

$2 \times 5 = 10$

(d) $5 \times 2 = m$

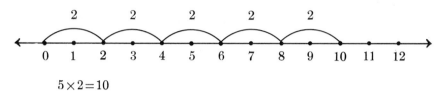

$5 \times 2 = 10$

(e) $\square + 3 = 10$

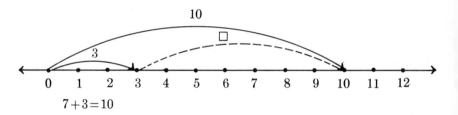

$7 + 3 = 10$

2. (a) When $\square$ is replaced by 0, 1, 2, 3, 4, 5, 6, 7 in the sentence $6 + \square < 14$, true sentences result; other replacements result in false sentences. The graph of the solution set is pictured below.

(b) When $\square$ is replaced by 10, 11, 12 in the sentence $\square - 5 > 4$, true sentences result; other replacements result in false sentences. The graph of the solution set is pictured below.

(c) When $\square$ is replaced by 6, 7, 8, 9, 10, 11, 12 in the sentence $\square \geq 6$, true sentences result.

(d) When △ is replaced by 0, 1, 2, 3, 4 in the sentence △≤4, true sentences result.

0   1   2   3   4   5   6   7   8   9   10   11   12

(e) When y is replaced by 2, 3, 4, 5 in the sentence $1 < y < 6$, true sentences result.

0   1   2   3   4   5   6   7   8   9   10   11   12

(f) When y is replaced by 1, 2, 3, 4, 5, 6 in the sentence $1 \leq y \leq 6$, true sentences result.

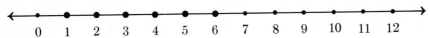

0   1   2   3   4   5   6   7   8   9   10   11   12

3. $7 + a = 12$

4. $x - 5 = 6$

$x - 6 = 5$

Exercise Set 9

1. (a) $n + 16$ (d) $n \div 4$, or $\dfrac{n}{4}$

   (b) $13 \times n$ (e) $5 \times (n + 2)$

   (c) $\dfrac{1}{5} \times n$, or $\dfrac{n}{5}$

2. (a) $(6 \times n) + 8 = 44$ (d) $8 - n = 4$

   (b) $n + 8 > 14$ (e) $n + 7 > 3 \times n$

   (c) $n \div 4 < 17$

3. (a) Number of cents Sue saved   354

       Number of cents Sue earned   75

       Number of cents she needs $795 - (354 + 75)$

       Number of cents she needs n

         Sentence: $795 - (354 + 75) = n$

         Solution: $n = 366$

             She needs $3.66 to buy the sweater.

   (b) Number of dollars George has   15

       Number of dollars for baseball shoes   6

Number of dollars for baseball shirt   5

Number of dollars he can spend $0 \leq n \leq 15 - (6+5)$

Sentence: $0 \leq n \leq 15 - (6+5)$

Solution: $0 \leq n \leq 4$

He can spend $4.00 or any amount less than $4.00 for the bat.

(c) The distance in miles from San Diego to
Chicago   2200

Average speed in miles per hour   535

Distance traveled in 3 hours 3×535

Distance from Chicago after 3 hours $2200 - (3 \times 535)$

Distance from Chicago after 3 hours x

Sentence: $2200 - (3 \times 535) = x$

Solution: $x = 595$

The jet is 595 miles from Chicago.

(d) Number of days for summer vacation   93

Number of days spent on fishing trip   9

Number of days spent at camp $93 - 9$

Number of weeks spent at camp $(93 - 9) \div 7$

Number of weeks spent at camp n

Sentence: $(93 - 9) \div 7 = n$

Solution: $n = 12$

He spent 12 weeks at camp.

(e) Temperatures for San Francisco   70, 72, 78, 69, 74

Average temperature for 5 days $(70 + 72 + 78 + 69 + 74) \div 5$

Average temperature for 5 days n

Sentence: $(70 + 72 + 78 + 69 + 74) \div 5 = n$

Solution: $n = 72\frac{3}{5}$ degrees.

The average temperature was $72\frac{3}{5}$ degrees.

4. There are many verbal problems that could be written for each open sentence. Here are some samples.

(a) John has $8.00. How much money does he need to buy a transistor radio which costs $39.00?

(b) Mary has saved $19.00 which is $\frac{1}{4}$ of the cost of a record player she wishes to buy. What is the cost of the record player?

(c) In a basketball game, the final score of the winning team was less than 26 points. If they made seven free throws worth one point each, how many regular baskets worth two points each could they have made?

(d) On an exam containing questions worth 1 point and $\frac{1}{2}$ point, pupils made scores which were between 39 and 45 inclusive. What are the possible scores the pupils could have made?